structural principles. The structural analysis of simple and complex polysaccharides, modern analytical techniques, separation techniques, and the roles of biochemical methods in both synthetic and analytical carbohydrate chemistry are discussed. The book's formulas are almost exclusively three-dimensional, a sharp departure from the classical use of projection or Haworth formulas. There is a frequent use of tables to repeat specific points. A general bibliography for each chapter provides the reader with a selection of pertinent review articles or texts for more detailed treatments of specific topics. In these bibliographies, there are references to original literature as well.

ABOUT THE AUTHOR

Eugene A. Davidson (Ph.D., Columbia University) is Professor of Biochemistry at Duke University. The author of over seventy scholarly publications, Professor Davidson has been actively engaged in amino sugar and complex polysaccharide chemistry since 1951. His current research has been supported by the National Institutes of Health since 1958. He was a Guggenheim Fellow as well as consultant to the National Cancer Institute and National Institutes of Health. Presently, he is a member of the Panel on Materials of Life and their Transformations of the Committee on Science and Public Policy, National Academy of Sciences.

CARBOHYDRATE CHEMISTRY

Eugene A. Davidson

DUKE UNIVERSITY

Holt, Rinehart and Winston, Inc.
New York   Chicago   San Francisco   Toronto   London

Preface

The concepts of stereochemistry, optical isomerism, and configurational relationships have received enormous impetus and development over the past 50 years through studies in the carbohydrate field. The outstanding contributions of Fischer, Haworth, Hudson, and others are models of logical reasoning. During more recent times, however, striking progress in organic chemistry has been made. The advances have been primarily of a conceptual nature rather than additions to an already large catalog of "name" reactions. The mechanism of displacement and elimination reactions, the role of ionic intermediates, kinetic behavior, solvent effects, and so on, have all been extensively studied and, as a result, reaction courses can be effectively predicted. In some cases, they can be designed to achieve a desired result. Comparable advances have been made in spectroscopic techniques, especially infrared, proton magnetic resonance, and optical rotatory dispersion.

The average student of chemistry or biochemistry is able to select from among numerous modern texts, all of which offer up-to-date treatments of organic reaction mechanisms, stereochemistry, and current synthetic techniques. The study of organic chemistry has thus been transformed from catalog-like memorization into that of a discipline with broad reaching fundamental principles. However, the discussions of carbohydrate reactions in these texts are rather cursory and tend to emphasize the early classical studies as opposed to modern developments. This "neglect" by most organic chemists has provided one of the major stimuli for this book. An equally strong and largely complementary reason is the failure of books on carbohydrate chemistry to apply modern organic chemical developments to discussions of reactions.

After numerous discussions with colleagues and students, the major topics thought desirable for a contemporary approach to carbohydrate chemistry were enumerated. The conclusions of such discussions can be summarized as follows: A useful book in the area of carbohydrate chemistry might begin with a discussion of stereochemical and conformational analysis. The reactions given by various functional groups can then be discussed in light of current structural

iii

knowledge with some effort being made to provide underlying principles. An extensive discussion of optical rotation, infrared, and nuclear magnetic resonance as applied to carbohydrate problems is a necessary adjunct. In view of the current interest (and importance) in the biological roles of various sugar derivatives, the chemistry of amino sugars, sugar phosphates and sulfates, glycopeptides, and glycolipids deserve detailed discussion. For similar reasons, attention should be given to synthesis of certain isotopically labeled sugars and to degradative methods. The classic methods of structural analysis of oligo and polysaccharides deserve attention as well as problems of homogeneity, molecular weight, and biosynthesis.

It is hoped that this text provides a view of the chemistry of this class of compounds from a predominantly structural and mechanistic approach. In a sense, it is an attempt to update the reader's chemical orientation toward the carbohydrates sometime beyond 1920.

As with any rapidly growing field, the elapsed time between writing and printing witnesses the publication of several important results. *Carbohydrate Chemistry* represents a natural compromise between waiting for posterity and reaching today's audience.

Durham, North Carolina   EUGENE A. DAVIDSON
March 1967

Contents

PART 1
Structural Analysis

INTRODUCTION

It may reasonably be said that the beginning of organic chemistry coincided with Woehler's discovery in 1828, that ammonium cyanate on standing, slowly gave rise to urea via an internal rearrangement. This definition would be consistent with the proposal that organic chemistry is that science which deals with the chemical behavior of carbon compounds.

It would appear to be more realistic and more accurate to think of organic chemistry as beginning when those concepts were formulated which lead to much of our present-day understanding of molecular structure. These fundamental ideas were proposed not for lack of experimental data, but rather were suggested by the accumulation of a considerable amount of chemical information on natural and synthetic compounds. The underlying principles initially described nearly 100 years ago have stood the test of time better than most concepts in chemistry and physics.[1]

The proposal by Van't Hoff and LeBel that the various types of isomerism, which were known by the end of the nineteenth century, could in part be explained by visualizing a saturated carbon atom as having its four valence bonds projecting toward the corners of a regular tetrahedron, was certainly not greeted with unbridled enthusiasm on the part of the scientific community. The ridicule showered on this idea was, however, countered by experimental verification of equal and necessarily greater force. These concepts were subjected to repeated laboratory tests and it was shown with unceasing regularity that the structural behavior of organic (carbon) compounds could be satisfactorily accounted for on the basis of the proposed tetrahedral orientation. This is certainly one of the most fundamental principles of organic chemistry as we know it today.

The structure of a molecule of the simplest organic compound, methane, reveals a perfectly symmetrical, uniform arrangement, as illustrated in Figure 1.

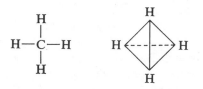

FIGURE 1   Structure of methane.

<hr>

[1] Mathematicians excepted because they *derive* everything from first axioms.

3

The position of each hydrogen is equivalent in terms of distance from the central carbon, distance from the other hydrogens, and relative orientation in space. It is probably fair to say that almost no other aliphatic compound possesses such a simple spatial formula as does this one, and few undergo reactions that are consistent with a completely symmetric structure. It is conceivable that some preferred spatial orientation might exist for such a molecule, but experimental evidence for this has not yet been found. In addition, the valence bonds expected for a saturated carbon based on a quantum-mechanical solution are four, with tetrahedral orientation. As the number of atoms increases and molecules become structurally complex simple spatial assignments for individual atoms cannot be easily made on a theoretical basis. The ideal structural knowledge that chemists and biochemists wish to have may be stated as follows: (1) the detailed three-dimensional arrangement (conformation) of the constituent atoms of given molecules; and (2) a reasonable prediction as to the likelihood of this conformation remaining fixed, or failing that, some information as to what other conformations are likely, their relative probabilities of formation, ease of inter-conversion, and reactivity in specified chemical and biological systems.

The tools that have become available to the chemists of today allow a far more probing examination of three-dimensional molecular structure than has hitherto been possible. Techniques such as infrared and nuclear-magnetic-resonance spectroscopy, optical rotatory dispersion, mass spectrometry, and so on, have become commonplace in the hands of the practicing chemist. However, it frequently happens that the combined use of several of these is still insufficient to permit an accurate three-dimensional array to be written. Ultimate structural tools, such as x-ray or neutron diffraction, which are capable of giving the requisite information, still have relatively limited application, are very tedious and time consuming in development, and as a result, have received limited use in this field. The efforts expended have been primarily on compounds of considerable biological interest or those where the structural problems are felt to be relatively easily solved from the corresponding diffraction patterns. In view of the practical difficulties of applying x-ray analysis to every compound where detailed structural information is desired, considerable effort has been devoted to other methods of obtaining such structural information as is related to chemical behavior and, in certain cases, biological activity. The level of success in this endeavor is quite variable but it is probably fair to say that a great deal of the fundamental work in molecular structure and stereochemistry has been carried out in the carbohydrate field.

The early studies of Fischer, Hudson, Haworth, and others established considerable fundamental groundwork upon which much of carbohydrate chemistry is solidly based. The rather unique structure of these compounds combined with the "brutal" approaches common in organic chemistry during the past century has probably been responsible for the lack of enthusiasm on the part of organic chemists toward sugars. The carbohydrates were considered either intractable for the normal type of organic reaction, too difficult to obtain suitable crystalline products from (as any practicing carbohydrate chemist will only be too happy to explain), and fraught with numerous isomerism difficulties not present in much of synthetic organic chemistry.

The underlying principles of organic reaction mechanisms—kinetic and solvent control, directed stereochemistry of newly formed asymmetric centers, use of neighboring group reactions, and so on—have only recently been applied to the carbohydrate field. As a result, there has been an increasing realization that the modern concepts of structural organic chemistry are no less valid when applied to carbohydrates than they are when applied to substitutions in complex polycyclic systems.

CHAPTER 1

Stereochemistry and Conformation

1.1 Rotational Isomerism

In an attempt to build up some fundamental information regarding molecular structure, let us consider the possible arrangements that a molecule such as ethane may adopt in the absence of any external stimulus. A flat projection formula for the ethane molecule, CH_3—CH_3, does not indicate any possibility of structural isomerism. A formula such as that illustrated in Figure 1.1, where two tetrahedra are joined together at an apex, may be pictured. Here

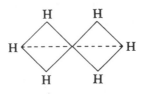

FIGURE 1.1   Structural formula for ethane with tetrahedral representation.

the hydrogen atoms appear equivalent and there is no reason to favor one structural array over any other. However, if an attempt is made to visualize this molecule in either the saw-horse form or in the extremely useful Newman projection[1] [1] (Figure 1.2), it is immediately apparent that other arrangements are possible for even as simple a molecule as this. Notice that the so-called eclipsed formula for ethane has all three pairs of hydrogens on the adjacent carbons in opposition with one another, whereas the skew or gauche form has an angle of 60 degrees between the hydrogens on adjacent carbons. The distance between hydrogens in the eclipsed form is approximately 2 Angstroms. This is insufficient for any steric repulsion to be significant yet the energy difference between the eclipsed form and the more stable gauche form is approximately 3 kcal per mole [2]. Several reasons have been suggested for this effect including interactions of the carbon-hydrogen bonding electrons, but the primary reason for the observed differences is not known. A plot of energy content versus the

[1] This views the molecule (or a portion of a molecule) along the bond joining the carbon atoms.

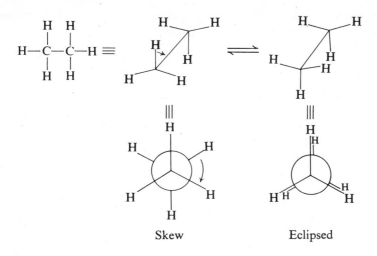

FIGURE 1.2   Structural formula for ethane in either the sawhorse or Newman projection diagram.

dihedral angle between hydrogens on adjacent carbons is sinusoidal in nature with the energy minimum corresponding to an angle of 60 degrees, at which angle the hydrogens are at the maximal distance from one another. The amount of a given form present can be assessed from the energy differences between forms and can be calculated for simple molecules. Between these two possible

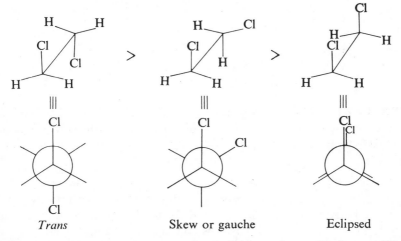

FIGURE 1.3   Rotational isomers of 1,2-dichloroethane. Under equilibrium conditions the *trans* form makes up about 75 percent, the skew form about 25 percent, and the eclipsed form less than 1 percent of the possible isomers present. An increase in temperature produces more of the skew form but proportions suggest that conversion via the eclipsed form is restricted.

structures are an infinite variety of rotational isomers all of which may exist to a greater or lesser degree in solution or in the gas phase. In molecules such as this where the barrier to rotation is only several kilocalories, there is sufficient thermal energy present at any reasonable temperature to permit all such isomers to exist. This thermal rotation will be very rapid until the energy barrier approaches 15 kcal. Accordingly, we can do little more than make probability statements about those forms that are most common or more common as opposed to those, which by energetic considerations, should be less common.

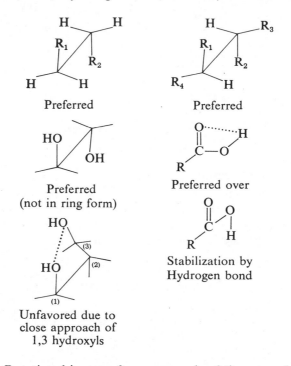

FIGURE 1.4   Rotational isomers for compounds of the open chain type containing more than two carbons. The preferred forms are those with minimum interactions. In the case of carboxylic acids, stabilization by hydrogen bond formation is possible.

The H–H interactions in ethane will all be uniform and for any possible structure a fairly accurate assessment of its total population can be made. However, when the rotational barrier is amplified by the introduction of polar substituents, the probability estimates become more difficult and selected structures much more (or less) favored. Molecules such as 1,2-dichloroethane show a very distinct conformational preference (Figure 1.3) and it is possible to show differences in physical properties and reactivity between the rotational isomers present in such a structure. This is true to a lesser extent for ethylene glycol and to a greater extent when other substituents are present, but the basic conclusions are quite clear. There is not completely free rotation about single bonds resulting in equiprobable rotamers, and we must allow for the preference of certain conformations over others. In general, the preferred conformation will be that in which interactions between atoms on adjacent carbons are kept to a minimum. Naturally, stabilizing interactions such as hydrogen bonding may result in exceptions (Table 1.1 and Figure 1.4).

TABLE 1.1

Dipole moments of 1,2-dichloroethane and carboxylic acids as a function of temperature or rotational isomer present.

COMPOUND	DIPOLE MOMENT
1,2-dichloroethane (32°)	1.12
1,2-dichloroethane (271°)	1.54
1,2-dichloroethane (Skew form, calc.)	2.5
Carboxylic acid (*Cis*, calc.)	1.2
Carboxylic acid (*Trans*, calc.)	3.7
Carboxylic acid (Measured)	1.7–1.9

1.2 Stereoisomerism

When a carbon chain becomes 3 carbon atoms long, spatial isomerism becomes possible (Figure 1.5). The number of such isomers increases rapidly

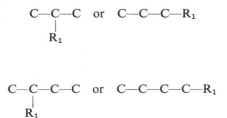

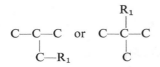

and so on

FIGURE 1.5 Structural isomerism possible as the carbon chain is extended to three or more carbons in length.

with increasing chain length so that when a chain is 6 or more carbons long, the number of possible isomers is very great. This, taken together with the number of rotational isomers for any given structure, makes the prospect of writing consistent three-dimensional formulations for such compounds very dim. Therefore, structures written for open chain compounds are compromises, approximations, and little more than probability statements regarding conformations most likely to be present in solution. The graphic symbols may depict the most probable conformer but this is not always certain. Indeed, straight chain compounds are usually depicted as Fischer projections in which no attempt is made to illustrate any conformational preference.

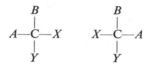

FIGURE 1.6   Schematic representation of two compounds which are mirror
images of one another.

The phenomenon of optical isomerism is now superimposed on those that have been previously discussed. The original proposals of Van't Hoff regarding the tetrahedral orientation of bonds on a saturated carbon atom were in part developed to explain optical isomerism. Compounds that are optical isomers or enantiomers have identical chemical behavior, solubility, and melting point, but exert opposite effects on polarized light and usually have markedly different biological properties.[2] This effect arises by the very nature of the tetrahedral arrangement of the groups.

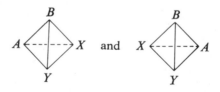

FIGURE 1.7   Tetrahedral representations of mirror images.

The problem can be visualized by inspection of the structures of two compounds, each of which contains a carbon atom with four different substituents (Figure 1.6). Without any insight into the structure other than that of the tetrahedral orientation of the substituents, it is possible to construct two formulas (Figure 1.7). These two structures cannot be superimposed upon one another by any device of rotation or translation which does not involve actual bond breaking and reforming. This may not be the only three-dimensional

---

[2] In the latter case, the difference is due to the interaction with asymmetric reagents such as enzyme proteins.

representation that accommodates isomerism of this type, but it is the only one that is consistent for all models examined.

The nature of the four different functional groups represented does not have to be remarkably different. For example, enzymatic reduction of acetalde-hyde in the presence of a specific, deuterated reducing agent yields monodeutero-ethanol, which can be shown to possess optical activity (Figure 1.8) [3]. This is

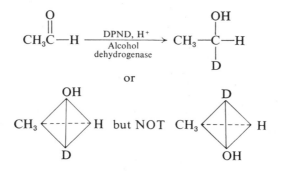

FIGURE 1.8   Stereospecific reduction of acetaldehyde to ethanol using mono-deuterated reducing agent and alcohol dehydrogenase. The monodeuteroethanol may be considered the simplest asymmetric organic compound.

perhaps the simplest compound exhibiting this property. This interesting reaction also underlies the type of enzyme specificity which frequently occurs in biological systems. Whereas "right-handed" molecules may be completely active in some biological system, "left-handed" molecules may be inert, and vice versa. The fundamental origins of such structures and the mechanism for retaining their stereospecificity are unknown, but in some respects we deal with a right-handed universe for one type of compound and a left-handed universe for some others.

Before extending this discussion to the type of optical isomerism en-countered in carbohydrate structure, a brief discussion of optical rotation will be presented.

1.3 General Introduction and Theory

The phenomenon of optical activity has been known for an extremely long time. The initial attempts to formulate a physical theory to explain optical rotation were made in 1824 by Fresnel who attributed the rotatory phenomenon to circular double refraction[3] [4]. In an attempt to account for the rotation

---

[3] Circularly polarized light is defined as electromagnetic radiation wherein the locus of the projection of the time-dependent electric vector onto a plane perpendicular to the direction of propagation describes a circle.

The optical properties of a molecule depend on its orientation relative to the plane of polarization of the radiation used to observe it. Differences in polarizability along different directions cause a change in the refractive index for polarized light. This phenomenon is known as *double refraction*.

exhibited by crystalline materials, he suggested that the atoms in a crystal were arranged in a helical fashion. This was not an adequate explanation because liquids and solutions were also optically active and this type of helical arrangement was very unlikely for them.

Biot was one of the earliest workers to examine optical rotation as a function of wavelength. He formulated an equation relating the square of the wavelength to the optical rotation, which was constant for a given species [5]. He was perhaps the first to observe rotatory dispersions and also studied the effects of temperature, solvent, and concentration on optical rotatory power. A classic experiment in this field, post-dating that of Biot, is the well-known one carried out by Louis Pasteur. He managed to separate enantiomeric crystals of tartrates which had different crystalline forms by picking them apart under the microscope. The success of his painstaking achievement is underscored when we understand the fact that it is unusual for the crystal forms of optical isomers to be mirror images, the tartrates being one rare example of such a pair having this kind of crystal isomerism as well. Thus, Pasteur's achievement was slightly fortuitous, but nonetheless a dramatic demonstration of optical activity.

Attempts to explain the rotation of plane polarized light have been made more or less continuously since the end of the nineteenth century. The "sphere of action of the molecule" and the vibrational periods of the charged particles in the absorbing medium were suggested reasons but are inadequate descriptions, especially as far as relating the rotatory behavior of a molecule to specific structural features.

Drude, approximately at the turn of the century, suggested that if the medium were nonsymmetric and isotropic (all molecules were regular tetrahedra of a similar kind) then, because of the molecular structure, the paths of electrons would not be short lines but helices twisted in the same direction with their axes randomly oriented in space [6]. He related the wavelength to the number of vibrators[4] as follows:

$$\alpha = \sum_m \frac{Km}{\lambda^2 - \lambda_n^2} \tag{1.1}$$

α is the optical rotation and is also given by the expression:

$$[\alpha]_\lambda = \frac{A \times 100}{l \times c}$$

A is the symbol for measured rotation, l is the path length in decimeters, and c is the percent concentration of solute. λ_n is the wavelength corresponding to a characteristic frequency of vibration, and K is a constant whose magnitude is a function of the number of vibrators.

---

[4] A general term for particles that absorb or respond to the incident radiation.

This equation is valid in the region where there are no absorption bands. Because the natural vibrations of electrons lie in the ultraviolet range, this equation can be expanded to a two-term expression initially suggested by Boltzmann. Drude extended this application into absorbing regions by introducing a term which he called the *fraction coefficient*. This was an attempt to explain the anomalous dispersion curves observed in regions where chromophores are present in the molecule.

All of this early work was carried out before the development of contemporary quantum mechanics. In 1914, a valence electron theory of optical rotation was suggested which did not involve complex mathematical treatment. This may be briefly summarized as follows: The action of the electric vector of the light wave upon a valence electron produces a displacement which is opposed by a restitutional force which is a function of the electronic environment, the

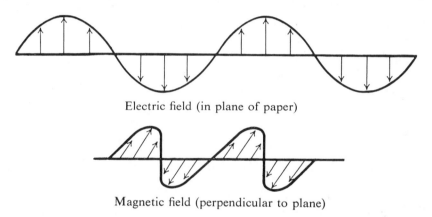

Electric field (in plane of paper)

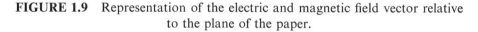

Magnetic field (perpendicular to plane)

FIGURE 1.9 Representation of the electric and magnetic field vector relative to the plane of the paper.

nature of the nucleus to which the electron is attached and its localization. In an isotropic field, this restoring force would be directed toward the position of "rest" of the electron or what we might consider as the ground state. However, in this theory, the field is not isotropic because it is assumed that the restoring force acts along the direction of the chemical bond. The combined action of displacing and restoring forces on the electron thereby produces a displacement that is not parallel to the electric vector. As a result of this, the polarization of the molecule is rotated from the field direction. This rotation vanishes when averaged for all random positions as long as the system contains 1, 2, and 3 uncoupled valence electrons. However, 4 valence electrons will give a definite rotation provided that they are present in a *nonsymmetric* or *noncancelling* arrangement. Interchanging two of the four electrons will change the sign of rotation and, if two of the electrons are identical, the molecule thereby acquires a plane of symmetry and the resultant or net rotation will be 0.

Contemporary theories also relate the influence of one moving electron upon other electrons in the molecule. This modification is required to account for the profound effect that polarizable groups (such as carbonyls, which are themselves symmetric) have on the optical rotation of neighboring asymmetric centers. One of the several current theories (theories have been proposed by Kauzmann, Kirkwood, and Eyring, among others) is that suggested by Kauzmann, briefly summarized below [7].

A light wave is composed of oscillating electric and magnetic fields, each perpendicular to the other and both perpendicular to the direction of propagation of the wave (Figure 1.9). The intensity of the electric field will vary with time, and the magnitude at any two times may be represented by the relative lengths of the vectors at these times. The electric field will be of a sinusoidal type moving along a direction perpendicular to the propagation of the wave. The intensity obviously will be maximal at the peaks and troughs of the sine curve. The magnetic field will be oscillating in a similar way, again perpendicular to the plane, and the sum of these represents the light wave as illustrated in Figure 1.10.

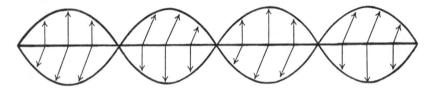

FIGURE 1.10   Representation of the light wave as the sum of the electric and magnetic field vectors.

A molecule that is optically active will induce a change in the electric field which in turn changes the magnetic dipole moment of the molecule. The change in the magnetic field will induce an electrical dipole moment. Thus, for optical rotatory power to be exhibited by a molecule one of the two following conditions must hold:

$$M = \frac{-\beta}{c} \left(\frac{\delta H}{\delta t} \right) \tag{1.2}$$

$$\mu = \frac{\gamma}{c} \left(\frac{\delta E}{\delta t} \right) \tag{1.3}$$

In the above equations, M represents the induced electric dipole moment and μ the induced magnetic dipole moment, β and γ are constants, and H and E are the magnetic and electrical field of the light wave at time t. The motion of electrons along helical paths of parallel orientation is assumed to be requisite for rotatory power to be exhibited. If polarized light is allowed to interact with such a system so that the direction of the propagation of the light is perpendicular to the plane, and the magnetic field parallel to the axis of the helices, then a changing magnetic field will induce an electromotive force in any conductor which encircles the magnetic lines of force. Therefore, an electromotive force is induced in the helix, tending to make the electrons move along that path which, in turn, will produce a change in the electric dipole moment of the molecule. This results because the center of charge moves away from its equilibrium position. This changing dipole moment may be represented as a vector which changes in both magnitude and direction and may be resolved into components perpendicular and parallel to the helical axis. The perpendicular components tend to cancel as the electron makes one turn of the helix but the parallel component is of the same sign as long as the electron moves along the helix in a given direction.

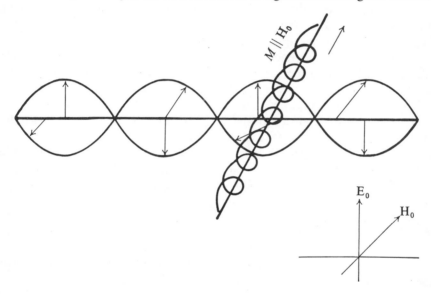

FIGURE 1.11 Interaction of the electric and magnetic field of incident light. E_0 is the electric field of the incident light. H_0 is the magnetic field of the incident light. E_i, the induced electric field, is in the same direction as H_0.

By this representation, the parallel component determines the average direction of the induced dipole moment. The motion of the electron along the helix results in an induced moment in the direction of the axis of the helix. The magnitude of the moment will depend on the magnitude of the electromotive force and also, therefore, on the magnitude of the magnetic field of the incident light. Because the parallel component of the induced dipole moment is negative as the electron moves along a left-handed helix (arbitrary representation) (Figure 1.11), the concept that molecules, which are mirror images, will have optical rotatory signs of opposite nature is satisfied.

The exact reason for the change in electric moment leading to optical rotation itself is not entirely clear. The oscillating moment gives rise to an electromagnetic wave in which the electric vector is parallel to the direction of the dipole and in phase with the wave of the incident light. When the two are combined vectorially, the resultant is still plane polarized but is changed slightly in direction. Thus, when plane-polarized light is acted upon or passes through a layer of molecules whose behavior is governed as described above, rotatory power will arise when an electric dipole moment can be induced by a change in the magnetic field. In a sense, this may be considered as a change in the index of refraction for the polarized light.

Consider a system wherein the axes of the helices along which the electrons move are parallel to the electric field of the incident light beam. This forces the electrons to move along the helix and thereby produces a magnetic field similar to that produced by a current flowing through a solenoid. The changing electric field of the incident light induces the molecule to act as a magnet with a separation of centers of positive and negative charge. The resultant dipole is parallel to the electric field and increases the rate of change of the magnitude of the electric field. The sign of the constant γ in the equation above will depend upon whether the electron follows a right- or a left-handed helical path and this is assumed to be positive for a right-handed helix and negative for a left-handed one.

The oscillating magnetic dipole moment resulting from the field emits radiation in which the electric field is parallel to the electric field induced by the changing magnetic field. It is also in phase with this other field and can be treated in the same way. Thus, the field induced by the oscillating dipole moment may be combined with the electric field of the incident light and the resultant is light, which is still plane polarized but rotated away from the plane of the incident light.

Although the above may seem relatively straightforward, a problem still arises in the attempt to relate the constants β and γ (the parameters governing the magnitude of rotation) to some physical expression. Hopefully, we should be able to examine a molecule of known conformation and make some intelligent prediction regarding the magnitude and sign of its optical rotation. The converse, if true, would be equally valuable. If the dimensions of the helix along which the electrons move are known, then it may be possible to calculate β and γ and the actual rotatory power for the molecule under consideration. Nevertheless, the problem of predicting the rotation of a real compound introduces several complicating factors.

Kauzmann, in a discussion of secondary butyl bromide, presents the following argument (see Figure 1.12). Examining formula (a), the curve made up of the bonds $Br-C-C_b-C_a$ is a right-handed helix. The same curve in formula (b) is a left-handed helix and these are analogous to the helical paths considered above. Formula (c) has the atoms coplanar and therefore no helical path connects them. To determine whether this particular *configuration* of butyl bromide is dextro or levo rotatory requires a knowledge of the following points: (1) the relative amounts of the various possible conformations in the mixture, and (2) the relative effectiveness of helices derived from the chains Br—C—C—C and C—C—C—C.

The latter point is relatively easier to estimate as long as there are atoms present in the molecule which are more readily polarized than others. Chains involving hydrogen atoms alone would be expected to contribute relatively

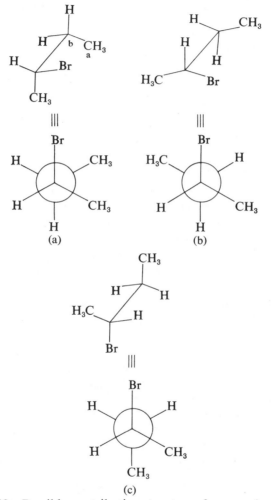

FIGURE 1.12   Possible contributing structures for monobromobutane.

little to optical rotation, whereas those involving the very polarizable bromine might be expected to have large contributions. The number of possible chains becomes very large as the number of asymmetric centers increase. In addition, it will be necessary to be certain that the electrons would tend to move along the direction of the bonds. With all this in mind and with the realization that it is not easily possible to differentiate conformation (a) and conformation (b), an educated guess as to the more likely structure is still required. When the number of asymmetric centers grows and when similarly polarizable groups are present (such as hydroxyls), an attempt to predict optical rotatory magnitude is extremely difficult.

Quantum-mechanical considerations in addition to the optical and electromagnetic ones discussed above may provide answers to these problems.[5] The application of current theories to carbohydrate structure will be discussed subsequently.

Despite the somewhat uncertain understanding of optical rotation, there are a large number of empirical and practical rules. Structural inferences can be drawn from optical rotatory behavior, particularly when dealing with compounds of similar nature and predictable conformation. In addition, the recent developments of rotatory dispersion and circular dichroism techniques have made possible conformational determinations based on empirical considerations of rotation. This approach to optical rotation may not be aesthetically pleasing but has indeed produced results.

The structure of more complex molecules containing additional carbons leads to compounds with more than one asymmetric center. A compound containing two asymmetric centers would be expected to have four possible structural representations, one containing three asymmetric centers would have eight, and so on. This simple formulation is completely valid as long as no other kind of molecular symmetry exists. However, that present in the tartrates illustrated in Figure 1.13 represents a special type of symmetry found in molecules with identical functional groups at each terminus (like-ended). This type of structure is frequently encountered among carbohydrates, especially those with 5 or 6 carbons, and the presence or absence of molecular symmetry is of considerable importance.

Several simple considerations will assist in predicting the number of isomers expected for like-ended and unlike-ended molecules. Straight chain molecules with dissimilar ends will have 2^n possible structures when n is the number of asymmetric centers. Like-ended molecules containing an odd number of carbons, as illustrated in Figure 1.14, present no problem in deciding whether or not a center of symmetry is present. The central carbon atom is chosen as the reference point and the functional groups attached above and below are compared. If these are mirror images, the molecule will be optically inactive (meso, internally compensated). However, where an even number of carbons are

---

[5] We are tempted to feel that we are in the same position with regard to optical rotation that physicists have been with regard to the hydrogen atom. We may very shortly know everything about the optical rotation of compounds with a single asymmetric center (a complete description of the hydrogen atom is available) and perhaps in certain specialized cases, the behavior of compounds with two asymmetric centers (some people are willing to talk about helium). However, as soon as the molecule contains three or more asymmetric centers, or as soon as the two asymmetric centers present are not sufficiently similar so that easy treatments are available, the predictions become much less certain. (No one is willing to talk about lithium or anything more complicated.)

present in the chain, the visualization is not quite as clear cut. As indicated for tartaric acid, the "center" of such a molecule is not an individual carbon atom but rather some point in space on a line joining the centers of two adjacent carbons. Van't Hoff and Fischer attempted to develop logical rules for dealing with compounds of this type in the carbohydrate series, (the most common

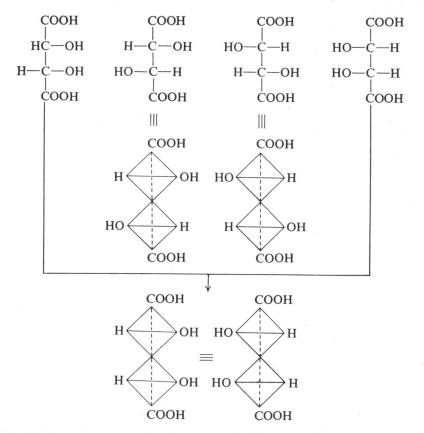

FIGURE 1.13 The tartaric acids. View the upper asymmetric carbon from above and the lower asymmetric carbon from below. If the substituent groups hydrogen, hydroxyl, and carboxyl appear in clockwise order on one of the asymmetric centers and counter clockwise order on the other, the two centers are compensating and the depicted structure nonasymmetric (meso).

examples by far) for predicting when internal compensation would result and where optical isomerism would occur. These rules may be briefly summarized as follows: In order to draw a projection formula (usually termed a Fischer projection), the carbon atoms are arranged so that their projection would fall in a straight line on the plane of the paper. This results when the centers of the tetrahedra are lined up one above or beneath the other. This cannot be coplanar,

of course, but the projection can be a linear array (Figure 1.15). Such free
rotation as exists on individual carbon–carbon bonds is then exercised so that
the bonds that join hydroxyl groups and hydrogen atoms to these carbons
project *above the plane* of the line joining the carbons to one another. The
molecule is now viewed from above and the projection formula drawn on a
plane beneath. This is illustrated in Figure 1.13 for tartaric acid; the various
forms of tartaric acid lead to different projection formulas, one pair of the
individual forms is superimposable and the other is not.

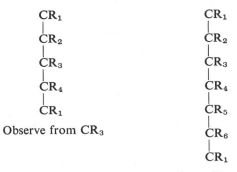

Thus,

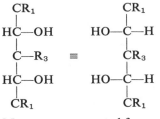

Meso or compensated form

FIGURE 1.14 Schematic representations of open chain compounds with
identical substituent groups on the termini of the carbon chain.

The optical activity or "compensation" for like-ended compounds with an
even number of carbon atoms requires visualization from a position at the
actual center of the carbon chain. Whether this is between carbons 3 and 4, or
2 and 3, and so on, will depend on the number of carbons in the linear chain.
Hydroxyls that project on the same side in such a formula and are the same
distance from the center are compensating; thus, in the formula for meso-
tartaric acid, both hydroxyls project either to the right or to the left, depending
upon which "end" is up. The D or L form would have one hydroxyl on either
side; these are not compensating.

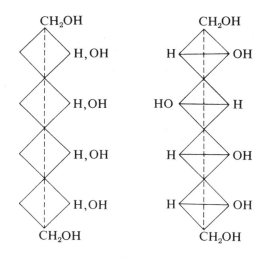

FIGURE 1.15 Tetrahedral representation of a 6-carbon sugar alcohol. The tetrahedra are rotated so that the hydrogen and hydroxyl groups adopt the orientation described in the text. A number of arrangements are possible, the one indicated is D-glucitol. When the stereochemistry of the hydrogen and hydroxyl groups of a particular center are not known, it is customary to represent them as H, OH.

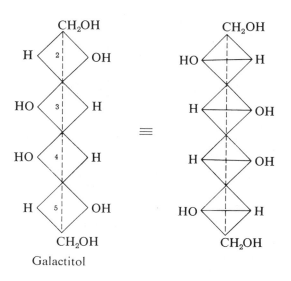

FIGURE 1.16 Tetrahedral representation of galactitol which on inspection is seen to be internally compensated.

This general method is easily extended. Compare the projection formulas of galactitol and mannitol (Figure 1.16 and 1.17). Applying the indicative rules: for galactitol, carbons 3 and 4 compensate one another and carbons 2 and 5 likewise cancel, whereas for mannitol no such compensation is present, and therefore D and L forms are expected. This representation of compensation

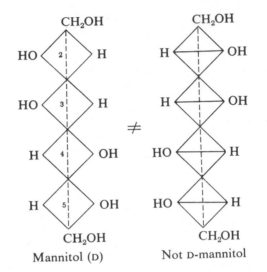

FIGURE 1.17   Tetrahedral representation of D-mannitol and its mirror image. The mirror image structure is, of course, L-mannitol, but on superficial inspection appears to be identical with the D-mannitol. Visualization of such structures can be significantly improved by use of models. Open or stick models rather than space filling models are recommended for this purpose.

rules serves to simplify and perhaps make more apparent the properties which lead to meso forms. The actual number of forms possible for straight chain compounds is represented by the formulas below.

For nonlike-ended molecules with n asymmetric centers:

$$\text{number of forms} = 2^n$$

For like-ended molecules:
If an even number of carbons is present,

$$\text{number of forms} = 2^{n/2-1}(2^{n/2} + 1)$$

If an odd number of carbons is present,

$$\text{number of forms} = 2^{n-1} \tag{1.4}$$

CHAPTER 2

Development of Carbohydrate Structure

2.1 Terms and Definitions

Anomer: Refers to the orientation of the hydroxyl group at the carbonyl carbon which arises due to internal condensation to form a 5- or 6-membered ring hemiacetal or hemiketal. Assignment of spatial position was originally made on the basis of optical rotation. A more accurate designation would indicate axial or equatorial as well as ring form.

Axial: Bonds perpendicular to the plane formed by carbon atoms 1, 2, 4, and 5 in a 6-membered strainless ring.

Configuration: Representation of a three-dimensional structure in a projection formula. Conventional usage is largely restricted to so-called stick formulas. Usually a gross distortion of molecular shape but may have utility for assessing relative arrangements of groups about a given center.

Conformation: Three-dimensional structure of a molecule. Representation of a given conformation on a planar surface (paper, blackboard) is an exercise in geometry. Proficiency is achieved by practice.

Conformer: A specific conformation of a given molecule. Many may exist but the most stable will predominate (energetic considerations). Differences between alternate conformers may be small but considerations of activation energy may prevent interconversion under normal conditions.

D: Any sugar derivable from D-glyceraldehyde by addition to the aldehydo carbon.

Diastereoisomers: Compounds with identical formulas which have different spatial distribution of atoms; for example, galactose and mannose.

Enantiomorphs: Mirror images, DL pair, a special case of diastereoisomers; D-glucose and L-glucose.

Epimer: A term that is useful when discussing molecules with several centers of asymmetry. Refers to configuration at a single center (others are usually

23

the same). For example, glucose and galactose are C-4 epimers. A special case of diastereoisomers.

Equatorial: Bonds radiating from the plane formed by C-1, -2, -4, and -5 in strainless 6-membered ring. Angle to the plane is not quite 0 degrees.

Glyceraldehyde: The simplest asymmetric carbohydrate (Figure 2.1). In the D forms, the position of the hydroxyl group on the central, asymmetric carbon is toward the right.

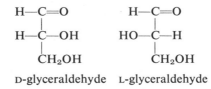

D-glyceraldehyde   L-glyceraldehyde

FIGURE 2.1   D- and L-glyceraldehyde, the simplest asymmetric carbohydrates.

Inversion (Walden): Alteration of configuration at a given asymmetric center as a result of a bimolecular displacement reaction.

Isomers: Any pair or group of compounds with the same empirical formula.

L: Any sugar derivable from L-glyceraldehyde. See D.

Meso form: Internally compensated structure, possesses a plane of symmetry.

Rotamer: Refers to a specific conformation for a compound having free or relatively free rotation about C—C bonds.

2.2 *Development of Structure for* D-*Glucose*

Despite the fact that several of the reaction sequences employed may not yet be familiar to the reader, this discussion can be followed as an exercise in stereochemistry alone [1].

Several fundamental facts were known to Fischer before he undertook his configurational studies. These can be summarized as follows:

1. The carbohydrates were straight chain compounds containing carbon, hydrogen, and oxygen with the empirical formula $C(H_2O)_n$.

2. The 6-carbon sugars contained 5 hydroxyl groups as determined by esterification with acetic anhydride.

3. The terminal group in one class of carbohydrates, aldoses, had properties like those of an aldehyde (reduction to an alcohol, mild oxidation to an acid, and addition reactions). A second class, ketoses, contained a non-terminal carbonyl function.

4. Several sugars with the same empirical formula satisfied all of the above criteria and therefore could only differ in the spatial arrangement of their functional groups.

Once these relationships had been established, it was possible for Fischer to derive a completely consistent and correct projectional formula for the structure not only of D-glucose but D-mannose and several other sugars related to these. It is worthwhile to follow through Fischer's reasoning in a somewhat modified form and to examine carefully the actual assumptions and experimental evidence upon which he based his conclusions.

Fischer found that three sugars, namely glucose, mannose, and fructose, on treatment with phenylhydrazine gave rise to identical crystalline derivatives termed *phenylosazones*. The reaction leading to the formation of phenylosazones destroyed the center of asymmetry at C-2. Because fructose was known to be a keto sugar, it was clear that glucose and mannose differed only at carbon 2 (epimers). Without any firm configurational assignment, glucose could therefore be represented as one of the two formulas presented in Figure 2.2, and mannose would necessarily have to be the other.

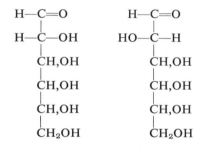

FIGURE 2.2 Structural formulas for glucose and mannose as described by Fischer after he demonstrated that both sugars give rise to identical phenylosazones wherein the stereochemistry at carbon atom 2 is destroyed.

At this point, Fischer introduced his single assumption. In earlier studies, he had established that 6-carbon sugars could be synthesized from glyceraldehyde (the simplest asymmetric carbohydrate) by successive applications of the cyanohydrin synthesis. He arbitrarily chose the glyceraldehyde that could be converted to the naturally occurring, optically active glucose as that represented by the projection formula which had the hydroxyl group on the right (Figure 2.1). It was quite immaterial for his argument whether this initial assumption was correct or incorrect. If it had been incorrect, Fischer would have ended up proving the structure of L-glucose as that for D, and vice versa. In addition, all of the carbohydrates represented in the early literature would have turned out to be their mirror images. We are tempted to speculate that this might have been the case had Fischer come from a civilization where writing occurred from right to left rather than the opposite. It was quite natural to put the hydroxyl group on the right because this was the manner in which we write things down. Accordingly, glucose and mannose could be represented as illustrated in Figure 2.3.

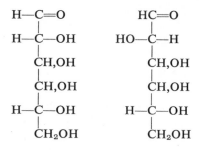

FIGURE 2.3 Structural representations of glucose and mannose after Fischer introduced his single assumption regarding the configuration around carbon atom 5.

It was known that both glucose and mannose could be reduced or oxidized to alcohols or dicarboxylic acids that had identical functional groups (CH_2OH or COOH) at carbons 1 and 6. *Both* types of derivatives for *both* sugars possessed optical activity, therefore ruling out structures such as those shown in Figure 2.4, wherein it is clear that internal compensation is present.

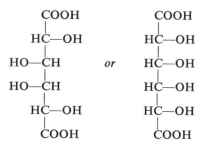

FIGURE 2.4 Like-ended 6-carbon dicarboxylic acid, which cannot represent derivatives from either glucose or mannose because the forms shown are internally compensated.

A naturally occurring 5-carbon sugar, arabinose, when carried through the cyanohydrin synthesis, yielded a pair of 6-carbon sugars. The major reaction product was identical in physical properties to natural mannose but the sign of the optical rotation was negative rather than positive. This was therefore the *mirror image* (enantiomorph) of the natural mannose. Similarly, the minor product was the mirror image of the natural glucose (Figure 2.5).

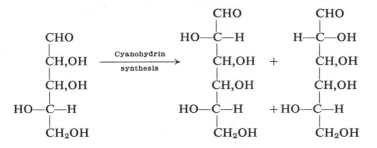

FIGURE 2.5 Cyanohydrin synthesis carried out on a 5-carbon sugar which gives rise to two 6-carbon sugars. As indicated in the text, the products of the reaction with L-arabinose were the mirror images of the natural glucose and mannose and therefore must have the opposite stereochemistry, not only at carbons 2 and 5 but at carbons 3 and 4 as well.

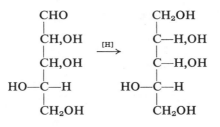

Product cannot be:

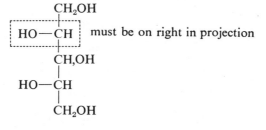

Product must be:

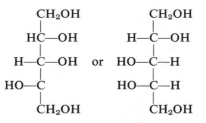

FIGURE 2.6 Conversion of L-arabinose to like-ended 5-carbon sugar alcohol. Because the product alcohol was optically active, it is impossible for the compensated form to satisfy the structural requirements. Therefore, the original L-arabinose must have been one of the two possible structures indicated.

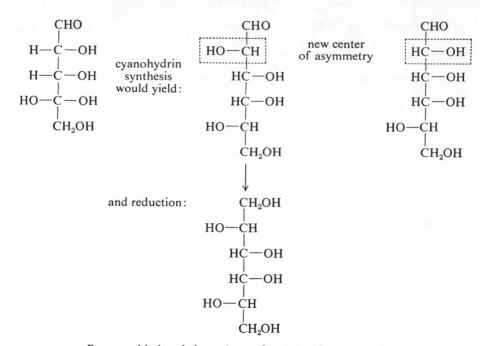

	CHO				CHO		new center	CHO
H—C—OH				HO—CH		of asymmetry	HC—OH
H—C—OH	cyanohydrin		HC—OH				HC—OH
HO—C—OH	synthesis would yield:		HC—OH				HC—OH
CH₂OH			HO—CH				HO—CH
			CH₂OH				CH₂OH

and reduction:

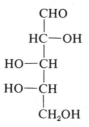

CH₂OH
HO—CH
HC—OH
HC—OH
HO—CH
CH₂OH

Because this is ruled out (meso form) arabinose *must* be:

CHO
HC—OH
HO—CH
HO—CH
CH₂OH

and glucose and mannose therefore become:

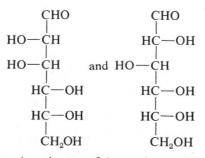

CHO   CHO
HO—CH   HC—OH
HO—CH and HO—CH
HC—OH   HC—OH
HC—OH   HC—OH
CH₂OH   CH₂OH

Note: These are mirror images of the products derived from arabinose.

FIGURE 2.7 Cyanohydrin synthesis on one of the two possible arabinose structures. This gives rise to two products, epimeric at carbon 2. However, one of these, as indicated, upon reduction would give rise to a meso 6-carbon sugar alcohol. *Because it is known that both glucose and mannose give rise to optically active like-ended derivatives, the arabinose must have* the indicated structure. The glucose and mannose therefore can be depicted.

This natural arabinose could be reduced to a sugar alcohol or oxidized to a dicarboxylic acid. Both products possessed optical activity and were therefore not internally compensated. Accordingly, this limits the structure for the natural arabinose, as shown in Figure 2.6. Because two of the four possible 5-carbon sugars would yield meso, like-ended derivatives, only the other two had to be considered. *One of these will give rise to a hexose that in turn forms a meso like-ended derivative.* Thus, only one possible structure remained once the assignment of the *original C-5* of the 6-carbon sugar had been assumed (Figure 2.7).

It is clear from the foregoing that the complete representations of glucose and mannose were already available. It simply remained to be decided which of the two depicted structures was glucose and which was mannose. One final piece of information was necessary to establish this point. It was shown by Fischer that the reduction or oxidation of glucose gave rise to a like-ended compound which could also be obtained from *another* sugar (gulose). A similar comparison for mannose showed that the compounds obtained could only be formed from the parent mannose. Inspection of the structures reveals that the optically active mannose derivatives are analogous to the tartaric acids. We would expect that symmetric reagents would be unable to distinguish the two "ends" of the dicarboxylic acid formed from the natural mannose or its mirror image but that asymmetric reagents (enzymes) could do so. A similar type of "asymmetry" is exhibited by citric acid. These data are only consistent if the structure of glucose is represented by that in Figure 2.8 and that of mannose by that in Figure 2.9.

The previous discussion assumed some rudimentary knowledge on the part of the reader as regards several carbohydrate transformations, but can be assimilated quite independently of the chemical reactions being carried out. This formulation of the structure of glucose and mannose was extended by Fischer to most of the other simple carbohydrates and his deductions have proved entirely sound.

It is appropriate now to review the logical development of carbohydrate structure with the foregoing information in hand. It was obvious that for 6-carbon sugars, at least 16 isomers were possible and that a more consistent nomenclature was necessary than that which could be accommodated by trivial names.[1] In the early literature, assignments of configuration were frequently made on the basis of the direction of optical rotation; thus, sugars were termed *d* or *l*, depending upon whether they rotated plane-polarized light to the right or to the left, respectively. However, Fischer himself as well as several other workers

---

[1] Some currently accepted rules of carbohydrate nomenclature are presented in Appendix 1. Several of the rules will be formulated in the text but the reader should familiarize himself with current usage. Some useful terms are as follows:

   1. The term *aldose* or *ketose* is used in a generic sense to denote the character of the carbonyl or potential carbonyl function. In an aldose, the aldehyde function is carbon 1 and in a ketose, the carbonyl function has the lowest possible number.
   2. The number of carbon atoms in the chain is designated by one of the following: triose (3), tetrose (4), pentose (5), hexose (6), heptose (7), and so on.

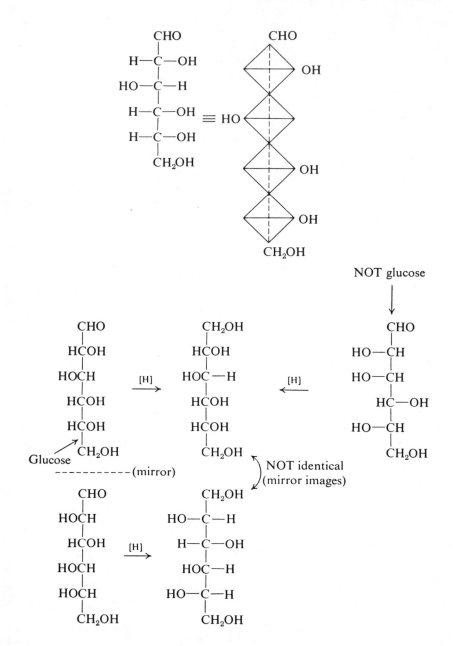

FIGURE 2.8   Representation of D-glucose as deduced by Fischer. Reduction of D-glucose yields a like-ended compound which is also derived by reduction of L-gulose *but not* L-*glucose.*

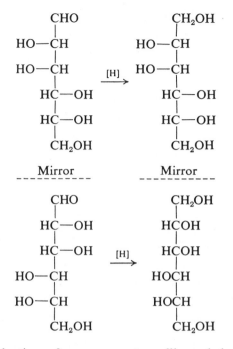

FIGURE 2.9 Reduction of D-mannose to a like-ended compound yields a product which is the mirror image of that obtained from the reduction of L-mannose, *but no other sugar.*

were well aware of the inadequacies represented by this convention. Thus, glucose represented originally as *d* had a positive optical rotation, whereas fructose was represented as *l*-fructose because it had a negative rotation although it was clearly configurationally related to glucose because both of them gave rise to identical phenylosazones.

The ambiguities and inconsistencies of the optical rotation convention were not resolved until Rosanoff, in 1916, proposed a system of nomenclature that has become universally adopted since that time [2]. He reasoned as follows: Because we can derive all of the simple carbohydrates from glyceraldehyde as the starting compound, let us assume that the parent glyceraldehyde for 8 of the 16 possible aldohexoses or 6-carbon sugars is that represented by Figure 2.10,

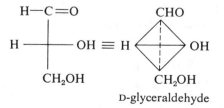

D-glyceraldehyde

FIGURE 2.10 Fischer projection and tetrahedral formula for D-glyceraldehyde.

and that the parent compound for the other 8 6-carbon sugars is represented by Figure 2.11. In a completely arbitrary fashion, one of these will be designated D-glyceraldehyde (in this case not referring to optical rotation but rather to the configuration of the hydroxyl group in the projection formula as being on the

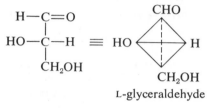

L-glyceraldehyde

FIGURE 2.11   Fischer projection and tetrahedral formula for L-glyceraldehyde.

right or on the left-hand side). The mirror image shall be designated L-glyceraldehyde again referring to the projected configuration of the hydroxyl group. All sugars that can possibly be derived from D-glyceraldehyde by application of the cyanohydrin synthesis are termed D-sugars and all those which could possibly be derived from L-glyceraldehyde are designated as L-sugars. The examples are given for the 4-carbon sugars; the reader can easily work out the remaining ones (Figure 2.12).

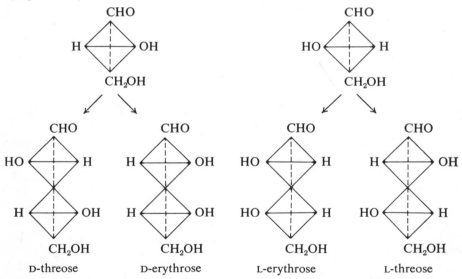

D-threose   D-erythrose   L-erythrose   L-threose

FIGURE 2.12   Conversion of glyceraldehydes to 4-carbon sugars, threose and erythrose.

2.3 Development of Cyclic Structures for Carbohydrates

The information that was accumulated regarding the configurational relationships of the monosaccharides permitted satisfactory projection formulas to be written for all known sugars. However, it was clear that these structural representations were inadequate to account for all of the properties and reactions of carbohydrates. Although carbohydrates, such as glucose, galactose, and mannose, gave many typical aldehyde reactions such as reduction to alcohols, mild oxidation to acids, and condensation reactions with aldehyde reagents—(phenylhydrazine), there were several properties of these sugars which were uncharacteristic of aldehydes and rather more difficult to explain. These included the following:

1. failure to react with amines to form typical Schiff bases;

2. the formation of two products on treatment with either an esterifying agent such as acetic anhydride or methanol and hydrogen chloride;

3. the change in optical rotation exhibited by freshly prepared crystalline sugars, apparently reaching an equilibrium value. For example, two crystalline forms of D-glucose were isolated. One had a rotation of +109 degrees and the other of +12 degrees. On standing, solutions of either form changed in optical rotation to an equilibrium value of +52.5 degrees. This phenomenon was termed *mutarotation*.

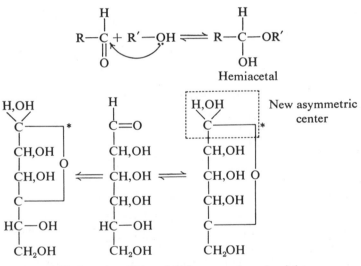

* Hydroxyl at C-4 and C-5 assumed on the right.

FIGURE 2.13 Reaction leading to the formation of hemiacetal rings in carbohydrates. In a carbohydrate the groups R and R′ are part of the same carbon chain. Note that a new asymmetric center has been created at position 1.

These properties could best be explained by a formation of an internal hemiacetal structure as illustrated in Figure 2.13. Because internal hemiacetals are in equilibrium with the open chain form in aqueous systems, the mutarotation phenomenon could be explained by interconversion of the two forms of the sugar through the open chain form. The formation of two derivatives on either esterification or acetalation reactions could be explained by reactions of the two different forms of the hemiacetal to yield full acetals (Figure 2.14), no longer in equilibrium with an open chain form. The general unreactivity or atypical behavior of the terminal aldehydo function could be explained by

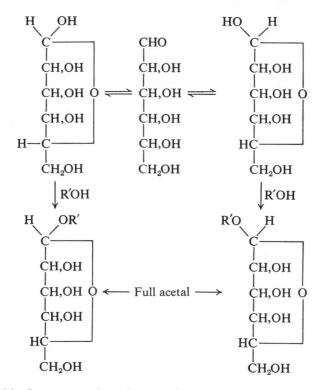

FIGURE 2.14   Interconversion of anomeric forms through equilibrium with the open chain structure. The formation of a full acetal by reaction of the carbohydrate with an alcohol leading to substitution at position 1 gives rise to a compound in which the ring is fixed and not in equilibrium with any open chain formula. The products thus derived from a single sugar are not mirror images, but are epimeric at carbon 1.

assuming that the great majority of the carbohydrate existed in this internal ring form.

The position of linkage of the ring form was originally assumed to be to carbon 4 of the carbohydrate chain. The structure was formulated in this manner by Fischer in analogy with the ready formation of 5-membered lactone rings with which he had considerable experience. The easier accommodation of the carbonyl function in a 5-membered ring is readily understood in contemporary structural terms and will be discussed in detail subsequently. More

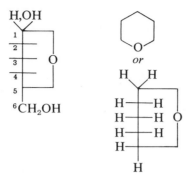

FIGURE 2.15 Fischer projection formula of 6-carbon aldose sugar in the ring form. The parent heterocycle is tetrahydropyran and the 6-membered ring structure is termed a pyranose.

recent work, particularly by Haworth, based on methylation and periodate studies, as well as modern studies of conformation, has conclusively proved that the predominant (in most cases the exclusive) form is the 6-membered ring, illustrated in Figure 2.15. Note that the formation of this new ring gives rise to another asymmetric center at carbon 1 and introduces additional nomenclature and isomerism problems. In accord with early conventions, the form for a D-sugar having the higher optical rotation was designated α and the other anomer β. This arose out of the fact that one of the two crystalline glucoses

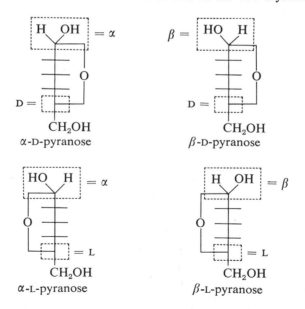

FIGURE 2.16 Projection formula and nomenclature rules for α and β and D- and L-pyranoses.

isolated was named α-glucose and in fact turned out to be the one of the higher optical rotation. This is conventionalized somewhat more rigorously as follows: In the D series, the α form is the one having the higher optical rotation and in which the hemiacetal hydroxyl appears on the right in the projection diagram. In the D series, the β form has the hemiacetal hydroxyl on the left side of the projection diagram. *The reverse holds true for* L-*sugars so that α-*D- *and* α-L-*sugars represent true mirror images* (Figure 2.16). In an α-L-sugar, the rotation is larger in a negative direction than for the corresponding β-L-sugar.

2.4 Applications of Optical Rotatory Behavior to Configurational Studies

The major contributor to the development of empirical optical rotation rules has been C. S. Hudson [3]. Many of his experimental investigations were in part dictated by attempts to verify some of the hypotheses regarding optical rotation which he himself had proposed. His first publications on optical rotation rules appeared at a time when there was still much confusion with regard to both the configuration of carbohydrates and their nomenclature. Hudson officially proposed that the assignment of α and β forms of a given sugar be done in such a way that for sugars related to D-glucose the subtraction of the rotation of the β form from that of the α form would give a positive difference, and for sugars related to L-glucose, this difference would be negative. This was a modification of the rule that assigned the more strongly rotating form the α configuration. To be consistent with this latter formulation, the mirror image of α-D-glucose would be called β-L-glucose, and Hudson correctly felt that this misrepresented the relationship between these sugars. With the nomenclature in mind, let us consider the development of some of Hudson's rotation rules.[2] It is assumed throughout that the carbohydrates are present in the ring form.

The rotational contribution due to the end asymmetric carbon was designated A and that due to the remainder of the molecule was termed B. The molecular rotation of the form on the left in Figure 2.17 is expressed as $A + B$, whereas the rotation of the form on the right is expressed as $-A + B$ since the two isomers are identical except for the asymmetric carbon at position 1. The molecular rotations of similar isomers for the other sugars that have the same configuration at carbon 1 as does α- or β-D-glucose may be considered. Whereas it is true that in these sugars the remainder of the carbon chain is not identical

---

[2] The specific rotation, [α], is calculated from the observed rotation, α, according to the following expression:

$$[\alpha] = \frac{100\alpha}{lc}$$

where l is the length of the light path in *decimeters* and c is the concentration of solute in grams per 100 ml of solution. The molar rotation M is equal to the specific rotation times the molecular weight.

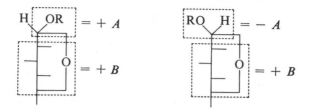

FIGURE 2.17 Schematic representation of full acetals or glycosides in terms of the rotational contribution of the center at carbon 1 and the centers of the remainder of the molecule. Contribution of carbon 1 is termed plus A when the substituent is α and minus A when the substituent is β.

to that in glucose, this seems to have very little effect on the rotatory contribution of the anomeric center. By the same token, it is found that the carbon chain itself retains a fairly constant rotational contribution when only the group at carbon 1 is changed. This rotatory effect is independent of and uninfluenced by the chain. Stated in equation form, the differences between the *molecular* rotations of α and β forms of all aldehyde sugars is nearly constant.

$$
\begin{array}{r}
\text{Sum of } \alpha + \beta \text{ forms} = \quad A + B \\
-A + B \\
\hline
2B
\end{array}
\tag{2.1}
$$

$$
\begin{array}{r}
\text{Difference of } \alpha + \beta \text{ forms} = \quad A + B \\
- \; -A + B \\
\hline
2A
\end{array}
$$

$2A$ may be independent of configuration of chain.

The two anomers of D-glucose will have molecular rotations whose sum is $2B$ and this value will be substantially the same for a large number of derivatives. Table 2.1 illustrates the close correlation between theory and the experimental observations.

Since the rotatory power of many naturally occurring glycosides is known, it is possible to predict the specific rotations of the corresponding anomeric glycosides from the above rules. This is obviously applicable to a situation where the A and B values are known for the parent sugar in question. The agreement is very good for glucose and galactose derivatives but has been relatively less studied for other sugars. Also, Equation (2.1) is only valid where the substituent group (aglycone) itself is not optically active.

If the molecular weight of a known glycoside is w, and its specific rotation is r_β, the specific rotation of the anomer r_α would be a constant over w minus r_β. For glucosides, the value of this constant is 23,200. Obviously, the substituent R group can vary considerably in molecular weight. Because the contribution of the glycosidic carbon alone can be calculated from these rules, it is possible to

TABLE 2.1

Specific and molecular rotations for selected monosaccharides and a disaccharide.

SUGAR	SPECIFIC ROTATION	MOLECULAR ROTATION[a]	DIFFERENCE $(\alpha - \beta)$
α-D-glucose	+109	19,600	16,000
β-D-glucose	+20	3600	
α-D-galactose	+140	25,200	15,700
β-D-galactose	+53	9500	
β-L-arabinose	+104.5	28,610	−16,050
α-L-arabinose	+48	11,560	
α-D-lactose	+86	29,400	17,400
β-D-lactose	+35	12,000	

[a] Specific rotation × molecular weight.

deduce a relationship of the effect on optical rotation of the weight of the aglycone grouping (Figure 2.18). Although this expression fails to take into account the nature of the aglycone, and the polarizability of its electrons with the effect that this may have on the contribution of neighboring asymmetric centers, the curve is clearly asymptotic.

The influence of temperature on the equilibrium between the α and β forms of free sugars has also been studied polarimetrically. Experimentally, a sugar solution is heated to a given temperature and then rapidly cooled while the change in optical rotation is observed. Without exception, it was found that the α form of the sugar predominates at elevated temperatures with a return upon

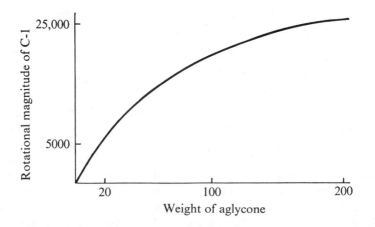

FIGURE 2.18   Variation of the rotational contribution of carbon 1 with the weight of the substituent group.

cooling to equilibrium where the β form may predominate. There is no thermal lag in this situation for sugars that do not mutarotate.

There are two other rotation rules that were formulated to answer questions of asymmetry regarding the products obtained by the application of the cyano-hydrin synthesis. In a typical cyanohydrin reaction, the first isolable products are a pair of sugar acids which are epimeric at carbon 2. When one of these is then crystallized from the reaction mixture, it would be advantageous to have some method for assigning its structure without having to resort to extensive degradative or other structural techniques. It was well known that open chain compounds, partly because of their relatively unrestricted rotation about carbon–carbon bonds, exhibit a great deal of rotational cancellation and the absolute magnitudes of their optical rotation are small. However, the formation of a suitable derivative, or conversion of such acids to a ring form (lactone) has a marked effect upon the magnitude of the optical rotation. The first of these rules is called the *lactone rule* and may be stated as follows: The optical rotation of the lactone derived from a sugar acid will be significantly increased over that of the parent acid when, if written in the standard Fischer projection formula, the ring is on the right-hand side. The lactone with the ring projecting to the left will be more levorotatory than the parent acid.

Because the difference in magnitudes of the rotations is very substantial, this was a convenient empirical tool. However, the application of rotatory dispersion studies to the sugar lactones will probably make the above unnecessary, since the entire configuration can be deduced from an analysis of dispersion curves (see Section 4.13).

The second rule proposed by Hudson was the phenylhydrazide rule: The phenylhydrazides of aldonic acids will be more dextrorotatory than the acid if the hydroxyl group at carbon 2 projects to the right and more levorotatory than the parent acid if the hydroxyl at carbon 2 projects to the left.

This is easily rationalized in the sense that the proximity of the phenyl-hydrazide grouping will probably have a very significant effect on the rotational contribution of the asymmetric center at carbon 2. However, why the effect should be in one direction for a given configuration cannot be resolved at our present level of understanding.

The above rotation rules have been of great historical interest in the field of carbohydrate chemistry and also of very considerable utility in assignment of configurations for unknown new compounds. They are particularly valuable where conformational instability is not likely and where the gross structure of the molecule can be established with a reasonable degree of certainty. However, as the chemistry of more unusual carbohydrates begins to be developed and the possibility of more than one conformational isomer remains, it becomes apparent that the rotation of a molecule is a function of its three-dimensional shape rather than of its projection formula. Thus, from the projection formula for D-idose, it is immediately apparent that it is not possible to predict the predominant or "correct" three-dimensional structure (Figure 2.19). Accordingly,

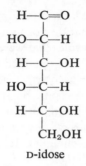

D-idose

FIGURE 2.19   Fischer projection formula for D-idose.

an application of rotation rules in the absence of conformational information could lead to entirely erroneous conclusions. The current state of optical rotation theory is not at such a sophisticated level that satisfactory structural information can be deduced from this type of analysis alone.

CHAPTER $\boxed{3}$

Conformation and Conformational Analysis

3.1 Strainless 6-Membered Rings

While in many ways they explained much of the chemistry that was known at the time, the structural representations of the hemiacetal forms of the sugars as 6-membered rings proved unsatisfactory for a variety of reasons. It was perfectly apparent that the fact that the carbohydrates could best be represented as internal hemiacetal forms did not convey any unusual elastic properties on the carbon–oxygen or carbon–oxygen–carbon bonds involved in the formation of the 6-membered ring. Several attempts were made to represent these rings in a more spatially accurate way than the simple planar or stick representation depicted. The best known and most commonly used of these is the Haworth form illustrated in Figure 3.1 [1]. The ring is formulated as a hexagon with the plane of the ring perpendicular to the plane of the paper. The front edge is shaded so as to accentuate this and bonds above and below the plane of the ring would represent those to the left and to the right of the Fischer projection, respectively. The nomenclature rules for the use of this form are indicated. Although this represents an improvement over the Fischer projection, it still falls far short of an accurate projection. The very fact that the carbohydrate hemiacetal structure exists as a 6-membered ring *in equilibrium* with the open chain form argues that this structure is thermodynamically stable. In fact, the properties of the sugars in solution strongly suggest that ring form predominates. Accordingly, we must ask if this relatively strainless form can be visualized as a planar hexagon and, if not, what structures can be written to satisfy the stability requirements.

A consideration of the bond angles for a tetrahedral carbon atom immediately leads to the realization that a 6-membered alicyclic ring, in order to be free from bond strain, will not exist in a planar form. The planar hexagon would have bond angles of 120 degrees, appreciably different from 109° 28′, introducing considerable distortion. An evaluation of the structure present for most carbohydrates, and indeed for alicyclic structures generally, leads to a

41

consideration of *conformational analysis*. Conformational analysis is the study of physical and chemical properties of a compound in terms of its conformation in the ground state and in transition states when it is undergoing a reaction.

The tools employed in conformational analysis are quite numerous. These include reactivity of specific functional groups, measurement of bond distances

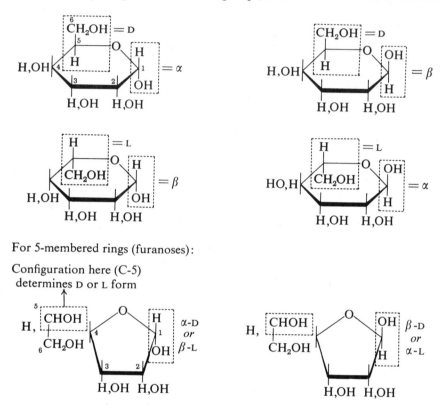

For 5-membered rings (furanoses):

FIGURE 3.1   Haworth formulas for D- and L-pyranoses and furanoses.

by use of complexing agents, infrared and nuclear-magnetic-resonance spectroscopy, optical rotatory dispersion, chromatographic behavior, melting point, solubility, dipole moment, and so on. The determination of the absolute three-dimensional structure of a molecule is usually only available through X-ray diffraction analysis of crystals. Even in the relatively simple cases that we shall consider, description of chemical behavior in solution must be regarded as a kind of probability statement wherein a given conformation represents to a limit of approximation the most likely structure for the molecule under consideration. Where the strain elements are few, such as in highly stable structures, the proposed structure will likely account for many of the reactions that a given molecule undergoes. Where the strain elements become many, the proposed structure may or may not be the most favored one, and other more flexible or less obvious structures may predominate. It is also true that there is little accurate data regarding the energy barriers between interconversions of conformers of different types. Therefore, it is difficult to state with any certainty whether a given compound exists as a conformer equilibrium or whether an apparently unstable (less likely) form might predominate because of considerations of activation energy. Superimposed upon this general problem is the realization that when details of fine structure are considered, distances calculated from examination of molecular models will frequently be in error by a few percent. If this error is not critical, or if a molecule is flexible within the area of uncertainty, these are not likely to be serious drawbacks with regard to interpretation of chemical behavior. However, where several physical properties are concerned, small differences become magnified. An understanding of these properties will help provide a more accurate assessment of three-dimensional structure.

TABLE 3.1

Heats of combustion of ethylene and cyclic hydrocarbons.

COMPOUND	HEAT OF COMBUSTION		DEVIATION FROM "NORMAL" ANGLE [a]
	kcal/mole	kcal/CH_2	
Ethylene	340	170	$+54$
Cyclopropane	506	169	$+24$
Cyclobutane	663	166	$+9$
Cyclopentane	797	159	$+0°, 44'$
Cyclohexane	939	158	-5
Cycloheptane	1103	158	-9

[a] Based on calculation for planar structure.

Accordingly, the subsequent discussion will consider the types of conformers which may exist for a 6-membered ring and the various methods that are used to determine which of these is most likely for a given structure. The utility of these methods in predicting a three-dimensional molecular structure can best be evaluated in terms of chemical results. As with most "rules," exceptions occur with disturbing frequency but are easily rationalized.

The early proposals of Bayer relating ring strain to deviations from the tetrahedral bond angle were consistent as long as 3-, 4-, and 5-membered rings were being considered. His angle deviation for 6-membered rings was quite large and did not explain the thermochemical properties and generally inert behavior of cyclohexane which argued for extreme stability for such a 6-membered ring [2] (Table 3.1). The proposals of Sachse, first advanced in approximately 1890, were of considerable merit (although largely ignored at the time and still given insufficient attention) and have gone far toward explaining the properties of 6-membered rings [3]. He pointed out that 6-membered rings could be constructed in nonplanar shapes, wherein all the valence angles were tetrahedral. He distinguished a flexible and a rigid form and further recognized that there could be two monosubstitution products of the rigid form.

The strainless formulation of the 6-membered ring of cyclohexane is illustrated in Figure 3.2. It can be seen that this representation is that of an equilibrium mixture of two ring forms which are *mirror images* of one another. The conversion from one ring form to another probably goes through an

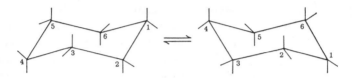

FIGURE 3.2   Structural formula for cyclohexane in a strainless representation.

intermediate stage such as that represented in Figure 3.3, and in the case of cyclohexane, is extremely rapid at room temperature. Suffice to say that all positions interchange during this ring conversion and once a substituent group other than hydrogen is present in the molecule, these interconversions are no longer of trivial importance.

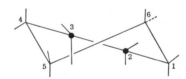

FIGURE 3.3   Skew form of cyclohexane which is the presumed intermediate in the interconversion of one ring form to its mirror image.

It is generally difficult to visualize the geometry of the strainless 6-membered ring and an examination of molecular models at this point is strongly recommended. There are several features that may be noted:

1. The ring may be formed by starting with a planar hexagon and successively raising and lowering opposite vertices.

2. The ring as drawn has 3 pairs of parallel sides.

3. The carbon atoms designated 2, 3, 5, and 6 are essentially coplanar, with carbon 1 and carbon 4 above and below this plane, respectively.

In the alternate ring isomer, the positions of C-1 and C-4 are reversed, but carbons 2, 3, 5, and 6 still remain in their coplanar arrangement.

It is apparent from consideration of this structure that there are two general classes of bonds attached to the cyclohexane ring. The first is a group of six which radiate perpendicular to the plane of the "original" hexagon; these are termed *axial bonds*. The second group of six radiate in this plane and are parallel to the nonadjacent pair of parallel sides. Since the angle between valences is not 90 degrees, it is not quite accurate to state that these bonds are in the plane of the ring as formed by carbons 2, 3, 5, and 6 but rather that they are approximately in the plane or radiate in the plane; these positions are termed the *equatorial positions*. The ring form itself is termed the *chair form*.

If we follow a single hydrogen substituent on a given carbon atom, as illustrated in Figure 3.4, *the interconversion of one ring form to the other results in the change of this hydrogen from an axial to an equatorial position, or vice versa.*

There have been several attempts to measure the energy barrier for this inter-conversion and to obtain substantiating evidence that the two ring conformers shown are in fact present in cyclohexane. The most recent results have been obtained by examining nuclear-magnetic-resonance spectra as a function of temperature [4]. (See Chapter 4.) When the equilibrium between the two con-formers is extremely rapid compared to the time of measurement of an individual parameter, then only an average response from the various structures will be

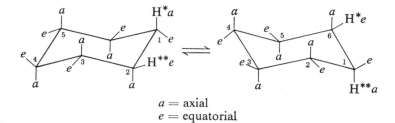

$$a = \text{axial}$$
$$e = \text{equatorial}$$

FIGURE 3.4 Representation of cyclohexane with axial and equatorial bonds. Note that conversion from one ring form to another involves the change of groups from an axial to an equatorial orientation or vice versa.

obtained. However, if the interconversion between the two ring forms is slowed down sufficiently by reducing the temperature at which the observation is made, it is then possible under suitable conditions to resolve the spectral behavior of the hydrogens present in cyclohexane. These split into two equal groups, those that are axial and those that are equatorial. By an assessment of the rate of conversion of these two forms or the rate of "time-averaging" as a function of temperature, it is possible to arrive at an estimate of the energy barrier (activation energy) for the ring interconversion. The figure thus derived is approximately 10 kcal per mole; it is apparent that thermal energy is more than sufficient at ordinary operating temperature in the laboratory to allow for very rapid equili-bration of these isomers.

For any given pair of hydrogens in cyclohexane, those present on adjacent carbons are translated at an angle of + or − 60 degrees relative to the carbon–carbon bond (Figure 3.5). It is clear that the distance between an axial and an equatorial hydrogen on adjacent carbons is exactly the same as the distance between two equatorial hydrogens. This fact is of very considerable importance in an understanding of carbohydrate reactions.

It is also clear that the distance between two axial substituents on adjacent carbons is quite large. These actually project on different sides of the molecule and therefore interactions between axial substituents on adjacent carbons are of relatively minor consideration. A second type of interaction is termed the

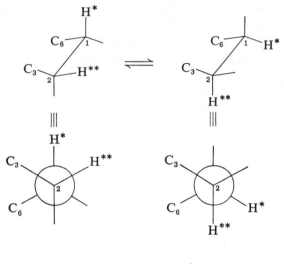

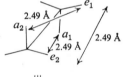

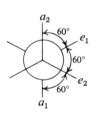

$a_1 - a_2$ distance is 3.0 Å

FIGURE 3.5   Distances between groups on adjacent carbon atoms in a cyclohexane ring.

transannular, or *1-3 interaction.* Axial groups on the same side of the ring, such as the hydrogens, illustrated in Figure 3.6, are at a distance of relatively close approach to one another. This distance is substantially the same as that between axial and equatorial or diequatorial hydrogens on adjacent carbon atoms. When polar groups are present or bulky substituents occur in an axial

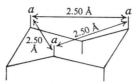

FIGURE 3.6 Distances between transannular axial substituents on a cyclo-hexane ring.

conformation, these steric repulsions will play a large part in determining ring distortion and other factors in the molecular structure.

The total number of interactions present in such a structure for cyclohexane may be conveniently expressed as the sum of all the hydrogen–hydrogen interactions, although as stated previously, the strain energy due to such interactions is not from steric repulsion and is incompletely understood. These are only of two types: Those that are 60 degrees translated (axial-equatorial or equatorial-equatorial) and those that are transannular or axial 1,3 on the same

TABLE 3.2

Calculation of the strain energy for the cyclohexane chair form.

INTERACTION	STRAIN OR REPULSION ENERGY (kcal)	TOTAL
Axial-equatorial hydrogen	1.07	6 × 1.07 = 6.42
Equatorial-equatorial hydrogen	1.07	6 × 1.07 = 6.42
Transannular (1,3) hydrogen	1.04	6 × 1.04 = 6.24
Axial-axial hydrogen	0	0
		Total for chair = 19.1 kcal

side of the 6-membered ring. Various estimates have been made as to the instability or strain energy associated with each of the listed interactions. These are given in Table 3.2 and indicate the strain energy to be expected in this representation of a 6-membered ring [5].

The chair form is not the only nonplanar structure that can be formulated for cyclohexane wherein no distortion of bond angles takes place. For purposes of comparison, examine the boat form of cyclohexane illustrated in Figure 3.7. In addition to the familiar skew interactions, hydrogens attached to carbon atoms along the side of the boat are in the eclipsed form where the angle of the translation between hydrogens on adjacent carbons is essentially 0 degrees. This brings these protons into a much closer approach distance than that found in the chair formula and imposes a larger strain energy. This phenomenon was previously discussed in considering the structure of ethane. There is one additional interaction that is quite prominent in the boat form and that is termed the *bow-stern interaction* (Figure 3.8). In this case, the protons of carbon 1 and carbon 4 are at a distance of approach that is much closer than either of the other interactions hitherto encountered, and steric repulsion does become

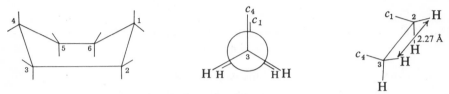

Same for C_6-C_5
Eclipsed H–H interactions (4): 2.14 kcal/mole = 8.56
Skew H–H interactions (12): 1.07 kcal/mole = 12.84

FIGURE 3.7   Boat or flexible form of the cyclohexane ring. The eclipsed hydrogen–hydrogen interactions have a repulsion energy of 2.14 kcal per mole and the skew interactions are the same as those of cyclohexane.

significant. It is this single interaction that makes the boat form rather unlikely. Although several workers have proposed alternative boat forms for carbohydrates by moving the oxygen around to any of six positions to allow for different types of ring isomers (Figure 3.9), an examination of molecular models reveals the following:

1. The chair form is a rigid structure permitting relatively little distortion of bonds without introducing some considerable strain.

2. The boat form appears to be a completely flexible structure which may adopt an infinity of possible conformations.

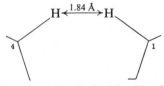

Bow-stern H–H: 8.25 kcal/mole

FIGURE 3.8   Bow-stern interaction for the boat form of cyclohexane. The repulsion energy is 8.25 kcal per mole.

3. It is apparent from energetic considerations that the highly stylized boat must, in real circumstances, give way to energetically more favorable half-chair or skew forms, as illustrated in Figure 3.10. The skew and half-chair forms of the 6-membered ring are encountered as possible intermediates in chair–chair interconversions and when the 6-membered ring contains a double bond or fused ring substituent which imposes certain planar restrictions.

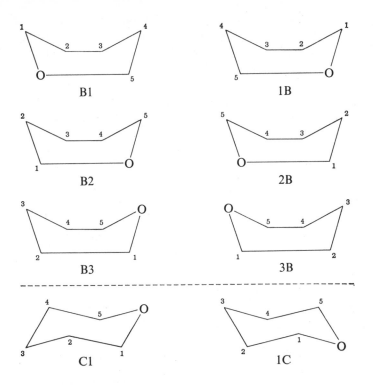

FIGURE 3.9 Possible boat forms for tetrahydropyran. Compare with the two rigid chair forms.

It is useful for certain types of considerations to regard formal boat structures as possible molecular entities but it should be obvious from the above that these are gross oversimplifications. The energy difference between either of the two chair forms and the "possible" boat forms has been calculated for cyclohexane simply on the basis of the interactions of the various hydrogen atoms involved. Typical data are summarized in Table 3.3, and show a net

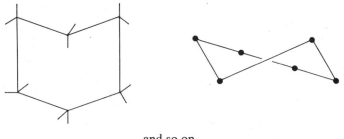

and so on

FIGURE 3.10 Skew boat form of the 6-membered ring.

difference in the neighborhood of 6 kcal per mole. However, it seems likely from consideration of cyclohexane and related molecules that the type of ring interconversion that takes place between the two cyclohexane chair forms does not occur between a given chair and the boat form. The free-energy difference of 6 kcal is accompanied by an activation barrier at least 10 kcal in magnitude and the properties of cyclohexane are satisfactorily explained assuming only the chair form to be present. It is possible, however, to impose secondary restrictions on a given molecule such as the presence of unusual substituent groups, bicyclic ring systems, and so on, wherein a boat form is dictated by the over-all geometry of the structure. In this case, it will be found that such structures are rather rigid

TABLE 3.3

Total strain energy present in chair, boat, and skew forms for the 6-membered ring.

FORM	TOTAL SKEW REPULSIONS	BOW-STERN OR TRANSANNULAR	TOTAL STRAIN ENERGY
Chair	12	6 (T-A)	19.1 kcal
Boat	12	1 (Bow-Stern) + 4 Eclipsed	29.6
Skew or half-boat	12 (at ~ 2.44 Å each)	2 (Bow-Stern) at 2.45 Angstroms + 4 (Eclipsed) at 2.33 Angstroms	25

and that only the unusual restrictions imposed permit the existence of such forms. A key consideration to translating structural results on the cyclohexane ring structure to the 6-membered ring of carbohydrates is that the bond angles for oxygen are substantially the same as those present for carbon. Thus, the tetrahedral orientation for the carbon atom valences is maintained and the oxygen atom may be substituted into the 6-membered ring without appreciable distortion of the ring shape. It is certainly true that the polar oxygen with its electron withdrawing capacity will probably have some effect on bond distances, on the actual positions of hydrogens near to it, and on interactions with polar substituents on nearby carbons. Nevertheless, the majority of properties are satisfactorily explained by assuming that no ring distortion has taken place. As a general rule, unless specifically mentioned, carbohydrates will exist in the most stable chair form as represented by the cyclohexane ring structure.

Although the foregoing considerations have been based primarily on the behavior of protons, it is apparent that the more polar and the more bulky substituent groups become, the more effectively they will repel one another and the more driving force will exist to keep them at distances as far apart as possible. In addition to all of the above considerations, there are interactions with the ring oxygen and, as a result, it is not always possible to predict what the most stable conformer will be for a given substituted carbohydrate. It seems likely that polar groups would prefer to be disposed in an equatorial arrangement rather than in an axial arrangement. Whereas it is true that polar groups which are transdiaxial on adjacent carbons will not interact together, they would both interact with transannular neighbors on their respective sides of the 6-membered ring. The strain energies imposed will total somewhat more than the interaction found for the diequatorial conformer. Nevertheless, when the polar substituents are sufficiently large as in *trans* 1,2-dibromo cyclohexane, then the diaxial conformer may predominate [6].

CHAPTER $\boxed{4}$

Optical Methods of Structural Analysis

4.1 Nuclear-Magnetic-Resonance Spectra

There have been few analytical techniques of structural analysis which have mushroomed with quite the same rapidity as has the application of nuclear-magnetic-resonance spectroscopy to conformational problems. The general advantages of this technique that render it so valuable are: (1) the ability to examine a molecule without losing it, (2) information is obtained regarding not only the number of protons but also their environment, (3) the environmental information provides data regarding the spatial relationships of the protons to one another as well as their electronic surroundings. Data of this nature have permitted the analysis of complex structures and the assignment of conformations which are not possible by other means.

When a compound is placed in a magnetic field, the nuclei of the constituent atoms that have the property of spin and therefore act as nuclear magnets will orient themselves in various fashions with respect to the externally applied field. Their directions relative to the field are quantized and thus will appear to exist in a selected number of orientations. The number of possible orientations depends on the spin state of the nucleus and is given by

$$I = \text{spin}$$

Spin states are given by

$$I, I - 1, \cdots -I + 1, -I \tag{4.1}$$

If $I = \frac{1}{2}$, only two spin states are possible: $+\frac{1}{2}$ and $-\frac{1}{2}$.

Each orientation that is adopted will have a different characteristic energy depending upon whether the nuclear magnet is aligned with or against the applied field.

The interaction of radiant energy with a molecule (absorption spectroscopy) follows well-established rules. A photon of light is absorbed by a molecule if, and only if, the energy of the photon is equal to the difference in energy between two states of the molecule. During this absorption process, the molecule is

52

promoted from one energy level to another and this change is due largely to an alteration in the electronic (ultraviolet, visible) or vibrational-translational (infrared) states of the molecule. In either case, the relationship between the wavelength of the absorbed incident radiation and the energy of each photon is given by

$$E = h\nu$$

Since

$$\lambda\nu = c$$

then

$$E = \frac{hc}{\lambda}$$

ν = frequency
λ = wavelength
c = speed of light

(4.2)

The wavelength necessary to promote the hypothetical transition is

$$E = \frac{1}{2}\gamma H_0$$

$$\Delta E = \gamma\hbar H_0$$

$$\hbar = \frac{h}{2\pi} \quad \text{(Planck's constant, } 6.6 \times 10^{-27} \text{ erg sec)}$$

$$H_0 = \text{Applied magnetic field}$$

(4.3)

The term γ is called the *gyromagnetic ratio* and is a *constant characteristic of the individual nucleus* under consideration. Radiation of the type observed in nuclear-magnetic-resonance spectroscopy is in the so-called radio-frequency or micro-wave region and accordingly is concerned with electromagnetic radiation of extremely low energy. In other words, the transitions observed in nuclear-magnetic-resonance spectra are between states separated by extremely small energy differences.

One additional advantage in the examination of organic compounds is that nuclear-magnetic-resonance absorption occurs only in specimens containing nuclei that possess the property of spin or have angular momentum. Carbon-12, oxygen-16, and sulfur-32 have zero spin and consequently do not exhibit nuclear-magnetic-resonance absorptions. In contrast, hydrogen-1, fluorine-19, phosphorus-31, and carbon-13 are nuclei with spin $\frac{1}{2}$. Successful nuclear-magnetic-resonance work has also been done with nuclei of higher spin, such as nitrogen-14, oxygen-17, and deuterium.

The spinning, charged nucleus must possess a nuclear-magnetic moment whose size depends both on the nature of the nucleus and on its spin state. The nuclear-magnetic moment of a *given spin state* can stabilize or destabilize this state by interaction with a prevailing magnetic field such as that in which the specimen is placed when an NMR experiment is being conducted. For purposes of argument, we may consider that the nuclei under discussion have the spin state $\frac{1}{2}$. Therefore, according to Equation (4.1), an isolated nucleus present in a given molecule can exist in *two* possible spin states: *plus one-half* and *minus one-half*, which respectively stabilize and destabilize these states. The energy relative to this transition is expressed by Equation (4.3).

The energy difference between the two states is therefore equal to

$$\Delta E = h\nu = \gamma \hbar H_0 \tag{4.4}$$

The absorption of electromagnetic radiation, which would effectively promote the transition between these two states, will occur when a photon of energy equivalent to this is absorbed. Such a photon would have the following properties:

$$\nu = \frac{\gamma}{2\pi} H_0 = \gamma H_0 \tag{4.5}$$

In the case of protons, which are the primary nucleus under consideration for carbohydrate studies (and indeed for most structural work at present), the gyromagnetic ratio is 4.2577 megacycles per kilogauss. In practical terms, this means that a sample of hydrogen nuclei in a magnetic field of 14,100 gauss will absorb radiant energy at 60 megacycles. *All other resonant nuclei* have appreciably smaller values of the gyromagnetic ratio and therefore require much higher magnetic fields to bring about resonance at a *given frequency*. Contemporary developments in the field of superconducting magnets have made possible the production of extremely high magnetic fields which have been applied in specialized cases to studies of fluorine, phosphorus, and other resonant nuclei.

4.2 Chemical Shifts

In any natural product or indeed almost any organic compound, no proton is without an environment. This environment will contain both similar and dissimilar nuclei as well as electrons that are involved in the molecular bonds. All of these elementary particles[1] can contribute to the actual magnetic field experienced by the hydrogen nucleus. The largest of these contributors to the local fields are the nearby electrons. The very strong, applied, external field causes the local electrons to endeavor to precess about the direction of the external field. The magnitude of the *locally generated* magnetic field *due to the precession of the electrons* depends not only upon the number of electrons surrounding the nucleus but also on the molecular or bonding orbitals in which they exist. The precession that results in the formation of the local field is generally in directional opposition to the externally applied field, and the *magnitude is approximately 10^6 times smaller* than is the external field. Naturally, the exact size of these local fields will vary from case to case and in a more general sense, this is only one of the contributions. The local field experienced by

---

[1] We are not aware of the current vocabulary or even if this term is acceptable. Accordingly our apologies to contemporary nuclear physicists.

a given nucleus will contain contributions from other sources as well. The effect of these small changes in the field is to cause the proton or the nucleus to absorb at a frequency very slightly different from that predicted by the gyromagnetic ratio, γ, when the sample actually is placed in a field of external field strength H_0.

The total environment of the nucleus is really what determines the size of the local field. This parameter is usually expressed as σ, the shielding constant, according to the following expression:

$$\nu = \nu(H_0 - H_{\text{Local}})$$
$$\nu = \gamma H_0(1 - \sigma) \tag{4.6}$$

As σ becomes very large, the nucleus is said to be more shielded. Because of the experimental difficulty of simultaneously measuring both magnetic field and frequency sufficiently accurately to characterize nuclei of a certain type, it is customary to refer the sigma of the compound under study to that of a standard reference sample. The one most frequently employed is tetramethylsilane (TMS) (Figure 4.1). This reference compound has several advantages.

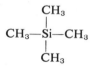

FIGURE 4.1   Tetramethylsilane.

1. It is volatile and thus easily removed.

2. It contains 12 identical protons and gives a single fairly intense signal so that large amounts need not be added.

3. The absorption of most protons is on one side of the tetramethylsilane resonance frequency so that spectra can be observed in one direction.

The shielding effect is a measure of the magnitude of the locally induced fields and will cause resonance to occur at a position different from that predicted by the gyromagnetic ratio. *This displacement is termed the chemical shift* and is defined as follows:

$$\delta_i = \sigma_{\text{TMS}} - \sigma_i$$
$$\gamma_0 = H_i(1 - \sigma_i) \tag{4.7}$$
$$\gamma_0 = 60 \text{ megacycles}$$

This value is usually reported in parts per million to give numbers of a convenient magnitude to be compared. (Recall that the local fields are 10^6 smaller than the external field.) *A large delta indicates a deshielded nucleus.* In connection with the above consideration, it is important to realize that the local field induced in the manner described above would be proportional to the externally applied field, H_0. Thus, the chemical shift observed will also be proportional to H_0; expressing the chemical shift in terms of delta or sigma, which contain no dimensions of frequency, becomes especially convenient because it allows direct comparisons between instruments of different magnetic field strengths.

A second parameter has been introduced in an attempt to standardize chemical shift values to the tetramethylsilane standard. This value, tau, arbitrarily assigns the delta of TMS as 10, and other shifts are related to it.

In most experiments, it is customary to present spectra with field strength increasing to the right (Figure 4.2). It can be seen that shielded nuclei will absorb at the high field, right-hand end of the spectrum and deshielded nuclei will absorb at the low field, left-hand end. Although the mechanics of this spectral scan actually involve the scan of field, distances are often measured

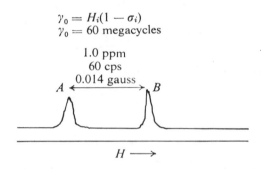

$$\gamma_0 = H_i(1 - \sigma_i)$$
$$\gamma_0 = 60 \text{ megacycles}$$

1.0 ppm
60 cps
0.014 gauss

A ←———————→ B

$H \longrightarrow$

FIGURE 4.2   Illustrated spectrum of two hydrogens absorbing energy as a function of magnetic field strength. The distance between them can be expressed as parts per million or cycles per second.

within the spectrum and expressed as cycles per second, which can be readily converted to field units or parts per million.

The chemical shift is created, as mentioned above, by differing electronic environments experienced by nuclei of the same atom. Protons in equivalent chemical environments will usually but not always have a different chemical shift.[2] As an example of this, the five aromatic protons of toluene resonate at an observably different frequency from the three methyl protons; but distinguishing between the ortho, meta, and para hydrogens by spectral methods is difficult if not impossible (Figure 4.3).

Protons bonded directly to a benzene ring resonate in a very limited region which is apparently rather characteristic of their total chemical environment. Similar generalizations can be made for olefinic protons, acetylenic protons, and so on. Thus, the chemical shift of a particular absorption when compared with other chemical shifts indicates a chemical environment of the proton and

---

[2] This is a well-known case of a converse not necessarily being true when the parent statement is true.

can show the presence of certain functional groups in the molecule. As indicated above, it is not necessary to have a numerical scale for measuring and reporting chemical shifts since the report in parts per million will be independent of the frequency of the spectrometer. It is desirable to have chemical shifts reflect purely intramolecular effects, and hence, the monomolecular structure of the substance under investigation. If compounds are present in considerable concentration, intermolecular effects may be present, and it may be desirable to run dilute samples in inert solvents using internal indicators.

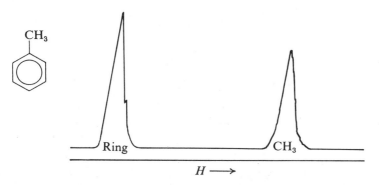

FIGURE 4.3 Illustration of the proton magnetic resonance spectrum of toluene. Methyl protons absorb at 2.32 parts per million and the ring protons at 7.17 parts per million. Although in theory the ring protons should resolve into three groups, present instrumentation does not achieve this type of resolution.

Deutero chloroform and carbon tetrachloride are typical inert solvents that are frequently used, although in the case of carbohydrates, solvents such as dimethyl sulfoxide and water (D_2O) have been employed. TMS is insoluble in aqueous systems and other internal standards, such as acetonitrile, dioxane, or a sulfonated silane derivative, have been used.

The relationship between the chemical shift and the environment of the carbon to which the resonant proton is attached is illustrated in Table 4.1. It should be noted that it is easy to distinguish between aromatic, olefinic, acetylenic, and aldehydo protons, that there is a considerable difference between alpha-substituted and beta-substituted aliphatic protons, and so on. Several useful generalizations are as follows:

1. Successive alkyl substitution of a saturated carbon almost always causes a shift to lower fields in the resonance of protons attached to that carbon.

2. In general, substituent effects are not additive and most frequently a second substituent causes a much smaller effect than does the first one.

3. The resonance of protons bonded to oxygen or nitrogen will be strongly influenced by hydrogen-bonding effects. As a result, the position of

these resonances in the spectrum can change markedly with concentration, solvent, and temperature, and relatively little structural information can be obtained from them. Exceptions are a carboxylic acid which forms a stable hydrogen-bonded structure, wherein the acidic proton resonance is found in the vicinity of $\delta = 11$, making this class of compounds easy to recognize.

4. Chelated protons such as those present in the enols absorb at very low fields.

5. In substituted cyclohexanes (also applicable to tetrahydropyran derivatives), axial protons almost always absorb at higher fields than do their equatorial counterparts. Obviously any substituents must be comparably disposed with respect to the axial-equatorial protons being compared. This

TABLE 4.1

Chemical shift[a] ranges for protons.

TYPE OF PROTON	τ	δ
Aldehydic	$-1-+1$	11–9
Aromatic	1–3	9–7
Olefinic	2.5–5	7.5–5
Aliphatic (α subst.)	5–8	5–2
Acetylenic	7–8	3–2
Aliphatic (β subst.)	8–9	2–1
Alicyclic	8–10	2–0

[a] $\Delta = (\Delta v \times 10^6)/v$, where Δ is the chemical shift between 2 absorptions with separation Δv observed.

difference in magnitude is frequently as much as 0.6 parts per million. This rule is very useful in determining the stereochemistry of substituted carbohydrate derivatives.

The mechanism of the chemical shift is essentially that of diamagnetism. The magnetic field that causes the circulation of electrons in the molecule creates a small local field whose net effect opposes that of the external field. The intensity of this field varies from point to point within a molecule so that the net field at a given point depends heavily on spatial orientation.

When an atom participates in a chemical bond, the atomic circulation is inhibited by bond formation. This inhibition is sensitive to the ionic character of the bond. This is the predominant effect in determining the chemical shift of nuclei other than protons, but is negligible or fairly constant for protons. Primarily because of this effect, proton chemical shifts are found over a range an order of magnitude smaller than those for other nuclei.

A consideration of the types of bonds found in organic molecules leads to the immediate realization that the factors controlling the electron density around a given proton are largely determined by the electronegativity of the attached groups, those with greater electron density, giving more shielding. Also important are the magnetic fields due to anisotropic circulation of electrons in the molecule, particularly those associated with bonding electrons and pi electrons of aromatic molecules. The effect due to such circulation of electrons in single bonds is illustrated in Figure 4.4. A nucleus residing within an hourglass-shaped region, where the bond lies at the center and on the cylindrical axis of the region, is shielded. The one outside this region is deshielded. The shielding at any given distance from the bond is greatest on the line extending from the ends of the bond, and the deshielding is greatest on a plane perpendicular to and bisecting the bond. The effect becomes zero somewhere in between and is directly proportional to the distance from the bond under consideration. The anisotropy of the carbon–carbon single bond accounts in large part for the axial-equatorial shift observed in cyclohexane and cyclohexane-type structures.

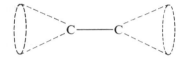

FIGURE 4.4   Areas relative to a carbon–carbon bond wherein protons would be shielded.

A proton must be held fairly rigidly or at least confined to a restricted region with respect to the bond or ring in order to observe an effect on the chemical shift. If the proton is free, or in a sense can be said to take any orientation with respect to the bond, the effect tends to average to zero. For this reason, intermolecular effects can usually be neglected.

4.3 Spin-Spin Coupling

The proton nuclear-magnetic-resonance spectrum of a typical organic compound contains many more lines than can be accounted for simply by the number of different kinds of protons on the molecule. This proliferation of lines is caused by an interaction of the magnetic moments of neighboring magnetic nuclei; for liquids and gases, the interactions that show up are relayed by bonding electrons. This interaction is called *spin-spin coupling* and the production of extra lines as a result of this is referred to as *spin-spin splitting*.

The energy of the coupling of two magnetic nuclei is measured by a term called the *coupling constant*, *J*, expressed in cycles per second. This depends on the nuclei involved, the bonds connecting them and their geometry. In contrast to chemical shifts, this coupling phenomenon is *independent of the strength of the magnetic field*. If the chemical shifts and coupling constants of all the magnetic nuclei in a molecule are known, it is possible to predict the positions and intensities (at least from theoretical considerations) of every line in an NMR spectrum. Frequently, it is possible to work backwards from the spectrum and deduce the shifts and couplings of the nuclei which give rise to the splitting pattern.

The most common type of coupling observed is between one proton and another, but it is also possible in many organic molecules to have couplings to phosphorus and, rarely, to nitrogen. In general, couplings are not observed with carbon-12 and oxygen-16, again simplifying the picture for most organic compounds.

In an attempt to understand the phenomena that give rise to splitting patterns without resorting to quantum-mechanical calculations, the spectrum of a simple organic molecule, such as ethyl bromide, can be considered. This is

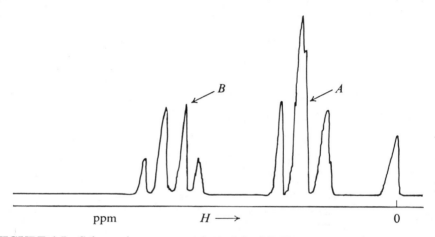

FIGURE 4.5 Schematic representation of the NMR spectrum of monobromo-ethane. The group of protons designated as A absorb at 1.67 parts per million, and that designated B at 3.43 parts per million.

illustrated in Figure 4.5 and, as can be seen, 7 peaks are observed, which can be divided into two groups, one a quartet and the other a triplet. Integration of the area under each of these peaks shows that the area under the quartet relative to that under the triplet is 2 to 3. Because the environments for the methylene and the methyl protons are not identical, we expect them to have different chemical shifts. These correspond to the center of the quartet and the triplet, respectively. Because the intensity or magnitude of a peak in an NMR spectrum, as it would be for any other type of absorption spectroscopy, is directly proportional to the number of protons in the given environment that gives rise to the peaks, the observed areas are consistent. The explanation of this splitting pattern can be arrived at in the following way. Assuming that only proton–proton couplings need be considered, first let us examine the behavior of the two methylene protons in an attempt to understand the appearance of the triplet. Because the spin quantum number of the hydrogen nucleus will either be $+\frac{1}{2}$ or $-\frac{1}{2}$, such protons can only have two possible orientations in a magnetic field, one with the field and one against the field. This may be symbolized by two arrows, one arrow pointing up and one arrow pointing down. When the two methylene protons are considered as a group, there are, therefore, four possibilities: both protons oriented with the field, both protons oriented against the field, and two cases where one proton is oriented with the field and the other against the field (Figure 4.6). Because the energy differences between these are *extremely small,*

Let ↑ indicate a nucleus aligned with the field and ↓ a nucleus aligned against the field. For the methylene protons:

$$ ↑↑ \quad ↑↓ \quad ↓↑ \quad ↓↓ $$

FIGURE 4.6 Possible orientation for the methylene protons aligned with and against the magnetic field.

a given proton has almost the same probability of being aligned with or against the field and thus each of the four two-proton combinations is equally probable. One quarter of the molecules at any given instant may be depicted by each pair of arrows as far as the orientation of the methylene protons is concerned. Because the methylene protons themselves have magnetic moments, this magnetic field is experienced by the nearby methyl protons and therefore *their* resonance frequencies are modified as a result. The fifty percent of the molecules where the methylene protons are oriented in opposite directions may be thought of as having cancelling fields, and it is expected that the methyl protons would show no net influence by the neighboring magnetic field of these methylene protons. Therefore, they will absorb at exactly the chemical shift frequency. The 25 percent of the molecules with the methylene protons aligned with the field will have a slightly displaced methyl proton resonance, and the

For the methyl protons:

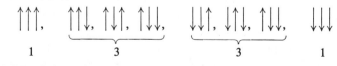

FIGURE 4.7 Orientations for the methyl protons aligned with and against the magnetic field.

25 percent aligned against the field will be displaced in the opposite direction. Therefore, the prediction from a consideration of this type is for three equally spaced lines with the middle of the three lines coinciding with the chemical shift and the areas in the ratio 1 to 2 to 1.

A similar consideration can be made for the three methyl protons. As illustrated in Figure 4.7, eight possible orientations of the three methyl protons may be observed, each one of which will have an equal probability of occurrence.

Examination of what may be termed the sum or net field resulting from each of these orientations reveals a distribution of 1 to 3 to 3 to 1, as indicated. Because none of these cancel out or sum up to 0 magnetic field, the exact chemical shift will not be indicated by any single peak and instead will be in the centre of the complex. As a result of this, the methylene protons will experience, at any given instant, four different types of local interactions arising from the orientations of the methyl protons, and will exhibit absorbancies at four slightly different positions in a ratio of 1 to 3 to 3 to 1. The intervals between the adjacent lines of the quartet should all be the same and will be numerically equal to the coupling constant J, which in the case of ethyl bromide is 7 cycles per second. The actual spectrum reveals that this prediction is reasonably well fulfilled.

A logical extension of this type of consideration leads to the following generalizations:

1. The resonance of a set of identical nuclei i will be split into $N + 1$ equally spaced lines by N nuclei, n, of spin $\frac{1}{2}$. This will be true provided all J are equal, all Δv are much larger than J_{in} and Δv_{nx} is also much larger than J_{nx}.[3]

2. The spacing between adjacent lines within the multiplet is equal to J_{in} with the relative intensities of the lines as expressed in a binomial expansion, being the coefficients of terms (Figure 4.8).

$$
\begin{array}{ccccccccccc}
 & & & & & 1 & & & & & \\
 & & & & 1 & & 1 & & & & \\
 & & & 1 & & 2 & & 1 & & & \\
 & & 1 & & 3 & & 3 & & 1 & & \\
 & 1 & & 4 & & 6 & & 4 & & 1 & \\
1 & & 5 & & 10 & & 10 & & 5 & & 1
\end{array}
$$

FIGURE 4.8 Expected splitting patterns as a function of the number of interactions.

When the above criteria are not met, that is, when the frequency differences are not of sufficient magnitude, the spectrum becomes extremely complex and overlapping patterns are observed. In cases of this type, without additional structural information it is very difficult to make an *a priori* interpretation of spectra, and as a result, quantitative information cannot be obtained.

Ideal spectra of the ethyl bromide type are observed only when the i and n nuclei are of different elements, which ensure a very large Δv. For example, in the case of the spectrum of trifluoroethanol, the methylene protons are split into a perfect quartet by the fluorine nuclei (Figure 4.9). The spectrum of ethyl bromide, however, clearly shows the expected quartet and triplet, but the integrated areas under each of these peaks do not exactly coincide with the distribution expected from the binomial expansion. In particular, a distortion occurs in such a way

---

[3] Δv_{in} is the chemical shift between the identical nuclei and one of the N nuclei, and J_{in} is their coupling constant.

Δv_{nx} is the chemical shift between one of the N nuclei and any other nucleus not in the set i or n; J_{nx} is their coupling constant.

that the lines *nearest* the absorption of the protons which *cause* the splitting are larger than expected and the lines farther away are smaller than expected. This type of distortion of areas is quite general and can be helpful in interpretation of spectra. Even when this so-called distorted splitting occurs, the coupling constant still corresponds to the spacing between adjacent lines, but the chemical shifts coincide with the *center of gravity* of the multiplet; in other words, with the weight average rather than with the geographical average. Table 4.2 illustrates the range for typical proton–proton couplings.

In general, couplings between protons, which are separated by three or more carbon atoms, are too small to observe in saturated acyclic molecules. However, in the case of rigid polycyclic systems, such long-range couplings may occasionally be observed. In aliphatic systems, the magnitude of the coupling

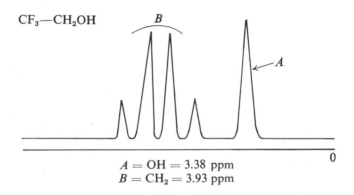

CF_3—CH_2OH

B

A

$A = OH = 3.38$ ppm
$B = CH_2 = 3.93$ ppm

0

FIGURE 4.9 Magnetic-resonance spectrum of trifluoroethanol.

constant varies considerably with the nature of substituents; electronegative substitutent atoms generally decrease the couplings, whereas electropositive atoms will cause an increase.

One of the most important features of the coupling constants, particularly for applications to carbohydrate chemistry, is their angular dependence. This is a theoretically predictable observation and it has been experimentally verified, that for vicinal protons, the coupling constant varies with the dihedral angle between them. This is illustrated in Figure 4.10. Note that J is near 0 at 90 degrees and appreciable at intermediate values with maximal coupling constants being found at 0 and 180 degrees. This phenomenon was first observed in the carbohydrate field by Lemieux and co-workers and has been extensively studied by Karplus, who proposed an equation of the form:

$$J = J_0 \cos^2 \phi + k \qquad (4.8)$$

where J is the coupling constant, J_0 and k are parameters, and ϕ the dihedral angle [1]. This relationship allows us to estimate the angle between vicinal hydrogen atoms based on the coupling constant they exhibit. As a result of this, the calculated angles can then be used to define the shape and conformation of the molecule.

Karplus derived many of his theoretical results by assuming that the carbon atoms to which the hydrogen atoms are attached are sp^3 hybridized and

TABLE 4.2

Coupling constants for protons on adjacent carbons as a function of structure.

STRUCTURE	J_{ab}, cycles per second
$\begin{array}{c}\diagdown\quad\diagup\\ C-C\\ \diagup|\quad|\diagdown\\ H_a\ H_b\end{array}$	2–9
$\begin{array}{c}H_a\\ \diagdown\diagup\\ C\\ \diagup\diagdown\\ H_b\end{array}$	0–20
$\begin{array}{c}H_a\\ \diagdown\diagup\\ C{=}C\\ \diagup\diagdown\\ H_b\end{array}$	0–3.5
$\begin{array}{c}H_a\\ \diagdown\quad\diagup\\ C{=}C\\ \diagup\quad\diagdown\\ H_b\end{array}$	11–18
$\begin{array}{c}\diagdown\quad\diagup\\ C{=}C\\ \diagup\quad\diagdown\\ H_a\qquad H_b\end{array}$	6–14
$\begin{array}{c}\diagdown\\ C-C{=}O\\ \diagup|\quad|\\ H_a\quad H_b\end{array}$	1–3

for the rest of his calculations followed a valence bond approach. More recently, calculations made by Conroy using a molecular orbital approach have arrived at similar but somewhat different results [2]. His predictions suggest larger couplings for protons at angles greater than 90 degrees and are in very good agreement with experimental data.

The observation of spin coupling itself depends upon the following fact: whenever two resonant peaks are separated by some energy unit, $\Delta\nu$, the uncertainty principle states that in order to resolve two such peaks, the molecular system as a whole must be fixed for a sufficient length of time. The magnitude of this time must be greater than the time uncertainty, Δt, which may be defined as follows: $\Delta\nu \times \Delta t$ must equal 1. A hypothetical situation may be envisioned whereby we allow $\Delta\nu$ to equal J between two peaks of the spin coupled signal. Then, if that part of the molecule in which spin coupling originates or through which the spin coupling is transmitted, changes sufficiently rapidly, so that any one state exists for a time less than $\Delta t = 1/J$, then the entire effect of J will be removed from the spectrum. This may be considered as a decoupled spectrum.

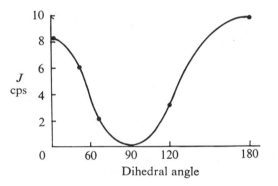

FIGURE 4.10   Coupling constant of protons on adjacent carbons as a function of the dihedral angle between them.

In other words, coupling is theoretically possible but is not observed due to a type of averaging effect wherein the molecule does not remain in a fixed state long enough for the coupling to be expressed.

There are two commonly encountered types of natural spin decoupling. The first one is particularly pertinent to carbohydrate problems:

1. The proton under consideration undergoes very rapid exchange between molecules or between a given molecule and the solvent. In this case, the proton will not exhibit any spin coupling with neighboring protons. The most common example of this is the hydroxyl proton of alcohols.

2. Natural spin decoupling also arises as a result of movement of quadrupolar nuclei (a nucleus with asymmetric shape, usually having a spin of 1 or greater).

In the case of alcohols, the intramolecular exchange of protons removes the proton from being coupled to nearby nuclei or prevents such coupling if the half-life of the exchange is less than 0.2 seconds. Obviously, the rate of this exchange will be a function of both pH and temperature.

The effect of spin coupling between nitrogen-14 (a quadrupolar nucleus) and protons is usually exhibited by a broadening of all proton lines except in the cases where symmetry decreases the effectiveness of the reorientations. For example, the proton spectrum of NH_4^+ clearly shows proton–nitrogen coupling.

4.4 Spin Decoupling: Double Resonance

In addition to natural spin decoupling, it is possible to bring about the same effect by external irradiation, and this technique (termed *double resonance*) is a very powerful tool for the analysis of complex NMR spectra. In order to remove the effects of spin coupling with nucleus B on the spectrum of nucleus A, the technique employed is to irradiate nucleus B at its resonance frequency while observing the spectrum of nucleus A in the usual way. The irradiation of B speeds up the flipping of the nucleus B until it passes the critical time value. This may be visualized in a slightly different way. When spin coupling is taking place, the nucleus that is undergoing the splitting phenomenon does so due to the influence of the spin states of the coupled nucleus, which has a different chemical shift. If the coupled nucleus is irradiated *with its own resonance energy* (slightly different from that of the splitting nucleus), it undergoes transitions between its own different spin states. Effectively, if this is occurring sufficiently rapidly, the nucleus being split is affected only by the average quantum spin state (of nucleus B, for example) which is 0. Thus, it appears not to be split at all and appears as a singlet. The effect of double resonance is analogous to the chemical exchange discussed above although the reason for the phenomena are quite different.

The applications of decoupling techniques are very general in nature. The most useful aspect results in the fact that the spectrum itself is greatly simplified due to the disappearance of multiplets. As a result of this, these peaks usually appear at the exact chemical shift value and integrated peak intensities can be obtained from what previously may have been very difficult to interpret spectra. It is even possible in proper circumstances to determine the chemical shift of a completely hidden proton if that proton is coupled with another nucleus that is easily detectable. The most useful and pertinent application in the field of carbohydrate chemistry is that small relative chemical shifts give rise to significant changes in the double resonance system. This will therefore be useful for measuring chemical shifts and coupling constants in molecules where the nuclei are in nearly equivalent chemical environments, such as axial and equatorial hydrogens, and where effects of substituents on potential shielding atoms change the electron density to a very small degree.

It is worthwhile to consider a detailed example of the application of this technique to conformational analysis. An elegant structural study on cyclohexane tetrol was recently reported where the conformational characterization was achieved by the use of spin-decoupling techniques [3]. A cyclohexane tetrol will have three possible configurations: ortho, meta, and para, as shown by Figure 4.11. Examination of the normal NMR spectrum showed a quartet at 2.2τ due to the methylene protons and complex split peaks at 4.43 and 4.66, which resulted from the 4 OCH protons. When the OCH protons were all irradiated with a large field, these were completely decoupled and the methylene quartet collapsed to a *singlet*. Because this occurred as a singlet, it could be concluded that there was little or no difference between the chemical shifts of the

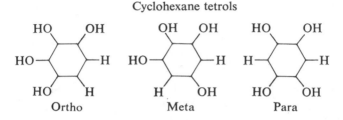

Cyclohexane tetrols

Ortho   Meta   Para

FIGURE 4.11   Planar projection of possible cyclohexane tetrol structures.

4-methylene protons and thus, the structure was assigned as meta in which all four methylene protons can be spectroscopically identical in certain conformations (Figure 4.12). Given the meta structure, there were six possible configurations, as illustrated in Table 4.3. To decide between these, the methylene protons were irradiated and the OCH protons were observed. The complex pattern previously exhibited by the OCH protons collapsed into two sharp singlets with relative peak intensities of 1 to 3. The smaller singlet was assigned to the proton of carbon 5, while the larger singlet was assigned to the protons of carbon 1, 2, and 3. Because the protons on C-1 and C-3 were *equivalent*, and

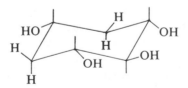

FIGURE 4.12   Strainless ring form of one of the possible cyclohexane tetrols.

because the methylene protons both above and below the ring were also equivalent, it could be concluded that the molecule had a plane of symmetry which passed through carbons 2 and 5 and was perpendicular to the ring (Figure 4.13). Thus, the two optically active forms listed above could be excluded. For the remaining 4 meso forms, although geometric equivalence between all four methylene protons does not exist, spectroscopic equivalence or near equivalence would be observed if these protons fulfilled two requirements. (1) The neighboring

TABLE 4.3

Configuration or conformation of hydroxyl groups for 1,
2, 3, 5 cyclohexane tetrols. The optically active forms are
indicated by an asterisk.

POSITIONS OF OH GROUPS	CONFORMATION
1, 2, 3, 5	*e, e, e, a*
1, 2, 3, 5	*e, e, e, e*
1, 2, 3, 5	*e, a, e, a*
1, 2, 3, 5	*e, a, a, e*
1, 2, 3, 5	*e, a, a, a**
1, 2, 3, 5	*a, a, e, a**

protons, that is, C-1–C-5 and C-3–C-5, have a *trans* rather than *cis* configuration.
(2) Each methylene proton must give a partial axial and partial equatorial
average response in NMR, and therefore there must be equilibrium between
chair forms of nearly equal energy. For this to be the case, the cyclohexane
tetrol must have two hydroxyl groups axial and two hydroxyl groups equatorial.
On the basis of the above, only one possible structure remained (Figure 4.14).

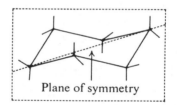

Plane of symmetry

FIGURE 4.13   Plane of symmetry in the 6-membered ring.

This was subsequently proved correct by independent chemical techniques. This
is illustrative of the type of analysis that can be carried out in complex systems.
Although relatively few applications of spin-decoupling techniques have thus
far been made in the carbohydrate field, the potential is quite obvious.

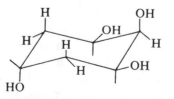

FIGURE 4.14   Structure of the cyclohexane tetrol as deduced from considerations of the NMR spectra—see text for discussion.

4.5 Relaxation; Time Averaging

Two other phenomena that occur commonly in NMR spectra are the so-called relaxation phenomena or saturation, and time-averaging effects.

In the absence of exchange, the width of the NMR signal is determined by a variety of factors, usually described in terms of relaxation effects and relaxation times. The relaxation time may be considered as the characteristic time for nuclei at equivalent sites to come to firm equilibrium with their surroundings. It is also the lifetime of those nuclei at their respective energy levels. The magnitude of this relaxation time depends on the efficiency of the coupling of the nucleus with those motions of the molecules in the sample which permit energy exchange between the nucleus and the molecules. In solids, the coupling is generally poor or almost nonexistent so that this time is of the order of hours or days. Protons in organic liquids have a relaxation time of about 1 second; should this time become much shorter than 1 second, a noticeable broadening of the proton absorption usually occurs. This follows directly from the uncertainty relationship.

A second relaxation phenomenon results from spin-spin collisions which decrease the life span of the spin states without changing the thermal energy of the nuclei. Because NMR energy levels are so close together in energy, even at room temperature they are almost equally populated. This is true for protons where the energy difference in the quantum states of the nucleus, whether oriented with or against the magnetic field, are extremely small. If the *energy* levels were *exactly equally* populated, no NMR signal would be observed because the very same protons, which would absorb energy and promote a nucleus from one energy level to a higher level, would also stimulate the nucleus at the higher level to drop back to a lower level. Thus, just as many photons would be emitted as absorbed. The spectrometer only detects *net absorption* of energy; this would only occur when there is some excess population in the lower energy state. The two states would tend to become equally populated during irradiation were it not for the relaxation processes which allow energy to be transferred to the surroundings and a firm equilibrium population to be maintained. Should the energy be absorbed faster than the nuclei can dissipate it, then the lower level becomes depopulated and the system is said to be saturated. The usual method of avoiding saturation is to keep the radio-frequency power sufficiently low. The primary reason for avoiding saturation is that when this occurs, the relative areas of absorption due to the various kinds of protons no longer become proportional to the number of protons of a given kind. In a general way, the signal-to-noise ratio improves with greater radio-frequency power; common laboratory practice is to use the highest possible power that will avoid saturation effects.

As indicated in several of the above comments, the NMR spectra does not give an instantaneous picture of a molecule but rather one which is averaged over a finite period of time. An examination of the spectrum of cyclohexane reveals a single sharp resonance at δ1.4 (Figure 4.15). Because we know that cyclohexane exists essentially exclusively in a chair conformation with 6 axial and 6 equatorial protons, the question arises as to why this one sharp line exists. The expectation would be that because axial and equatorial protons have different chemical shifts, two lines should result. The answer is that the chair conformation is in rapid equilibrium with the inverted chair (Figure 4.16) and as

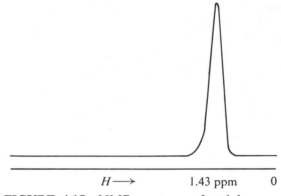

$H \longrightarrow$ 1.43 ppm   0

FIGURE 4.15   NMR spectrum of cyclohexane.

a result of this inversion, the axial protons become equatorial, and vice versa. The uncertainty principle states that in order to resolve two separate lines for the axial and equatorial protons, a given proton must remain in one of the orientations for longer than some time period, Δt.

$$\Delta t = \frac{1}{\Delta \nu} \tag{4.9}$$

where $\Delta \nu$ is the frequency difference between the two types of protons.

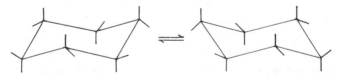

FIGURE 4.16   Equilibrium of the two forms of cyclohexane.

Cyclohexane has a $\Delta \nu$ of the order of 25 cycles per second at 60 megacycles, whereas the lifetime of a given chair conformation is much shorter than the critical time, 0.04 seconds. Thus, a single line at the average chemical shift is observed.

Consider a proton that spends half its time in environment A and half in B. The resonance frequencies corresponding to these two environments are ν_A and ν_B, respectively. If the lifetime of the proton in either state is long, two lines of equal intensity will be observed at ν_A and ν_B. If the lifetime is short, then a single line with twice the intensity will be observed at the average frequency. At intermediate lifetimes, appropriate intermediate behavior is observed. The two lines will broaden, the maxima draw closer together, and the signals finally will coalesce into one broad signal. With extremely short lifetimes, the signal will sharpen with the total under the curve being the same and independent of the lifetime. Obviously, if the nucleus does not spend equal time in the two environments (where the equilibrium constant for possible conformers is no longer one), the two peaks will be unequal in size and the condensed signal will appear not at the numerical average but at the weighted average or center of gravity of the two frequencies.

Several important types of time averaging are observed in aliphatic and cyclohexane type systems.[4]

1. Because rotations about carbon–carbon bonds in nonrigid molecules are sufficiently fast at room temperature, the individual conformations are not seen, but rather the average effect of all conformations.

2. Protons bonded to oxygen and many bonded to nitrogen are so mobile that only an average chemical shift of all such protons is observed. Splitting of these protons is not resolvable even when instantaneous coupling is appreciable.

The first of the above cases concerns the problem of rotation or conformer interchange and may be experimentally examined by reducing the ability of the molecule to undergo this change. For very simple molecules such as ethane, where the rotational barrier for various forms is extremely small, this is not practicable. However, when the rotational barrier is of appreciable magnitude, such as in cyclohexane, the two chair forms may be resolved by lowering the temperature of the samples (in this case, to -80 degrees). A study of the temperature effect on this freezing-out phenomenon will give a value for the activation energy of the conversion of the chair forms of cyclohexane. The results of such a study indicated a value of 10 kcal per mole for cyclohexane itself [4]. Similar figures have not been deduced for carbohydrates but would be expected to be larger because the conversion from one chair form to another requires intermediate ring forms wherein hydroxyl functions are eclipsed. Adequate temperature-dependent NMR studies may serve to resolve this problem and permit some assessment as to the magnitude of the energy barrier for chair–chair interconversions.

4.6 NMR of Carbohydrates [5, 6]

The interpretation of resonance spectra for carbohydrates has led to the formulation of several empirical rules and quite a number of specific applications. These are based, in part, on studies with model compounds such as *cis*

---

[4] The homogeneity of the magnetic field is critical and enhanced by spinning the sample tube. This averages the envelope of lines due to different values of the magnetic field at different places in the sample to one sharp line.

and *trans* *t*-butyl cyclohexanols where the *t*-butyl group serves as a conformational control in the molecule.

1. Axial protons tend to resonate at higher field strengths than do equatorial protons. This is apparently without exception for the ring protons, but may not apply to protons of substituents. In the latter case, the resonance is usually indicative of positions, with axial methoxy protons, for example, resonating at lower field strengths than do the equatorial.

2. The coupling constants between axial protons on adjacent carbons (5 to 8 cycles per second) are two to three times larger than those observed between axial-equatorial or diequatorial protons. This is what would be predicted from a consideration of the Karplus curve. Studies to date have not distinguished between axial-equatorial and diequatorial coupling constants. Because these have the same dihedral angle (60 degrees), the expectation is that there will be relatively little difference between them. Several observations suggest that the diequatorial coupling is somewhat smaller than axial-equatorial coupling but good quantitative data are not yet available.

3. In general, axial and equatorial protons on the same carbon will be strongly coupled with a J of about 12 cycles per second.

4. The anomeric proton absorbs at a unique field strength and as a result, is particularly useful in conformational analysis especially in view of its interaction with the proton on carbon 2. The proton at position 1 is attached to a carbon bearing two oxygens and resonates at lower field strength than do any of the other ring protons.

5. The ranges in chemical shifts that may lead to overlap of equatorial and axial resonances, particularly as affected by substituents, may lead to conclusions about deformations from ideal chair conformations. The extent of the chemical shifts observed can be used as a conformational guide.

6. Protons on substituents such as acetoxy and methoxy groups are not coupled to other protons and thus give rise to fairly sharp spectral resonances.

7. The prevailing ring form in solution, particularly for pentoses, can readily be determined because if the pentose is in the pyranose ring form, the resonance signal of the hydroxymethyl group attached to the ring does not occur.

4.7 Specific Applications in the Carbohydrate Fields

A study of fully acetylated pentose and hexose pyranosides showed the methyl protons of axial oriented acetoxy groups to have lower chemical shifts than those of equatorially oriented groups [7]. The recent availability of 100-megacycle instrumentation has permitted complete resolution of all acetoxy methyl groups in several cases. Table 4.4 illustrates the resonance assignments that have been made for acetoxy groups on individual carbon atoms. Almost without exception, all of the tau values occur between 7.8 and 8. Although relatively few acetylated furanoses have been studied, the resonances are in the same region with a possible difference between exo and endocyclic acetoxy groups. Those within the ring apparently are not readily separable.

TABLE 4.4

Methyl proton resonances in acetylated carbohydrates.

	AXIAL	EQUATORIAL	
		PRIMARY (C-6)	SECONDARY
C-2	7.81–7.84		7.91–7.96
C-3	7.84–7.85		7.91–7.98
C-4	7.81–7.85	7.98–8.02	7.89–7.97

The chemical shifts of several other substituents have been examined: C-methyl substituents, equatorial acetamido functions, and equatorial acetamido in relation to neighboring hydroxyl groups. Table 4.5 lists the tau values for those several groupings for which assignments have been made [8].

Several unusual sugars have been described in mold and fungal antibiotics, and the application of NMR techniques (particularly coupling between protons of axial-axial and axial-equatorial orientation) have been particularly useful in this area. The conformation of desosamine has been deduced by this method; mycarose, which is 2,6 dideoxy 3-C-methyl L-ribohexose, and cladinose, its 3-methyl ether, have also been assigned structures based on NMR spectroscopy (Figure 4.17) [9, 10].

TABLE 4.5

τ values for various substituents in carbohydrate rings.

SUBSTITUENT	τ VALUE
Axial methoxyl	6.54–6.64
Equatorial methoxyl	6.46–6.47
Equatorial C-methyl	8.76–8.84
Equatorial acetamido	8.04–8.10
Equatorial acetamido *trans* to hydroxyl	8.00–8.02

NMR spectra can be used to differentiate diasteriosomers, and has been applied to a study of D-mannose 1,2 ortho acetates [11].

The determination of anomeric configuration is usually straightforward because the location of the anomeric proton and its coupling with the C-2 proton can be established.

There are several hazards of assignment based on assumptions of molecular geometry in cases where conformational information is desired. Thus, in systems where ring distortion may take place, or where fused rings are present, the assignment of dihedral angles is not always clear cut and deducing conformation from coupling constants can lead to errors. This is particularly true when polarizable substituents are present in the molecule which may influence either directly or by nonbonded interactions the shielding of the protons under study. This calls attention to the danger of indiscriminate use of the Karplus equation which should be supported by additional evidence whenever possible.

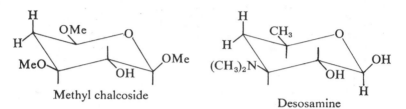

Methyl chalcoside

Desosamine

FIGURE 4.17 Methyl chalcoside and desosamine, 2 carbohydrates whose structures were initially deduced through NMR studies.

Studies by several groups have attempted to define the J_0 parameter of the Karplus equation. Examination of the spectrum of 3,6 anhydro isopropylidene D-glucofuranose and its 5-tosylate provided data on the coupling constants between protons on carbon 5 and carbon 6. Substitution of the values obtained into an unmodified Karplus equation gave bond angles of 136 and 140 degrees with the two derivatives, respectively. Based on the assumption that the correct angle would be 120 degrees, then the J_0 parameters change accordingly. This is a kind of cyclic reasoning and would be considerably substantiated if the true structure of at least one or two of these reference compounds could be determined by x-ray diffraction techniques.

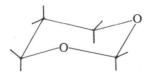

FIGURE 4.18 1,3-dioxolane.

A different approach to this problem has been made by Lemieux in a series of studies where the Karplus equation was "improved" by upward displacement of the entire curve by approximately 2.2 cycles per second [12]. This was based primarily on studies of the spectrum of the 1,3 dioxolane ring system (Figure 4.18). A calculation of the complete three-dimensional geometry of molecules of this type is beyond the scope of this text and probably no more accurate than any of the systems mentioned above. Because any accurate calculation will still involve assumptions whereby at least one or two reference angles are fixed, this approach has little to recommend it over the others. The molecular orbital technique may be better but has still received relatively little attention. All of the above calculations give values that are in reasonable agreement with experimental data, but in some cases, the cyclic nature of the reasoning is self-defeating.

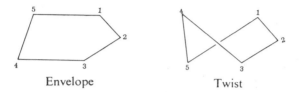

Envelope   Twist

FIGURE 4.19   Envelope and twist forms of 5-membered ring.

The use of the Karplus equation in the study of furanoses has led to predictions of nonplanarity for the furanose ring; both envelope and twist conformations are possible, as indicated in Figure 4.19 [13]. The very exact studies carried out by x-ray diffraction (see Section 4.10) will lead to some modification of these figures and also to some improvement of the experimental values upon which the structures are based. The derivatives employed have been isopropylidene acetals and cyclic carbonates; in all cases, the 5-membered rings are found to be not strictly planar (Figure 4.20).

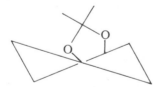

FIGURE 4.20   Schematic structure for isopropylidene ketal derivative of a 6-membered ring structure.

The conformation of free sugars as determined by NMR has received relatively little attention, primarily because good spectra are generally difficult to obtain; the study of deuterated sugars or borate complexes may provide some advantage in this area. Where 3-membered rings or double bonds are present in the 6-membered ring, the obligatory planarity of such structures has a profound effect upon the shape of the parent ring. The latter probably adopts a skew conformation which is energetically (3 kcal per mole) favored over the corresponding boat. The observed chemical shifts of protons in such derivatives are consistent with this type of conformation.

There have been relatively few applications of NMR spectra to the study of oligo and polysaccharides. It is likely that anomeric linkages of model compounds and simple oligosaccharides (wherein the exact composition and structure are known) could be assigned on the basis of NMR spectra. However, solubility problems and the high probability of interactions will make such spectra extremely complicated. It is conceivable that with the advent of computer techniques which increase signal-to-noise ratios appreciably, aspects indicative of changes from a regular structure may be identified or indicated. Relatively few solvent effect studies have been made, although in the case of carbohydrates, we would expect that the spectrum would be particularly sensitive to the nature of the solvent, especially when hydrogen bonding is possible.

In certain cases chemical modification of the parent carbohydrate may be useful in bringing out resonances of particular protons. Thus, the C-1 proton can usually be more easily resolved if the anomeric hydroxyl group is acetylated. Similarly, substitution by deuterium will permit identification of specific proton resonances. The use of double-resonance methods has already been discussed.

4.8 Phenylosazones

The structure of sugar phenylosazones, referred to previously, was established by NMR methods [14]. Studies of the chemical shift of the C-1 proton and the protons bonded to nitrogen and sugar in both dimethyl sulfoxide and fully deuterated pyridine strongly support the open chain chelate structure, originally

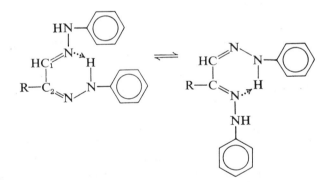

FIGURE 4.21   Schematic representation of a carbohydrate phenylosazone in the chelate form.

proposed more than 20 years ago (Figure 4.21). In compounds that have the aldehydo phenylhydrazone structure, such as D-galactose phenylhydrazone acetate (Figure 4.22), the chelate proton present in all of the osazones examined is not found, whereas a nonchelated imino proton signal at 11 parts per million can be demonstrated. This nonchelated imino proton signal is found in other compounds of this type as well. The identity of these signals with those present in dehydro D-glucosazone, which is known to have an axial hydroxyl, requires the type of chelation proposed. Examination of the spectra of the acetylated compounds in deuterochloroform shows a proton absorbing at approximately 7 parts per million; this resonance disappears on treatment of the sample with

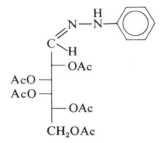

FIGURE 4.22 Phenylhydrazone acetate of D-galactose.

deuterium oxide, thus lending support to its ready exchangeability. Carbon-bound protons or protons not involved in chelation would not be expected to exchange under these conditions. Substitution of the α imino hydrogen of the *phenylhydrazine* residue with a methyl group is without influence on the position of the signal corresponding to the chelated NH, while the signal of the un-chelated NH disappears. This strongly indicates that its position is the same as the position of the methyl group in 1-methyl 2-phenylosazones (Figure 4.23).

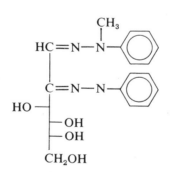

FIGURE 4.23 The phenylosazone derived from D-glucose by initial treatment with methylphenylhydrazine followed by treatment with phenylhydrazine.

In addition to these above considerations, long-range spin coupling between the C-1 proton and the unchelated NH proton was observed, also providing very strong support for this structure and its tautomers.

Double resonance spectroscopy at 100 megacycles confirmed that the C-1 proton is coupled with the nonchelated NH proton and not with the chelated NH proton. Similar spin coupling between the C-1 proton and the α imino proton has been reported for the syn isomers of aldehyde 2,4-dinitrophenyl-hydrazones (Figure 4.24). The position of the α imino proton and the C-1 proton in such derivatives and in the carbohydrate osazones is obviously very similar. The formation of such chelate structures permits the construction of a pseudoaromatic ring between several resonance forms. This latter structure is

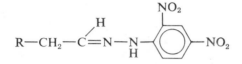

FIGURE 4.24   Syn isomer of an aldehyde 2,4-dinitrophenylhydrazone.

supported by x-ray data where the electron-density projection shows that the 6-membered chelate ring is approximately planar and approximately coplanar with the two benzene rings. This structure also helps to explain the difference between the phenylhydrazone groups at carbon 1 and carbon 2 with regard to methylation and triazole formation, as well as the markedly different reactivity of the hydroxyl group at C-3 which is undoubtedly due to the electron attractive effect of the chelate ring.

4.9 pH Effects

The conformation of the carbohydrate moieties in mono-di and poly-saccharides as a function of pH has been under study for some time. Treatment of both simple sugars and polymers such as amylose with alkali lead to marked

TABLE 4.6

Optical rotations of carbohydrates in water versus those in $1N$ potassium hydroxide solution.

COMPOUND	DIFFERENCE IN $[\alpha]_{436}$
Methyl α-D-glucoside	0.0
Methyl β-D-glucoside	-1.7
D-glucose	27
D-xylose	13
D-mannose	-9.8
Sucrose	7.8
Maltose	42.5
Amylose	40.0

shifts in optical rotation, as indicated in Table 4.6 [15]. This rotatory shift is apparent regardless of whether open chain or alkali stable glycosides are studied. An attempt to resolve the original suggestions made by Reeves regarding the possible change in conformation exhibited by such groups in alkali has been made by studies of the NMR spectroscopy of these compounds in D_2O or in potassium deuteroxide solutions. It was found for most of the cases examined that the NMR spectra were consistent with the carbohydrates remaining in the C-1 ring conformation regardless of the *p*H [16]. The interpretation was made that the change in optical rotation of the free sugars was due to a shift of the anomeric equilibrium in alkali toward the beta form.

An examination of the effect of *p*H upon optical rotation reveals an *S*-shaped curve very similar to what might be expected for a titration curve. The anomeric hydroxyl is a slightly stronger acid than any of the other chain hydroxyls and has a *pK* of approximately 12.8. This will be completely ionized in alkali and is the first of the functional groups to ionize on the carbohydrate. The accompanying ring expansion of this functional group due to ionization will tend to favor its equatorial orientation rather than the axial one which would result in appreciably more interaction with axial protons on the same side of the ring. β-D-glucose is known to be a slightly stronger acid than is α-D-glucose. Thus, a shift in an anomeric mixture from α to β is to be expected as the *p*H is increased, and accordingly, the optical rotation should decline somewhat. Whether or not this shift can completely account for the observed changes in optical rotation or whether this is the reason is not entirely clear. The ionization of hydroxyl groups and the subsequent formation of new types of chromophores such as CO^- functions are likely to have significant effects upon the optical rotation. Whether these would serve to increase or decrease the rotation is not clear and whether this is dependent on the wavelength of observation has not been studied up to the present time. Examination of similar phenomena for compounds such as methyl β-maltoside and amylose revealed similar results in that the ring conformation, as determined by NMR spectroscopy, was not observed to significantly change as a function of *p*H. It is possible that there is some increased freedom of rotation about the 1-4 glycosidic bond in these compounds perhaps due to ionization of a pertinent hydroxyl group. It is also possible that the changes for amylose are characteristic of the transition from a helix to a coil. Nevertheless, most of the rotational change can be explained by assuming changes in rotational freedom, although the exact contribution of these to specific rotation is not clear.

The foregoing discussion generally assumed that boat forms suggested as being present due to ionization of hydroxyl groups in the carbohydrates can have a specified and defined structure. If this were true, then the conclusions reached by examination of NMR spectral data (again assuming the Karplus equation holds) may be used to make conformational assignments. However, the so-called boat forms of the carbohydrates are flexible structures and can exist in an infinity of conformations. Therefore, assignment or ruling out of specific formulations on the basis of projected dihedral angles calculated from NMR coupling constants is tenuous indeed. It seems likely that much more refined measurements such as those based on a combination of rotatory dispersion, NMR, and x-ray information are required before changes in conformation can be ascribed. It is perfectly possible to conceive of specific protons having similar dihedral angles or coupling constants with the ring in a conformation different from C-1, but in view of the large effect that ring conformation may have on optical rotation, gross conformational changes on alkali treatment of simple carbohydrates are unlikely.

The structure of 3-deoxy osones which have been proposed as intermediates in various sugar degradations, particularly those leading to the formation of metasaccharinic acids and hydroxymethyl furfural, has been established partly on the basis of NMR spectroscopy [17]. Their probable precursors, which would

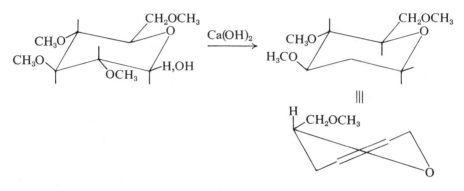

FIGURE 4.25 Reaction of 2,3,4,6-tetra-*O*-methyl-D-glucopyranose with calcium hydroxide.

be enolic forms, have been relatively little studied. The 4,6 di-*O*-methyl-3-deoxy-2-*O*-methylenol ether of D-glucopyranose was prepared by treatment of 2,3,4,6-tetramethyl D-glucose in saturated lime water. This compound was isolated as a crystalline product and showed an asymmetric carbon–carbon double bond at 1668 cm^{-1} in the infrared. Examination of the nuclear-magnetic-resonance spectrum in pyridine revealed that the ring was in a half-chair conformation with the C-5 hydrogen in an axial position (Figure 4.25). This product could be rapidly decomposed both with the formation of the 3,4 unsaturated osone (β-elimination) and also the formation of hydroxymethyl furfural.

Conclusions

The primary problems in NMR spectroscopy are likely to arise from overzealous interpretations of results. It is not to be expected that three-dimensional formulas will be derived by this technique which will have the same precision as those obtained from x-ray diffraction studies. However, several of the current drawbacks are likely to be overcome in the near future. Computer scanning of the spectrum permits resolutions 10 or more times as good as that currently obtainable.[5] Small amounts of material can therefore be studied as well as dilute solutions. Double resonance methods and expanded use of 100-megacycle instruments will greatly increase the data on which many empirical rules are currently based. Improved techniques for temperature studies should provide useful kinetic and energetic data regarding conformer equilibrium.

4.10 *Conformation of Ribofuranosides as Determined by NMR and X-ray Diffraction* [18, 19]

Early studies on the conformation of furanosides in solution utilizing nuclear-magnetic-resonance spectroscopy made an attempt to apply the Karplus equation to determinations of bond angles between hydrogens on adjacent carbons. The parameters employed do not correct to any significant degree, for the possibility that this ring, as does the 6-membered ring, can exist in preferred conformations. The problem is oversimplified by assuming that the 5-membered ring is substantially planar. Conformation differences as a function of the compound under study are presumed not to exist or if they do exist, are separated by sufficiently small energy barriers so that any given form is readily converted to any conformational isomer and reactions cannot be ascribed to only one structure.

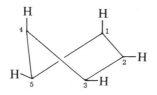

FIGURE 4.26 Predominant ring form for 5-membered ring. Note that this is not planar and that there are two out-of-plane carbons. This representation is a general one and the out-of-plane carbons will vary depending on the nature of the substituent groups.

Studies carried out by Hall on substituted D-ribofuranoses indicated that complete proton assignments could be made. The anomeric proton appeared as a characteristic low-field doublet with a coupling constant of 3.9 cycles per second to the proton on carbon 2. Coupling constants of 6.4 and 1.6 cycles per second were assigned to the interactions between protons on carbons 2 and 3, and 4, respectively. Using a modified Karplus equation where J is equal to $J_0 \cos^2 \omega - 0.2a$, where J_0 depends on whether ω is between 0 and 90 degrees or 90 and 180 degrees, the following dihedral angles were calculated: H_1–H_2, 48 degrees; H_2–H_3, 32 degrees; and H_3–H_4, 115 degrees (Figure 4.26).

---

[5] A technique very old in optics, more recently applied in Naval Warfare and currently very familiar to radar watchers on the DEW line.

If the 5-membered ring is assumed to be planar, the projected angle between *cis* hydrogens would be 0 degrees and between *trans* hydrogens 120 degrees (Figure 4.27). Because the angle between the protons on carbons 3 and 4 is very close to 120 degrees, it may be assumed that this section of the ring is relatively unaltered by deformations of the remainder of the molecule. Thus, carbons 2, 3, and 4 are coplanar with the ring oxygen, and carbon 1 is deformed out of the plane in what may be a stereospecific manner.

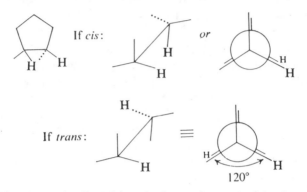

FIGURE 4.27   *Cis* and eclipsed interactions of protons in a 5-membered ring.

Calculations of the dihedral angles of a hypothetical 5-membered ring agree quite well with the observed values. The carbon that is deformed out of the plane is defined as being above the plane (see below, Figure 4.28). It lies on the same side of the reference plane as the group defining the configuration of the sugar; it would be below the plane if it were on the opposite side. Studies of 2,3-anhydrofuranosides showed that the coupling between the protons on carbon 1 and 2, and 3 and 4 were 0. It is clear that this conformation would require coplanarity due to the presence of the epoxide group.

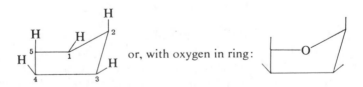

FIGURE 4.28   Schematic representation of tetrahydrofuran ring.

Recent studies have been carried out employing x-ray diffraction methods. The furanoside ring of the ribose moiety of simple mononucleotides such as cytidine or adenosine monophosphate and a nonreducing fructofuranoside, sucrose, were examined. These data were obtained on crystals (solid state) by x-ray and neutron diffraction studies.

The puckering of the ring that was observed involved the carbons at positions 2 and 3; and four different conformers could be distinguished (Figure 4.29). These were: C-2 and C-3 both endo, both exo, one endo and the other exo, and vice versa. The presence of an equatorial hydroxyl group on the carbon which is out of the plane leads to realignment of the carbon orbitals as seen by a shortening of the carbon–oxygen bond length to the hydroxyl and a widening of the dihedral angle relative to the adjacent carbon. This also introduces a resulting change in the carbon–hydrogen bond character.

The interaction of the protons present at C-5 with those present in the ring is different for the different orientations of the carbon–oxygen bond. The puckering present in the furanose ring is due to forces about the single bonds which arise from nonbonded interactions. These in turn are in opposition to those forces which attempt to retain tetrahedral orientation, and it appears that the energy gained in staggering the substituent atoms is somewhat greater than that

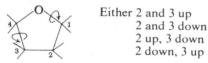

Either 2 and 3 up
2 and 3 down
2 up, 3 down
2 down, 3 up

FIGURE 4.29 Tetrahydrofuran ring with the rotations indicated allowing the distortions of carbons from the plane of the ring. Ring forms with carbons 2 and 3 either both up or both down or alternating can be pictured. Because any three atoms will determine a plane, there are ten possible constructions. If four of the atoms are coplanar, then only five are possible. In general, the carbon 1-oxygen bond is assumed to be in the plane of the ring and carbons 2 and 3 are most often distorted from this plane.

lost in increasing the angular strain. It has been previously pointed out in x-ray studies that for ribose and deoxy ribose, there is preferred puckering involving either C-2 or C-3. This is somewhat in contrast to the NMR data reported above, but since the x-ray studies are carried out in a solid state and may involve forces concerned with crystal lattice packing, the direct comparison of the two results is not possible.

The calculations of deviations from planarity are based on the assumption that four of the atoms present in the 5-membered ring would constitute a plane and that the fifth would be out of the plane; thus, all possible four-atom planes (five of them) were constructed and those that gave the least deviation from the calculated values were assumed to represent the most favorable energy state. As an example, for cytidinemonophosphate, fluorouracil deoxyriboside, and sucrose, the atom at C-2 is involved in the major puckering out of the ring, whereas in adenosine monophosphate and thymidine monophosphate, the atom at C-3 is involved (Table 4.7). It also is apparent from these calculations that when carbon 3 is associated with the major puckering, the next best four-atom plane that can be constructed is that for which carbon 2 is out of the plane, and vice versa. Thymidine monophosphate is an exception where the next best four-atom plane is formed with carbon 4 out of the plane.

A detailed consideration of the data revealed that the remaining four atoms were not strictly coplanar and that a secondary or minor puckering also is present. The standard deviations of these calculations were such that it was not entirely possible to estimate the magnitude of this puckering.

One not entirely unexpected finding was that conformation of the ribose in these derivatives is very much dependent upon whether the glycosidically bound nitrogenous base is a pyrimidine or a purine, and also whether carbon 5 is phosphorylated or free. Conformational sketches of several model compounds are indicated in Figure 4.30.

TABLE 4.7

Deviations (A) of the atoms from the best four-atom, least-squares plane of the furanose ring.[a]

ATOM	RIBOSE IN CMP	FRUCTOSE IN SUCROSE
C-1′	−0.020	0.028
C-2′	0.609	0.542
C-3′	0.018	−0.025
C-4′	−0.030	0.042
O-1′	0.032	−0.045
N	−0.860	1.265
O-2′	−0.434	0.250
O-3′	1.380	0.741
C-5′	−1.246	−1.048
O-5′	−2.485	−2.342

[a] The deviations of the atoms included in the calculation of the least-squares planes are shown in italic.

As a result of these studies, it seems possible that conformational conversions can take place in the furanose system and that transformation of a carbon from an endo to exo orientation will affect the size, shape, and possibly the biological, molecular, and physical properties of the molecule (nucleic acids). These will also depend upon the groups to which the pentoses are attached.

The orientation of substituents in these ring forms can be termed as pseudoequatorial and pseudoaxial depending upon which atom is out of plane, which substituents are present, and which conformers are adopted. Assignments can be made according to Table 4.8. It is apparent from the table that in most cases the assignments are consistent with what we would have predicted from simple planar geometry. The puckering can be described quantitatively in terms of the projected valency angle about each single bond. This is also equivalent to viewing the bond along the carbon–carbon axis and observing the dihedral

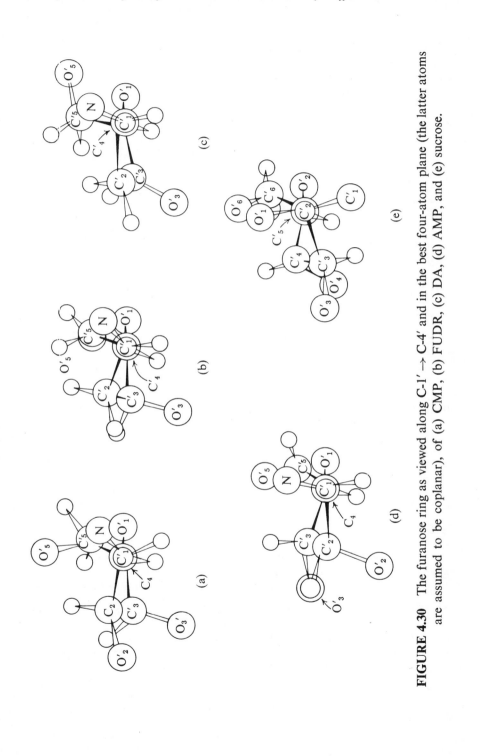

FIGURE 4.30 The furanose ring as viewed along C-1′ → C-4′ and in the best four-atom plane (the latter atoms are assumed to be coplanar), of (a) CMP, (b) FUDR, (c) DA, (d) AMP, and (e) sucrose.

angles. In this case, the angles calculated between the hydrogens are still in relatively good agreement with those calculated from NMR data. The bond that is opposite the out-of-plane atom, because it is the farthest removed, has the smallest value for the conformational angle and the next smallest is opposite the atom that is excluded in the calculation of the next best plane. Twisting the structure around the carbon 2–carbon 3 bond will result in changes from the endo to the exo configuration. Several general conclusions can be stated.

1. The bond lengths for carbon–carbon bonds within the ring are somewhat shorter than the standard 1.54-angstrom bond found in the diamond lattice. The C-4–C-5 bond is also shorter than the normal single bond value of 1.53 angstroms.

2. The bond adjacent to the glycosidic linkage, that is, the bond between carbon 1 and oxygen, is shorter than the ring carbon 4 oxygen bond by about

TABLE 4.8

The orientations of the substituents.[a]

OUT-OF-PLANE ATOM	N	H-1′	H-2′	O-2′	H-3′	O-3′	H-4′	C-5′
CMP C-2′-endo	*e*	*a*	*a*	*e*	*e*	*a*	*e*	*a*
FUDR C-2′-endo	*e*	*a*	*a*	*e*	*e*	*a*	*e*	*a*
DA C-3′-exo	*e*	*a*	*a*	*e*	*e*	*a*	*e*	*a*
AMP C-3′-endo	*a*	*e*	*e*	*a*	*a*	*e*	*a*	*e*
TMP C-3′-endo	*a*	*e*	*e*	*a*	*a*	*e*	*a*	*e*
Sucrose C-2′-exo	*a*	*e*	*e*	*a*	*a*	*e*	*a*	*e*

[a] *a* and *e* designate "axial" and "equatorial," respectively. It should be noted that these orientations are an oversimplification of what may be termed as quasiaxial, quasiequatorial, and bisectional.

0.02-angstrom units. This is perhaps due to the relative presence of the electronegative oxygen and the nitrogen of the purine or pyrimidine ring with its nonbonded electrons adjacent to carbon 1.

3. The exocyclic carbon–oxygen bond, which involves the carbon atom out of the four-atom plane, averages about 1.4 angstroms, and that involving the in-plane carbon atom, about 1.43 angstroms. This is in good agreement with the normal carbon–oxygen distance of 1.429 or 1.43 angstroms.

4. The internal dihedral angles for carbon that involve the out-of-plane carbon average about 101 degrees, which is about 2 degrees less than those that involve in-plane atoms. These are all appreciably less than the standard 109-degree tetrahedral angle.

5. The average internal carbon–oxygen bond angle is 106 degrees. This is somewhat greater than the carbon–carbon bond angle but still appreciably less than the tetrahedral angle.

6. The exocyclic carbon–carbon bond angle to the out-of-plane carbon averages 115 degrees, and is 6 degrees greater than that involving the in-plane carbon. The latter carbon–oxygen–carbon angle is the only one that is close to the true tetrahedral bond angle.

There appears to be a very marked correlation between the ring pucker, the exocyclic carbon–oxygen bond length, and the exocyclic carbon–oxygen–carbon bond angles. When the external angles open up approximately 6 degrees from normal, the carbon–oxygen distance contracts by about 0.03 angstroms, suggesting that the hybridization of the carbon is somewhere between sp^2 and sp^3. When the external angles are close to the tetrahedral bond angle, the carbon–oxygen distance is close to the expected or so-called normal value irrespective of whether the carbon atom involved is in plane or out-of-plane. This correlation between bond angle and carbon–oxygen bond length was found to hold true for several model compounds.

There is an appreciable difference in conformation depending upon the substituent groups. Although clear examples of conformational instability in the furanose series have not been put forth, and there is little or no evidence to suggest that D-sugars and L-sugars when in the furanoside form would have conformational isomerism as exists for pyranosides; in view of the above, there is every expectation that this will be the case. Whether these conformations differ by a sufficient energy barrier to permit their isolation and whether there is some biological significance ascribable to one or another preferred form of the ring is unanswerable with the present information.

This is the first of what is hopefully a series of detailed x-ray examinations of biologically important carbohydrate derivatives. It is interesting to note that although the crystal structure of sucrose was determined as early as 1947 [20], the advances in methodology and technique render the previous work of insufficient accuracy to permit determinations of conformational fine structure as indicated above. This study also underscores the relatively qualitative nature of conformational data obtained by other than x-ray methods.

4.11 Infrared Spectroscopy

General Introduction

Over the past two decades in organic chemistry, the development of infrared spectroscopy as a structural and analytical tool has been extensive. The accessibility of satisfactory commercial instruments that permit recording of infrared spectra on small amounts of material, and the advent of solid-phase pellet techniques for examining materials insoluble in nonpolar organic solvents has permitted a wide variety of structural correlations to be made. A general discussion of the mechanics and recording of such spectra is not pertinent but it may be useful to review some of the principles of infrared spectroscopy.

The intensity of an absorption band is usually expressed as strong, medium, or weak with an occasional modifying adjective. It is possible to record molecular extinction coefficients in the usual way although this is rarely done for infrared spectra.

A molecule of N atoms will be considered to have three N degrees of freedom. Three of these are assigned to translational and three to rotational motions. If the molecule is linear, there will be only two rotational degrees of freedom. The remaining degrees of freedom, $3N$-6 or $3N$-5 as the case may be, can be assigned to vibrational motions, and these give rise to infrared absorption bands. If the vibration does not induce any change in the polarity of the molecule, then infrared energy will not be absorbed and the number of peaks will be

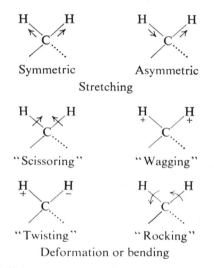

Symmetric   Asymmetric

Stretching

"Scissoring"   "Wagging"

"Twisting"   "Rocking"

Deformation or bending

FIGURE 4.31   Stretching and deformation modes for an ethylene group. Plus represents deformation out of the plane toward the reader and minus out of the plane away from the reader.

decreased accordingly. For example, the vibration of the central carbon–carbon double bond of ethylene does not absorb infrared radiation. Fundamental vibrations can be divided into those caused by stretching and those caused by bending or deformations. Figure 4.31 illustrates those that may be visualized for an ethylene group.

Overtones having twice the frequency of the normal vibration will occasionally be observed as weak bands. Combination tones occasionally appear at frequencies that are the difference of two or more fundamental bands. Two other phenomena may generally occur in infrared spectra.

1. Frequently a one-to-one correspondence between bond vibration and an absorption band is not observed. This coupling phenomenon occurs when

two bonds of the same symmetry are closely located within the molecule, the respective absorption bands are strong and the absorptions occur in the same region. In this case, only a single absorption band may be observed. These coupled bands frequently can be used as characteristic group frequencies, particularly for acids and amines.

2. When an overtone or combination band is located near a fundamental frequency, the band intensity of the former may be enhanced, or splitting may occur. This coupling between an overtone and a fundamental is called *Fermi resonance*.

The range from 0.75 microns (μ) to 200 microns (μ), which is from just above the visible range of the electromagnetic spectrum almost into the microwave region, is generally termed the infrared region. However, the practical use of infrared spectroscopy has been largely restricted to the range between 2 and 16 μ with relatively less experimental information available outside these limits. Because infrared spectroscopy is a form of absorption spectroscopy akin to ultraviolet and visible spectroscopy, it is more convenient to express the position of absorption peaks in terms of wave numbers, the reciprocal of wavelengths; these are expressed in cm^{-1} units. Thus, the range of 2 to 16 μ corresponds to 4200 cm^{-1} to 625 cm^{-1}. A consideration of the terminology shows that this term is directly related to energy and therefore a more appropriate expression for the phenomenon. The basic presumption is that molecules are made up of atoms linked together by chemical bonds. These chemical bonds are not rigid and thus the movement of atoms and the bonds holding them together can be represented schematically as a system comprised of springs and balls in constant motion (Figure 4.32).

The motion that can be visualized in such a system may be regarded as being composed of two components: those that involve stretching or compression of the bond, and those that involve its bending or distortion out of a particular reference plane. The frequencies of such vibrations depend on the nature of the particular bonds so that carbon linked to hydrogen would have one characteristic frequency, whereas carbon linked to oxygen would have another. They are also affected by the electronic and spatial environment of the atoms in relation to one another within a given molecule. The situation again may be analogous to that in the spring-ball system where the vibration of one spring is under the influence of the rest of the system and the motion of this particular one is enhanced if it is struck (absorption of energy). Thus, the vibrations of the chemical bonds will increase their amplitude if struck by an electromagnetic wave. Obviously, one of the differences between a molecule and our schematic representation of it is that the vibrational energy levels of the molecule are quantized and therefore only those electromagnetic radiations having specific energy contents will be absorbed. The amplitude of a particular vibration is increased in a quantized manner and not as a continuum. In practice, the frequency of the irradiating beam is continuously changed and the transmitted beam recorded as a function of this change. Those areas where absorption takes place are represented by decreases in transmission. Although it is true that the frequencies of a given bond in a molecule are affected by the molecular structure, certain bonds have rather specialized distinguishing characteristics.

1. Multiple bonds are stronger than single bonds.

2. NH, OH, and CH bonds have the characteristically light hydrogen atom and are more readily deformed than bonds involving heavier nuclei. The stretching vibrations of these hydrogen-containing bonds appear in the range of 3600 to 1500 cm^{-1}, whereas in the region below 1600 cm^{-1}, there are absorption areas due to the stretching of carbon–carbon, carbon–nitrogen, and carbon–oxygen bonds.

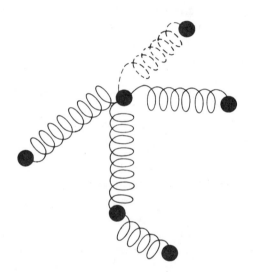

FIGURE 4.32   Schematic representation of a molecule as a series of springs and balls.

3. Single bonds have absorptions of roughly the same order of magnitude and are usually linked cumulatively. This results in a stronger mutual interaction, a wider range of appearance of absorption bands, and a great sensitivity of band positions to minor structural changes.

4. The frequency below 1300 cm^{-1} is known as the finger-print region. Assignments to specific bonds in this area are rather difficult and the spectrum is considered to be characteristic of the molecule as a whole.

5. The stronger the bond and the smaller the masses involved, the higher the absorption frequency of that bond and thus the more energy required to vibrate the bond. Bond strengths increase from single to double to triple bonds and the stretching frequency is associated with them and increases correspondingly. The stretching vibration of the OH bond is 3600 cm^{-1} but,

for example, if the hydrogen is exchanged for deuterium, this is lowered to 2630 cm^{-1}. The bond strength is substantially the same but only the mass has been increased.

6. Carbonyl vibrations that appear between 2000 and 1500 cm^{-1} are particularly sensitive to differences in structure and environment and usually quite intensely absorbing. A strongly polarizable group such as the carbonyl will be very much affected by the solvent. When polar solvents are employed, the absorption frequency of this functional group may be changed by its interaction with the solvent.

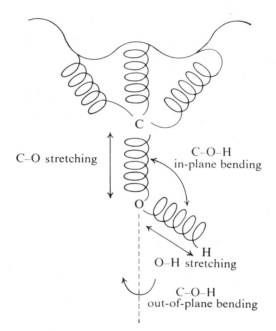

FIGURE 4.33 Stretching and deformation or bending expected for a typical hydroxyl group.

A given vibration is not necessarily accompanied by an absorption. The latter will only occur when this given vibration causes a change in the charge distribution within the molecule. Accordingly, the absorption bands of hydrocarbons (relatively nonpolarizable groups composed only of carbon and hydrogen atoms) are weak but bands associated with atoms that differ considerably in electronegativity such as carbon–nitrogen, carbon–oxygen, and so on, are usually quite strong. The term *characteristic frequency* or *characteristic absorption* band is usually applied to those absorption bands that appear with a high intensity in a range characteristic for a certain group. An enormous amount of empirical information regarding these characteristic frequencies has been accumulated in the past 20 years. Figure 4.33 indicates the type of absorptions that may be present in a typical hydroxyl function. There will be carbon–oxygen stretching, oxygen–hydrogen stretching, and carbon–oxygen–hydrogen bending both in and out of the reference plane. The location of absorptions in the infrared spectrum corresponding to these transitions will depend upon whether the carbon is primary or secondary, whether the hydroxyl group is hydrogen bonded, the strength of the hydrogen bond, and so on. The comparison of the bands for such a compound with those of similar, known compounds may help to make assignments for a specific functional group in a given environment.

Some general comments about technique may be mentioned. Simple carbohydrates are not soluble in organic solvents and can be examined as pellets suitably admixed with potassium bromide. Scattering is a problem but the KBr itself is transparent throughout the infrared region. Some distortion of specific absorption bands may occur and no information regarding solution behavior is available from this kind of spectral study. Examinations can also be made in solvents such as tetrahydrofuran and dioxane which are particularly useful for hydrogen bond studies. The use of specialized cell windows permits studies to be made in water. These are particularly complicated because of the strong absorption bands characteristic of water itself. Derivatives soluble in organic solvents are usually studied in carbon disulfide or chloroform. A consideration of the absorption bands of the solvent alone and of those bands which we wish to study in the unknown compound are helpful in selection of a suitable system for measurements.

Applications to Carbohydrates

The infrared absorption spectra of simple carbohydrates present several characteristic features from which functional group assignments have been made. There is a strong band at 3500 cm^{-1} due to the hydrogen–oxygen stretching frequency of hydrogen-bonded hydroxyl groups. The region of 1150 to 1000 cm^{-1} has several closely spaced vibration bands that are probably due to carbon–carbon and carbon–oxygen vibrations. Substituents or different functional groups will introduce their own absorptions. Thus, in glucuronic acid, the typical carbonyl absorption is found at 1750 cm^{-1}.

Most simple carbohydrates have absorption spectra which are extremely similar to about 1200 cm^{-1}. At lower frequencies, different structural isomers are shown to have different characteristic absorption bands; this is particularly pronounced in the finger-print region although the resolution and definition of spectra in this region is generally not as good as it is in the upper regions of the spectra.

One of the characteristic absorption bands for which a structural assignment has been made concerns the difference between α and β glycosides [21]. The α glycosides and also the α anomer of free sugars show an absorption peak at approximately 844 cm^{-1}, which is not exhibited by β anomers of the simple sugars or by β glycosides. Similarly, the latter group shows an absorption band at 891 cm^{-1}, which is not observed for the α. Table 4.9 illustrates the positions of the bands of this general group.

The pyranose derivatives of mannose, galactose, and glucose are all extremely similar but the small differences in absorption in the region between 900 and 750 cm^{-1} would almost certainly suffice for precise identification. Several derivatives of manno and galactopyranoses, however, display bands not exhibited by glucopyranose derivatives, and although this may be a result of the axial hydroxyl function, precise assignments have not yet been made in this area.

The vibration band observed in the area of 875 cm^{-1} is similar to a corresponding band in tetrahydropyran and may be due to carbon–oxygen–carbon stretching. The so-called ring breathing vibration found in tetrahydropyran at 813 cm^{-1} corresponds more closely to the carbohydrate bands at 765 to

TABLE 4.9

Infrared absorption bands for carbohydrate groupings.[a]

ASSIGNMENT	RANGE (cm^{-1})
Ring vibration (Asymmetric)	917 ± 13
Ring vibration (Symmetric)	770 ± 14
Anomeric C–H (Equatorial)	844 ± 8
Anomeric C–H (Axial)	891 ± 7
C–H (Equatorial)	880 ± 8
Ring methylene (Rocking, not adjacent to oxygen)	867 ± 2
CH$_3$ rocking (C-6)	967 ± 6

[a] Several of these will be modified; see text and subsequent discussion.

775 cm^{-1}. The stretching of the ring carbon–carbon bonds in this so-called breathing vibration contributes to the frequency but not to the intensity, whereas the small amount of COH stretching has very little effect on the frequency. The intensity of this band is much more susceptible to alteration than is the frequency; this is in agreement with experiments wherein there is relatively little change in the hydroxyl absorption.

Studies carried out by Isbell and his co-workers have indicated that absorption in the areas between 1160 and 1120 cm^{-1} may also be characteristic of different anomeric forms of the sugar [22]. A method of classification depending upon conformation is obviously more desirable than one which simply refers to D- or L-sugars. As might be expected, the difference is really whether the hydrogen at carbon 1 is equatorial or axial. Table 4.10 indicates absorption bands observed for several acetylated sugars where the conformation is known. When this assignment can be made, the infrared spectrum provides a means for determining anomeric configuration, which is relatively free of artifacts. This would be particularly useful in studies of polysaccharides, since these absorptions are not influenced either by the type of linkage or by the position.

Substantiation of the idea that the absorptions exhibited at 844 and 891 cm^{-1} involved the bending of the anomeric carbon–hydrogen bond rather than the bond involving the glycosidic oxygen was arrived at as follows. This absorption is relatively unaffected by modifications or replacements of the hydroxyl group at C-1 by a large number of groups ranging from deuterium to carbohydrate aglycones. Thus, the environment or restriction of movement of

TABLE 4.10

Infrared absorptions for selected carbohydrate derivatives.

COMPOUND	SYMMETRIC C—O—C VIBRATION	ABSORPTION BANDS	
		TYPE 1 [a]	TYPE 2 [b]
2-deoxy tetraacetyl α-D-glucopyranose	953	911	888, 849
6-deoxy tetraacetyl α-D-galactopyranose	943	898	881, 820
β-D-galactopyranose pentaacetate	966	894	896, 863
β-D-mannopyranose pentaacetate	933		896, 880

[a] Type 1 corresponds to the band found in tetrahydropyran and may be asymmetric C—O—C stretching.
[b] Type 2 is probably a vibrational mode of the C—H bond.

the external oxygen has relatively little effect on this absorption band. Because the α and β anomers of simple sugars, such as glucose, differ only in the positions of groups around carbon 1 (axial versus equatorial), it is postulated that the deformation of the axial hydrogen brings it into closer contact with the hydrogen at C-5 (Figure 4.34). This proximity of the C-1 and C-5 hydrogens results in

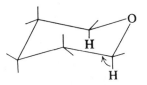

FIGURE 4.34 Possible closeness of approach between the axial hydrogen at carbon 1 and that present at carbon 5.

appreciable Van der Waals repulsion, giving rise to an increased frequency as is observed with β-D-glucopyranose. In agreement with this, the axial hydrogens on C-1 and C-5 are closer together in tetrahydropyran than they are found to be in cyclohexane.

The characteristic frequencies of ring methylene and C-methyl groups which occur in deoxy sugars have also been studied [23]. The assignment of absorption peaks to the methylene groups of the deoxy sugars has been approached by the study of the spectra of quercitols (pentahydroxycyclohexanes) and the corresponding inositols. The quercitols show an additional absorption peak at 853 cm^{-1}, which was assumed to be due to the methylene group. An extension of this study to 2- and 3-deoxy derivatives of glucose, galactose, and mannopyranoses show the deoxy compounds to have an additional absorption at 867 cm^{-1}, which is of moderate intensity for the free sugars or their glycosides compared to the parent sugar. Because the only part of the molecule that is different in the two groups is the replacement of a CHOH group by the methylene group, this was also ascribed to the rocking vibration of the ring methylene. This has been further strengthened by studies of the 4,6 benzylidene derivatives of α-D-glucopyranose (Figure 4.35) [24]. In this derivative, an absorption at 877 cm^{-1} was assigned to the ring methylene formed by C-6 of the α-D-glucopyranose attached to the benzylidene grouping. Comparable studies of D-xylopyranose derivatives found no such peak, although there is a ring methylene

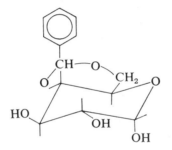

FIGURE 4.35   4,6 benzylidene α-D-glucopyranose.

at position 5 in this molecule. It was suggested that a single methylene next to the oxygen atom in the pyranose ring may absorb at a different frequency than a ring methylene grouping in another position. In the case of 6-deoxy sugars, where a methyl group is present, these show an additional peak at 967 cm^{-1}. However, precise assignment of this absorption band to the methyl function is difficult because many other carbon–oxygen absorptions are present in this region.

Compounds containing furanose rings exhibit absorption at 924 and 799 cm^{-1}, the former due to the symmetrical ring breathing frequency of the tetrahydrofuran ring. Fused cyclic acetals or ketals where two 5-membered rings are linked together usually show a doublet at 917 cm^{-1}. When a 5-membered ring is fused to a 6-membered ring, it is not possible to differentiate these completely.

The second type of absorption exhibited in furanoses is believed to be due to a deformation of a carbon–hydrogen bond where the hydrogen is present on a carbon directly attached to the ring oxygen of the 5-membered ring. In contrast to the pyranose ring, the carbon–hydrogen bonds are more equivalent than in the typical axial or equatorial orientations and hence a decision between α and β furanosides by infrared is not possible. In these cases, optical rotation behavior is generally found most useful. Several studies utilizing deuterium replacement, particularly involving the anomeric C-1 hydrogen, have indicated that modifications in early assignments are necessary. Table 4.11 lists the absorption bands that have been assigned based on the earlier work and which, in view of subsequent discussion, will require some modification [25]. The band at 917 cm^{-1} assigned to antisymmetrical ring vibration and the one at 770 cm^{-1} assigned to symmetrical ring vibration are fairly accurate and the bands at 844 and 891 cm^{-1} have been mentioned. Studies on crystalline versus noncrystalline polysaccharides reveal that these absorption bands are very

TABLE 4.11

Assignment of infrared absorption bands to carbohydrate structures.

STRUCTURE	ASSIGNMENT (cm^{-1})
Ring (asymmetric)	917
Ring (symmetric)	770
$\begin{array}{c} \text{H} \\ \mid \diagup \\ -\text{C} \\ \mid \\ \text{OH} \end{array}$	844
$\begin{array}{c} \text{OH} \\ \mid \diagup \\ -\text{C} \\ \mid \\ \text{H} \end{array}$	891
C–O–C stretching	1160
O–H stretching (primary)	3642
O–H stretching (secondary)	3629

sensitive to the physical state. The failure of substitution by deuterium to lead to a significant shift in these absorption bands suggests that the entire grouping at carbon 1 is responsible rather than just the carbon–hydrogen deformation (Figure 4.36). Recent work (deuterium replacement) has assigned the CH deformation between 1300 and 1400 cm^{-1} [26]. Specific assignments in the region between 960 and 1500 cm^{-1} are extremely difficult because of the large number of bands in this region. Careful studies carried out with cellulose have permitted assignment of over 15 specific bands in this area to functional groups. Those occurring primarily between 1200 and 1500 cm^{-1} have been assigned to OH and CH vibrations, whereas those below 1200 cm^{-1} are usually assigned to carbon–oxygen and carbon–carbon. Carbon–oxygen stretching at 1110 cm^{-1} and carbon–carbon ring stretching at 1120 cm^{-1} have also been identified.

The use of infrared spectra in the carbohydrate field has also been particularly widespread for identification of specific functional groups in derivatives. The methoxyl function in methylated sugars has an absorption at 2882 cm^{-1}, probably due to the methyl group, since this is not observed in ethoxyl or simple sugars. 2-keto sugars show characteristic absorptions at 810 and 874 cm^{-1}, *regardless of whether the ring is 5-membered or 6-membered.*

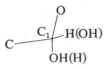

FIGURE 4.36 Functional group at carbon 1 of a carbohydrate responsible for indicated infrared absorption band. See text for amplification.

The general area for this absorption is very similar to that assigned to α and β anomers of glycosides of 6-membered rings. In this case, because the classical axial and equatorial orientations for the anomeric proton are not present, this supports the assignment for the 6-membered ring aldose absorption to the acetal grouping as a whole. Accordingly, these absorptions are considered characteristic of the ketal grouping (Figure 4.37).

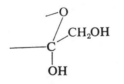

FIGURE 4.37 Grouping responsible for assigned absorption in ketoses.

Derivatives of the reducing group of carbohydrates including oximes, phenylhydrazones, osazones, semicarbazones, and thiosemicarbazones have all been studied. Although many of the absorption bands occur in regions where complexities are introduced due to other similar absorptions, several specific assignments can be made and are illustrated in Table 4.12.

TABLE 4.12

Absorption bands for nitrogen containing derivatives formed by reaction of carbohydrates with hydroxylamine, semicarbazide, and related compounds.

STRUCTURE	BAND POSITION
Oxime	1667 cm^{-1}
Semicarbazone	1646–1675
Thio semicarbazone	1630–1650
Phenylhydrazone	No distinctive band found

Specific assignment for absorptions of groups such as phosphate and sulfate can easily be made because of their very polar nature and the correspondingly intense absorption. A study of the sulfate absorptions of chondroitin sulfates has shown that axial and equatorial sulfates may be distinguished by the differing positions of the absorption bands corresponding to the sulfate grouping [27] (Figure 4.38). In general, axial bands occur at lower wave numbers and structural assignments have been made on this basis. The few studies that have been made on monosaccharide model compounds substantiate this although there have been no studies carried out with axial sulfates. Sulfated hyaluronic acid, which would have only equatorial substituents, exhibited absorptions consistent with the above.

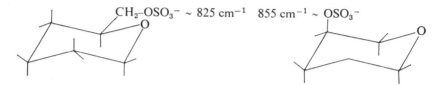

FIGURE 4.38   Differing infrared absorption for axial and equatorial sulfate esters.

It is apparent from much of the above discussion that it is extremely difficult to make precise band assignments on an *a priori* basis. Axial hydroxyls, anomeric or equatorial hydrogens may have specific absorptions, but these are frequently masked by other groups.

Infrared spectra in the carbohydrate field have been used primarily for identification of substituent functional groups such as acetamido, carbonyl, phosphate, nitrate, sulfate, and in addition, as an identification technique by comparison of unknowns with compounds of known structure. Where a new compound has been isolated, comparison of its infrared spectrum with that of suspected structural analogs can frequently provide useful information. It is almost equally probable that confusing information will be obtained if, for example, the compounds are not in the same crystalline state, are not examined in the same solvent, and so on. Nevertheless, as a means of structural identification, this is an extremely powerful tool particularly when insufficient material or time is available to permit x-ray diffraction analysis or a comparable structural proof; assignments of structure based on infrared spectra are difficult, but functional group assignments will always be possible.

Hydrogen Bonding

An estimate of the strength of hydrogen bonds can be made from the separation in wave numbers (Δv) between the bands due to free and hydrogen-bonded hydroxyl groups. As a general rule, the smaller the length of the hydrogen bond, the stronger the bond itself and the greater the value of the Δv.

Foster and co-workers have shown that the $\Delta\nu$ values also reflect the size of the ring formed by intramolecular hydrogen bonding as long as no unusual steric effects are present. Measurement in an inert solvent of the extent of intra-molecular hydrogen bonding of homologous glycols and homologous mono-methyl glycols, show that in compounds where hydrogen bonding allows the formation of different size rings, the 5-membered ring was formed more frequently than the 6 which in turn was formed more frequently than the 7-membered ring [28].

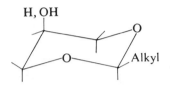

FIGURE 4.39   Alkyl substituted 1,3 dioxanes.

The synthesis of *trans* derivatives of two alkyl 5-hydroxy–1,3-dioxane was carried out, and the effects of the bulk and orientation of the alkyl groups on the hydrogen bonding between the hydroxyl group and the oxygen atom of the ring was studied [29] (Figure 4.39). The extinction coefficients and positions of the absorption bands were measured in this study. The latter were found at 3636 cm^{-1} for the free and 3595 cm^{-1} for the hydrogen-bond conformer. The

TABLE 4.13

Comparison of free and hydrogen-bonded hydroxyls in 1,3 dioxanes.

DERIVATIVE	CONFIGURATION	FREE OH	H-BONDED OH	RATIO (BONDED TO FREE)
Parent		3636	3593	5.70
2-methyl	*Cis*	—	3592	
2-methyl	*Trans*	3633	3604	0.40
2-ethyl	*Cis*		3592	
2-ethyl	*Trans*	3634	3602	0.29
2-phenyl	*Cis*		3590	
2-phenyl	*Trans*	3633	3601	0.32

extinction coefficient of the hydrogen-bonded derivative was approximately five times that of the free, indicating that it predominates in an equilibrium mixture. The introduction of substituents, such as phenyl, stabilized the hydrogen-bonded conformer to a very considerable extent. Table 4.13 illustrates the difference between the free and bonded hydroxyl groups and also the assignment of the *cis* or *trans* configuration to the alkyl substituent.

Most of the hydroxyl groups are clearly hydrogen-bonded but in the case of alkyl substituted *trans* derivatives, negligible hydrogen bonding is seen. Intramolecular hydrogen bonding in disubstituted derivatives of 5-hydroxy–1,3-dioxane does not appear to predominate in the chair form as indicated from the lack of effect of the bulk of the C-2 substituent on hydrogen bonding (Figure 4.40). It seems unlikely that the compound would be in the chair form, because this would have an equatorial hydroxyl having a dihedral angle between the hydroxyl group and each ring oxygen of 180 degrees (greater than that in cyclopentane *trans* 1,2 diol which does not exhibit hydrogen bonding).

In the case of 5-membered rings, primary hydroxyl groups and the neighboring oxygen atom are involved in hydrogen bonding, whereas both primary and secondary hydroxyl groups may be involved in hydrogen bonding in 6-membered rings. The ability of hydroxyl groups to form hydrogen bonds is influenced by steric effects and also to a certain extent by their acidity. Thus, tertiary hydroxyls are better than secondary which in turn are better than primary.

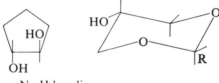

No H bonding

FIGURE 4.40   Structures of 5- and 6-membered rings in which hydrogen bonding is not present.

The model compounds of tetrahydropyran and tetrahydrofuran which have been examined, show that the ring oxygen may be involved in hydrogen-bond formation with suitably located hydroxyl groups. Tetrahydropyran 3-ol exists as an equilibrium conformer of the axial and equatorial hydroxyl. In this case, the former structure is stabilized by intramolecular hydrogen-bond formation with the ring oxygen, whereas the energetically (hydrogen-bond considerations aside) more favorable equatorial isomer cannot interact in this way. Under suitable conditions the chemical properties of functional groups can be greatly modified by hydrogen bonding. Selective sulfonation of 1,4:3,6 dianhydro D-glucitol can be carried out, and the formation of 1,3 benzylidene arabitol is more readily explained on this basis as opposed to the formation of the 3,5 derivative [30].

Hydrogen-bond studies on polymers such as cellulose indicate that there is intramolecular hydrogen bonding involving the oxygen atoms attached to carbon atoms 6 and 2 of adjacent glucose residues; this, in part, is responsible for the relatively rigid structure of the cellulose polymer. It is suggested by several workers that the insolubility of the cellulose in water is in part due to the complete hydrogen-bonded region of the cellulose molecule. X-ray investigations have confirmed this and also confirmed the fact that the crystalline region is completely hydrogen bonded, whereas the amorphous is not. This is another area where deuterium replacement studies permitted distinction between hydrogen-bonded and nonhydrogen-bonded hydroxyl functional groups.

Conclusions

Several recent developments offer promise for attack of problems that have hitherto been impossible to solve. It is possible to measure attenuated total reflectance which is relatively independent of sample thickness. This permits study of spectra in aqueous solution without serious interference of the absorption of water, which is very intense. This technique, developed by Fahrenfort, has not been widely applied in the carbohydrate field although potential applications, especially in hydrogen-bonding studies, are very great.

The study of polymer conformation and in particular the orientation of groups in polymers using infrared dichroism has been approached by several groups. Although model studies for those polymers that can be conveniently stretched into films have provided useful information, the general applicability of this technique in the carbohydrate field is probably limited. Limitations here may be primarily of a mechanical nature in the sense that the equipment is relatively unavailable. The advent of high-resolution grating spectrometers permits a great degree of confidence for band assignments and has facilitated the hydrogen-bonding studies discussed above.

4.12 Optical Rotatory Dispersion

The phenomenon of optical rotatory dispersion although known for a long period of time has had relatively little application to carbohydrate structure until fairly recently. The primary reason for this has been the lack of chromophores in the carbohydrates which absorb at a wavelength accessible to commercial instrumentation. The hydroxyl functional group has an absorption band at about 165 millimicrons (mμ) which is too far down for practical studies. Unless some other absorbing group is present, the expectation is that not too much structural information will be derived from dispersion studies. Several recent papers have appeared which indicate that dispersion techniques will be extremely valuable in the carbohydrate field although most simple sugars such as glucose give plain dispersion curves [31–33] (Figure 4.41). One immediate result is that D- and L-sugars give curves that are similar in shape but opposite in sign. Another parameter which is useful is the tremendously enhanced magnitude of the optical rotation at the lower wavelengths; D-glucose has a specific rotation in excess of 1000 degrees at 220 mμ. The only aldohexoses examined which did not show plain dispersion curves were D-galactose and D-talose. The curves for galactose are illustrated in Figure 4.42. The appearance

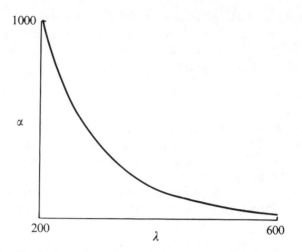

FIGURE 4.41   Typical rotatory dispersion curve for simple carbohydrates such as D-glucose.

of the Cotton effect at 208 mμ is not completely explained but may be related to the presence of a significant amount of the furanose form in this molecule, or the effect of the axial C-4 hydroxyl. Carbohydrates that have a significant amount of free aldehyde form in solution might exhibit Cotton effects above 200 mμ where *n*-π* transitions would be expected to occur. However, none were observed in water probably because the free aldehyde group is completely hydrated in aqueous solution. An alteration of solvent such as the use of

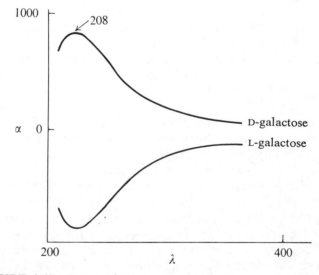

FIGURE 4.42   Rotatory dispersion curves for D- and L-galactose.

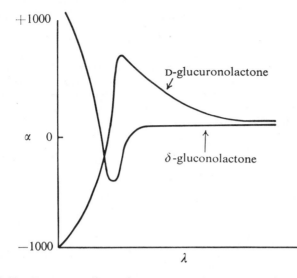

FIGURE 4.43 Rotatory dispersion curves of D-glucuronic acid lactone and delta gluconolactone.

dimethyl sulfoxide or methanol elicits such an effect but detailed solvent studies have not been carried out. The presence of a carboxyl or acyl group either in the chain or terminal leads to the appearance of Cotton effects which are exhibited at wavelengths corresponding very closely to the absorption maximum (Figure 4.43). The lactone rule of Djerassi (Figure 4.44) was found to be successful in predicting the sign of the Cotton effect curves from the configuration of the hydroxyl group in the lactones studied. This is illustrated in Table 4.14. The reverse is obviously also true since the shape of the curve can be used as a prediction of configuration. Correlation of these data with NMR conformational information should provide useful techniques for conformational assignments in the idose series and for those sugars where the ring form is unknown. It

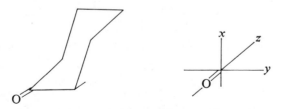

FIGURE 4.44 Representation of 6-membered ring containing a carbonyl group. The carbonyl group is considered to lie on a hypothetical axis as indicated. The rotational contribution of any group relative to this carbonyl will have a sign *which is the product* of the signs of its coordinates in this axis system.

TABLE 4.14

Predicted and observed rotations of simple cyclic ketones and carbohydrate lactones.

COMPOUND	PREDICTION	OBSERVED
3-methylcyclohexanone	+	+25
3,6,6′trimethylcyclohexanone	+	+81
9-methyl *trans* decalone 1	+	+38
9-methyl *trans* decalone 4	−	−32
9-methyl *cis* decalone 1	−	negative
D-arabono-γ-lactone, S^a	+	+
D-glucusono-γ-lactone, S	+	+
D-gluco saccharo, S 3,6 lactone	+	+
D-ribono-γ-lactone, R	−	−
D-glucono-γ-lactone, R	−	−
D-galactono-γ-lactone, R	−	−

[a] Refers to absolute configuration of 2 carbon.

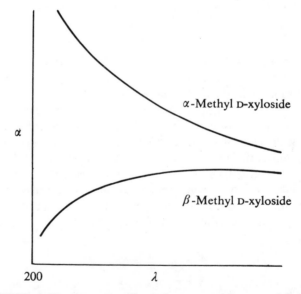

FIGURE 4.45 Rotatory dispersion curves for α and β methyl
D-xylopyranosides.

should also be noted that α and β glycosides of a given pyranose can be easily
distinguished since the shape of their dispersion curves is characteristic (Figure
4.45).

The application of these techniques to conformational problems has been
restricted due to instrumentation problems but a rapid expansion in this area is
anticipated.

CHAPTER 5

Carbohydrate Conformation

5.1 Use of Complexing Agents in Conformational Analysis

The application of structural information obtained for cyclohexane to the problem of carbohydrate conformation has been actively underway for some time. Various techniques have been employed and several experimental parameters have been measured and correlated in attempts to define the conformation of carbohydrates. The goal of such studies is to formulate some general statement regarding preferred structures and how these contribute to the physical and spectroscopic properties of the entire molecule.

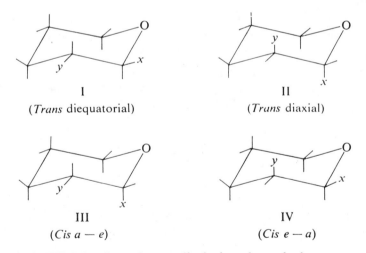

I
(*Trans* diequatorial)

II
(*Trans* diaxial)

III
(*Cis a — e*)

IV
(*Cis e — a*)

FIGURE 5.1 *Cis* and *trans* disubstituted tetrahydropyrans.

The formation of the 6-membered tetrahydropyran ring by a carbohydrate hemiacetal introduces several new problems. In contrast to the cyclohexane ring where all positions are equivalent, the presence of the ring oxygen (with no substituents other than carbon) permits a new type of asymmetry. Consider a disubstituted tetrahydropyran (Figure 5.1).

105

In the ring form illustrated, the two substituents may be diaxial, di-equatorial, or axial-equatorial. Recalling the effect of ring interconversion on substituents or hydrogens on cyclohexane (axial substituents become equatorial and vice versa), a similar transformation here yields Figure 5.2.

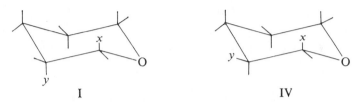

I   IV

FIGURE 5.2 Conversion of *trans* diequatorial to *trans* diaxial form (Figure 5.I) and *cis*, equatorial-axial to *cis* axial-equatorial form (Figure 5.IV).

As is readily apparent, the groups that were originally diaxial are now diequatorial, and so on. However, the projection formula of an open chain representation of this structure *has not changed*.

Extending the above to a typical sugar, we observe the following:

1. Groups that are *trans* (opposite sides of the carbon chain) in a projection formula are either diaxial or diequatorial in the ring form.

2. Groups that are *cis* in a projection formula are axial-equatorial in the ring form.

3. Epimerization of a hydroxyl group, as in the conversion of glucose to galactose involves change of this group from an equatorial to an axial position (or the reverse) *without any change in ring form*.

In an extension and illustration of the above, consider the structure of β-D-glucopyranose which, in a post-facto assumption, is depicted with all functional groups equatorial (Figure 5.3).

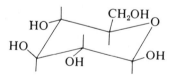

FIGURE 5.3 β-D-glucopyranose in the ring form with all substituent groups equatorial.

Epimerization at carbon 1 yields α-D-glucose (Figure 5.4).

Subsequent epimerizations at carbons 2, 3, and 4 yield α-D-mannose, α-D-altrose, and α-D-idose, respectively (Figure 5.5).

Finally, epimerization at carbon 5 yields β-L-glucose, the mirror image of the starting compound. However, in light of our earlier considerations (to be strengthened subsequently), β-L-glucose clearly prefers to exist in that ring form which has all groups equatorial rather than all groups axial (Figure 5.6).

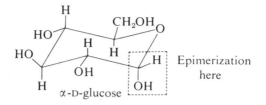

FIGURE 5.4 Epimerization at carbon 1 yields α-D-glucopyranose with the hydroxyl group at C-1 now axial.

A thorough understanding of these concepts is critical for an appreciation of conformational problems. The ability to decide on the most likely conformer for a given carbohydrate is, in a sense, proportional to our knowledge. The all equatorial structure of β-D-glucose permits an easy assignment of conformation. Indeed, it could logically be argued that the ubiquitous distribution of this sugar (it is the most widely distributed and most prevalent organic compound known) is what we would predict on thermodynamic grounds, given sufficient time for selection.[1] However, for a carbohydrate containing 2 axial groups in one ring form, and three in another, the choice becomes less certain. Problems of ring distortion, alternate nonchair ring forms, and possible interconversion of conformers all become pertinent. The methodology and interpretation of experiments aimed at solving these questions forms the major part of carbohydrate conformational analysis.

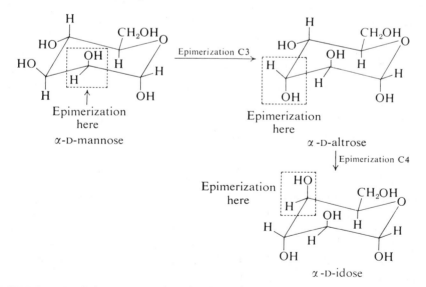

FIGURE 5.5 Subsequent epimerizations at carbons 2, 3, and 4 to form α-D-mannopyranose, α-D-altropyranose, and α-D-idopyranose, respectively.

[1] Perhaps β-L-glucose is equally popular in some other universe. We might venture that their local proteins would be composed of D-amino acids.

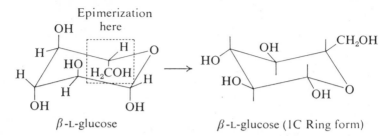

β-L-glucose β-L-glucose (1C Ring form)

FIGURE 5.6 Epimerization at carbon atom 5 of α-D-idopyranose to form β-L-glucopyranose which, as indicated, exists in that ring form where all groups are equatorial.

A chronological survey of the subject shows that much of the early work was carried out by Reeves, who for many years emphasized the fact that these molecules had to be visualized as somewhat more than planar stick formulas [1, 2]. The major experimental tool he employed was the use of a glycol complexing agent, *cuprammonium*.

Cuprammonium is a copper–ammonia complex prepared in a strongly alkaline solution according to one of two procedures; the solution (deep blue) has several rather interesting properties. When complexing occurs with a carbohydrate in cuprammonium solution, there is a change in the spectral absorption due to the copper complex; there is also a change in the electrical conductivity of the solution. This latter effect is primarily due to the fact that the strongly alkaline solution causes ionization of the hydroxyl groups and when these are chelated with copper, there is an associated change in conduction. Because the solutions have very high absorbancies, the spectrophotometric transformation is rather difficult to measure and, as a rule, most of the experimental work has been performed following changes in conductivity.

The absorbancy and conductivity changes themselves provide little structural information other than the ability of the compound in question to interact with the reagent. However, when complexing occurs between hydroxyls, which are on adjacent carbons (most common case) in skew (axial-equatorial or equatorial-equatorial) arrangements, a marked rotational moment is exerted upon the 6-membered ring, which in turn induces a large change in the optical rotation of the molecule. This arises due to the requirement for planarity or near planarity for the copper containing ring (Figure 5.7). The projected valence angle between hydroxyl groups on adjacent carbons will be 60 degrees (*cis*, or *trans* diequatorial), or 180 degrees (*trans* diaxial, no interaction with the reagent). However, the angle may be + or − 60 degrees when viewed along the axis of the carbon–carbon bond. If the translation is clockwise, the angle is considered negative and the observed rotational change is levo as for the 2,3 hydroxyl groups of D-glucose; if the translation is counterclockwise, the angle is considered positive and the observed rotational change dextro. It is neces-

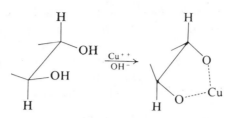

FIGURE 5.7 Schematic representation of the reaction between adjacent
hydroxyl groups and cuprammonium.

sary, in view of the dark blue color of the solution, to conduct rotational
measurements at a wavelength removed from that of the sodium light (yellow);
measurements are commonly carried out at 436 mμ (blue). This large change in
rotation is either positive or negative depending upon the actual direction in
which the molecule has been distorted in order to allow the formation of the
5-membered ring between the copper, the two hydroxyls involved in complexing

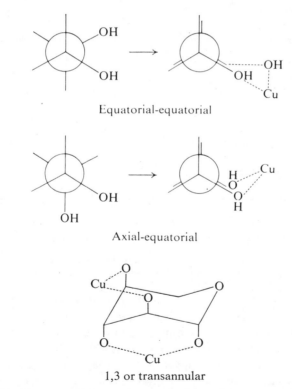

Equatorial-equatorial

Axial-equatorial

1,3 or transannular

FIGURE 5.8 Representation of complexing with cuprammonium in the
Newman projection for diequatorial, axial-equatorial, and transannular
hydroxyls.

and the two carbons which contain the hydroxyls. The several types of complexes are illustrated in Figure 5.8. Note that transannular complexing may also occur in a carbohydrate with axial hydroxyls at carbons 2 and 4. In this case, changes in conductivity would be observed *without concomitant changes in the optical rotation* of the complex. However, whenever axial-equatorial or diequatorial complexing takes place, both rotational and conductivity changes

TABLE 5.1

Rotational shifts observed for various glycosides on treatment with cuprammonium.

COMPOUND	ROTATIONAL SHIFT[a]	CHANGE IN CONDUCTANCE	INTERPRETATION[b]
Methyl 4-methyl β-D-glucopyranoside	− 2020		
Methyl 4,6-dimethyl β-D-glucopyranoside	− 1990	52	Levo complex C2–C3
Methyl 4,6-ethylidene β-D-glucopyranoside	− 1970	73	Levo complex C2–C3
Methyl 4,6-benzylidene β-D-glucopyranoside	− 2230	82	Levo complex C2–C3
Methyl 2,6-dimethyl α-D-glucopyranoside	+ 2110	58	Dextro complex C3–C4
Methyl 3-methyl-β-D glucopyranoside	− 83	16	No complex at 2,4, 2,6 or 4,6
Methyl 2,4 dimethyl-α-D glucopyranoside	− 74	7	No complex at 3,6
Methyl α-glucopyranoside	+ 244	50	Complex at 2,3 and 3,4[c]
Methyl β-glucopyranoside	+ 250	67	Complex at 2,3 and 3,4

[a] $([\alpha]_{436} \text{ Cupra} - [\alpha]_{436} \text{ Water}) \left(\dfrac{\text{Mol. wt.}}{100} \right)$

[b] Negative shifts interpreted as left (levo) rotational moments; positive as right (dextro) moments.

[c] Conductance change shows formation of complex. Low rotational change indicates near equal affinity of hydroxyls at 2, 3, and 4 for complexing.

are observed. Examination of a large number of glycosides and related derivatives led to several general results which are summarized in Table 5.1. The preferred conformations and three-dimensional structures for most of the simple sugars are listed in Table 5.2.

Although this method was novel in its conception and application, there are several drawbacks to the interpretations. The strong driving force favoring complexing permits some ring distortion to take place and therefore it is no longer entirely possible to reconstruct the initial situation with certainty. The changes in rotational moment are very large and can only be roughly correlated with the dihedral angle between groups on adjacent carbons. It is not always possible to determine whether a conformer change from one ring form to another has occurred as a result of the interaction of the sugar with the cuprammonium. The presence of very strong alkali in the solution also has some effect on group interactions. This technique may be viewed as one which is very valuable but which obscures part of the value of the measurement due to the rigorous conditions of the measurement process itself—a variation on the uncertainty principle.

TABLE 5.2

Correlation of the type of complex formed on interaction with cuprammonium with the predicted ring form.

METHYL GLYCOPYRANOSIDE	TYPE OF COMPLEX	RING FORM[a]
α-D-manno	Dextro	C1
β-D-manno	Dextro	C1
α-L-rhamno	Levo	1C
α-D-altro	Positive	C1, 1C
α-D-gulo	Dextro	C1
α-D-quinovo	Compensating	C1
α-D-ido	Compensating	1C
α-D-xylo	Compensating	C1
β-D-ribo	Compensating	C1
α-D-lyxo	Positive	C1, 1C

[a] See section 5.4 for definition of these terms.

A second complexing agent that has been widely used in determining carbohydrate conformation is borate [3]. The ability of sugars, and hydroxyl compounds generally, to complex with borate has been known for some time. There are several features of borate that provide information over and above that obtainable with cuprammonium. One essential difference between borate complexing and cuprammonium complexing can be visualized in Figure 5.9. It can be seen from the figure, that *cis* groups (axial-equatorial) on adjacent carbon atoms are capable of undergoing complexing with borate, whereas *trans* groups, which are diequatorial and presumably at the same distance from each other as the *cis* groups, do not undergo complexing. Contrast this with the situation for cuprammonium where both groups interact with the reagent. Consideration of molecular models does not provide an immediate answer to this problem because the distances between the axial-equatorial and the diequatorial groups are exactly the same. However, on attempting to distort the 6-membered ring so as to permit closer approach of the hydroxyl groups and thus binding of the complexing agent to the hydroxyls, it is apparent that considerably less physical force is required to bring the *cis* groups into an eclipsed arrangement than to achieve the same result with *trans*, diequatorial hydroxyls. This is *not* an artifact of the model and is a general rule that is often overlooked. Complexing of *cis* hydroxyls will tend to reduce transannular interaction with axial substituents, whereas for the *trans* hydroxyls, these interactions are created. In brief, it is possible to bring about distortion of the ring so that *cis* group are brought into *opposition*, but it is extremely difficult to bring *trans* groups into opposition. This result in itself emphasizes the strong driving force for cuprammonium complexing and underscores the possibility that ring conformation changes or other unknown distortions might take place during measurement of complexing by cuprammonium.

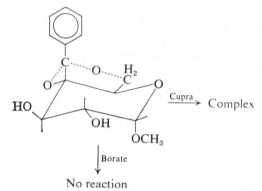

FIGURE 5.9   α-methyl-4,6-benzylidene D-glucopyranoside which will react with cuprammonium to form a rotating complex but does not undergo complexing with borate.

The extent of borate complexing is most often observed by measuring the changes in the conductivity of the solution or in the electrophoretic mobility of the respective carbohydrates. The complex formed is similar to the cuprammonium one and bears a net negative charge; it is a cyclic ester formed between boric acid and the sugar hydroxyls. Open chain esters are sufficiently unstable in aqueous solution so that complexing with single hydroxyl groups is not observed.

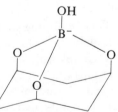

FIGURE 5.10   Schematic representation of tridentate borate complex.

The use of borate complexing as a chromatographic technique for separation of sugars is quite common. Borate-impregnated paper takes advantage of the fact that complexed carbohydrates move at a slower rate than those which do not interact with the borate. As is the case with cuprammonium, in addition to complexing with adjacent hydroxyls, borate also complexes with transannular hydroxyls. In this case, because there is no ring distortion involved, the same changes are observed as with cupra (conductivity). A special class of borate complex, the so-called bird-cage or tridentate ester, is encountered in the cyclitol series [4] (Figure 5.10). The rate of complexing in the cyclitols is very dependent on hydroxyl conformation (Table 5.3).

TABLE 5.3

Rate constants for the formation of tridentate complex as a function of cyclitol configuration.

COMPOUND	FORMULA	K FORMATION OF TRIDENTATE COMPLEX
Scyllo-quercitol		5
epi-quercitol		310
cis-quercitol		7900
myo-inositol		25
epi-inositol		7000
cis-inositol		1.1×10^6

Whereas the ability to complex with borate is a more subtle probe of the array or arrangement of the hydroxyl groups present in a carbohydrate, proportionately less information is obtained regarding the relative angles and distances for the groups and, as a result, other methods are generally employed to obtain fine conformational details. Nevertheless, the *ability* to complex with borate can be used as a diagnostic test for the presence of a *cis* hydroxyl function or a transannular hydroxyl pair in a given structure. The phenomenon is certainly not restricted to the carbohydrate field, although we may argue that any hydroxyl containing compound is a type of carbohydrate.[2]

Complexing agents of a somewhat different category include lead tetraacetate and sodium metaperiodate. Both of these are strong oxidizing agents and their role as preparative and analytic tools will be discussed subsequently. Nevertheless, considerable information can be gained regarding conformation from a consideration of the rate and extent of reaction of a given compound with

TABLE 5.4

Relative mobilities on paper electrophoresis for selected carbohydrates in borate, germanate, and arsenate buffers.

SUGAR	BORATE[a]	GERMANATE	ARSENATE
L-arabinose	96	150	30
D-lyxose	71	190	42
D-ribose	77	210	100
D-xylose	100[b]	140	17
D-allose	83	180	75
D-altrose	97	· · ·	77
D-galactose	93	130	28
D-glucose	100	100	16
D-gulose	82	· · ·	53
L-idose	102[c]	· · ·	115[d]
D-mannose	72	140	35
D-talose	87	· · ·	119[d]

[a] Mobility relative to glucose (100) for borate and germanate or ribose (100) for arsenate. The principles of metal complexing are discussed in detail in References 1 and 2.
[b] All equatorial (β-D-xylopyranose) as is glucose.
[c] Suggests C1 conformer predominant (only C-6 axial) because C-6 has little effect on complexing ability.
[d] Indicative of conformer instability. Both metal buffers roughly reflect this.

both sodium metaperiodate and lead tetraacetate. Part of the reason for this is based on the common mechanistic feature that planar or nearly planar 5-membered rings must be formed in order for reaction to take place. It is well known that open chain compounds, such as sugar alcohols, are extremely rapidly acted upon by periodate with complete destruction of the molecule. It is also well known, although perhaps not as well appreciated, that there is considerable difference in oxidation rates between compounds where the groups are primarily *trans*, as in D-glucose, and where *cis* hydroxyls are present, such as in D-mannose

[2] It is common for scientists in the nucleic acid field to regard a straight line as a degenerate helix.

and D-galactose. The difference is usually accentuated when other functional groups are present which tend to reduce the rate of periodate action.

Similar considerations entail with reactions involving lead tetraacetate. Rigid ring structures containing adjacent hydroxyl groups in transdiaxial conformation do not react significantly with either periodate or lead tetraacetate. In contrast, groups that have an eclipsed *cis* conformation react essentially instantaneously, while those with a skew orientation react more or less rapidly depending upon whether they are *cis* axial-equatorial or *trans* diequatorial, respectively. Because the action of both periodate and lead tetraacetate may be measured by spectrophotometric methods, rapid reactions are readily followed, and a quick assessment of the arrangement of hydroxyl groups may be obtained. The reaction itself is of an "irreversible" type because the parent compound will not be recovered. Nevertheless, the application of these reagents as conformational tools is not rare although they are primarily employed in structural determinations and, to a lesser extent, in analytic and synthetic procedures.

Several other complexing agents are known but their application to conformational problems has been rather minor. These include phenylboronic acid, germanate, sulfonate, and arsenate. The primary use of these has been as buffers for ionophoretic separation of carbohydrates. Typical mobilities and the associated structural parameter responsible are given in Table 5.4 [5].

5.2 Survey of Chemical Methods

The direct chemical assessment of conformation has been based primarily on the difference between the reactivities of axial versus equatorial functional groups. The normal consideration is that axial groups are shielded by the interaction of the entire ring and that approach of an attacking group will take place in a random fashion.[3] Based even on a crude version of reaction theory which requires collision to take place, such interactions will be at best 50 percent effective and at worst much less than that. Equatorial groups, on the other hand, are not protected by the ring and as such should be much more accessible to the action of reagents.

A series of studies has been carried out examining the reactivity of groups at carbon 1 of aldose sugars [6]. The rate of oxidation of the hemiacetal form of the sugar to the aldono-lactone has been measured under conditions illustrated below. The alkaline conditions of the oxidation require correction for the increasing rate of interconversion of the α and β forms (mutarotation). When appropriate corrections are applied, the following results are obtained: (1) The equatorial hydroxyl at carbon 1 is much more rapidly oxidized than is the axial hydroxyl. (2) This difference is directly related to the total number of equatorial groups. Stated in another way, the less conformational instability present in the

---

[3] This behavior is restricted to nonenzymatic systems since enzymic transformations are generally highly stereospecific.

molecule, the larger the difference in oxidation rates.[4] Typical figures are illustrated in Table 5.5. Whether (in the case of lyxose) these figures actually represent the presence of conformational equilibria, or whether they only represent small differences in rates due to interactions of other parts of the molecule is not entirely clear at present. However, the difference between the axial and equatorial forms of the conformationally stable glucose, galactose, and others, is sufficiently marked so that there can be no doubt about the relative reactivities of the two groups.

Some oxidizing agents are known to attack directly at the hydrogen rather than the hydroxyl and, in these cases, the axial hydroxyl is more readily oxidized because the equatorial hydrogen is more accessible. Agents that act by this pathway include catalytic oxidations with platinum and oxygen, and chromium

TABLE 5.5

Rate of oxidation of aldoses at 0 degrees with aqueous bromine as a function of configuration at carbon 1.

	$k \times 10^2 \min^{-1}$	$k\beta/k\alpha$	
β-D-xylose	1660	19	
α-D-xylose	89		
β-D-lyxose	450	2.9	
α-D-lyxose	160		
β-D-glucose	1250	39	
α-D-glucose	32		
β-D-galactose	1600	38	
α-D-galactose	42		
β-D-mannose	770	15	$\Delta 2$ effect
α-D-mannose	51		
β-D-gulose	416	6	
α-D-gulose	71		
β-L-arabinose	96	0.05	Strongly suggests C1 conformer
α-L-arabinose	1160		

trioxide [7]. The terminal hydroxymethyl group is usually readily oxidized under these conditions but constitutes an exception since it is not in a strictly axial or equatorial orientation regarding the OH function.

A parameter that has been employed to assess conformation and conformational instability is the rate and mechanism of glycoside cleavage. Energetic considerations suggest that there should be a direct relationship between the rate of hydrolysis of a given glycoside and the ring strain that is present in the derivative under consideration [Figure 5.11 (energy diagram)]. One striking fact is that furanosides are hydrolyzed much more readily than are pyranosides. This has been used to advantage in studies on complex polysaccharides isolated from

---

[4] The term conformational instability has little quantitative meaning at this stage. Attempts to use such data in a predictive fashion as regards reactivity, and so on, form the basis of much current work.

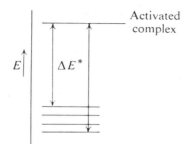

FIGURE 5.11 Energy level diagram for hydrolysis of glycosides. The lowest energy level might be considered to represent that carbohydrate with all functional groups equatorial.

wood and wood products wherein the arabinose units occur almost exclusively as furan derivatives and are easily removed, whereas the xylose derivatives occur almost exclusively as pyranosides and are far more stable to acid treatment. The classic example of the relative rates of hydrolysis of sucrose and trehalose (15,000 to 1) might also be mentioned. In a general sense, the greater the number of axial substituents present in the molecule, the greater the ring strain, the higher the free energy, and therefore, the higher the rate of hydrolysis (Table 5.6).

It is obvious from the above discussion that some consideration must be given to the size of the activation energy for this reaction. If different ring conformers may exist for a given compound, the activation energies required to form the intermediate transition states may be quite different since the initial structures will have different energy levels. Similarly, it is not possible to compare D- and L-sugars of intermediate instability unless the ring conformers are known in each case. When the compounds under consideration contain bicyclic ring systems, then rigid steric requirements are imposed such that still different conformations may be favored. The nature of the aglycon group is a factor

TABLE 5.6

Hydrolysis constants of synthetic and natural glycosides.

COMPOUND	k (min^{-1} × 10^4)	ΔE^*
Methyl α-D-glucopyranoside	2	38,190
Methyl β-D-glucopyranoside	3.8	33,730
Methyl α-D-mannopyranoside	4.8	
Methyl β-D-mannopyranoside	11.4	
Methyl α-D-galactopyranoside	10.4	
Methyl β-D-galactopyranoside	18.5	
Methyl α-L-arabinopyranoside	26	
Methyl β-L-arabinopyranoside	18	
α-D-glucopyranosyl-α-D-glucopyranoside (Trehalose)	0.52	40,180
α-D-glucopyranosyl-β-D-fructofuranoside (Sucrose)	7800	25,830

TABLE 5.7

Rate constants for hydrolysis of aryl β-D-glucopyranosides.

COMPOUND	k (min^{-1} × 10^4)	HAMMETT SUBSTITUTION CONSTANT σ
p-cresyl	2.32	−0.17
phenyl	1.15	0.00
p-nitrophenyl	0.33	+1.27

in the rate of glycoside hydrolysis insofar as it can contain electron withdrawing or electron repelling groups which will affect protonation of the
ring or glycosidic oxygen. This in turn will influence the rate of hydrolysis.
Acid catalyzed hydrolysis of substituted glycosides is facilitated by electron
repelling groups. Thus, p-nitrophenylglycosides are somewhat more stable than
their unsubstituted analogs [8] (Table 5.7).

Studies on several model compounds show that methyl-β-glycosides
hydrolyze faster than do methyl-α-glycosides. The explanation usually given
relates to the relatively more exposed equatorial position of the aglycon. This is
not true, however, where the phenylglycosides are concerned and cellobiose
(β-D-glucopyranosyl 1 → 4 β-D-glucopyranose) is not hydrolyzed any more
rapidly than is maltose; in fact, it is somewhat more stable [9]. Accordingly, the
"exposure" theory alone is inadequate to account for the hydrolysis properties
of the methyl glycosides.

The rate of hydrolysis is also greatly influenced by the nature and type of
functional group present at carbon 2 as well as its stereochemistry relative to
that of carbon 1. When these are suitably disposed in a *trans* configuration, then
glycosides may be displaced by neighboring group reactions involving internal

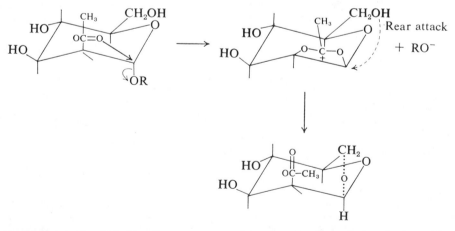

FIGURE 5.12 Neighboring group participation in hydrolysis of glycosides
with an axial acetoxy group at position 2.

attack by the C-6 oxygen on C-1, leading to the formation of 1-6 anhydro sugars. Epoxide intermediates can be formed as well and either case leads to retention of configuration at carbon 2 (Figure 5.12). Glycosides are also somewhat stabilized by polar effects due to the chain hydroxyl groups; these appear to be partly additive and deoxy-sugar glycosides are less stable than are regular aldosides.

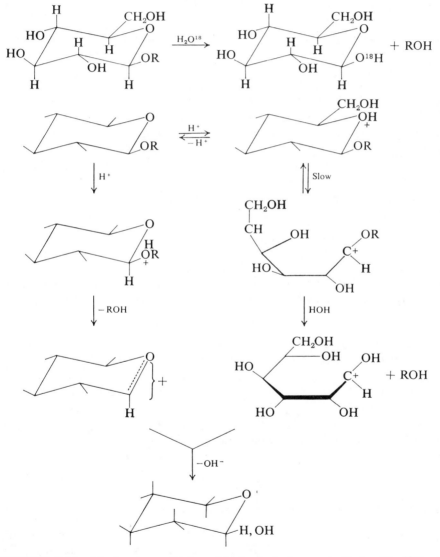

FIGURE 5.13 Mechanism of glycoside hydrolysis as studied with ^{18}O. A summary of the proposed mechanism involving cyclic or acyclic ionic forms.

The introduction of sulfur into the glycosidic linkage results in a change in the stability of the glycoside such that thioglycosides are more stable to acid hydrolysis. This is to be expected based on the nucleophilic character of the sulfur which is much more difficult to protonate than oxygen.

Mechanistic studies of glycoside cleavage show that when hydrolysis is carried out in the presence of H_2O^{18}, ^{18}O appears in the hydroxyl group of the resulting sugar rather than in the R group that has been cleaved from it [10]. It seems unlikely that bimolecular displacement at C-1 takes place, and thus, the rate determining step should be the formation of a cyclic or acyclic carbonium ion as illustrated in Figure 5.13. The two proposed mechanisms are given. The bulk of experimental evidence favors the latter, and this will be discussed in detail in Chapter 6.

Conformational problems in the carbohydrate series have also been studied in a chemical post-facto fashion by noting the rate and extent of formation of isopropylidene derivatives (Figure 5.14). In this case, the formation of a cyclic ketal by condensation of the sugar with acetone results in either a new 5- or a new 6-membered ring. The 6-membered ring product is infrequently observed but can occur when transannular axial hydroxyls are present and bond distances

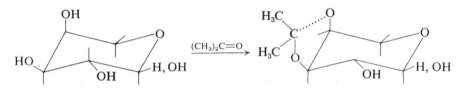

FIGURE 5.14   Reaction of acetone with a carbohydrate containing *cis* hydroxyls at carbons 3 and 4 to form the *cis* isopropylidene derivative.

and angles satisfy the easy formation of such a ring structure. The formation of the 5-membered ring is favored although this appears to induce some ring strain within the carbohydrate chain. In general, it is found that only compounds possessing suitably disposed *cis* hydroxyls can form such derivatives, and that all ring junctions are *cis*. The majority of stable isopropylidene derivatives are those with residues in the equatorial positions, and a consideration of even projection formulas reveals that more than one derivative can be formed from a given carbohydrate. As a result, reactions are frequently complex with mixtures of products being obtained. General rules and a more detailed discussion will follow.

5.3 *Physical Properties and Conformation*

The study of conformation is greatly facilitated by an examination of a number of physical properties. Mutarotation behavior was one of the earliest to be correlated with structural features. Consider a carbohydrate for which a single conformer is present. The mutarotation phenomenon should simply result in the equilibration between the α and β forms of the carbohydrate in this given conformer. In that case, the rate equation for this reaction can be written

$$\frac{-d[\alpha]}{dt} = k_1[\alpha] - k_2[\beta] \tag{5.1}$$

Integration of this expression between limits of time zero and equilibrium time gives

$$k_1 + k_2 = \frac{2.303}{t} \log_{10} \frac{\alpha_0 - \alpha_{eq}}{\alpha_t - \alpha_{eq}} \tag{5.2}$$

This states that constants k_1 and k_2 should be independent of the nature of the sugar as long as the initial assumption has been met. In other words, values for these parameters should be obtained for the α and β forms of all sugars if only two contributing forms are present. Experiments immediately reveal that most sugars do not follow this equation; therefore, contributions from open chain forms, furanosides, and other ring conformers all must be taken into account. Unfortunately, the shape of the curves obtained cannot (yet) be used to deduce the nature of the contributing structures. The only statement that can be made regarding the "complex" mutarotation behavior of most sugars is that several isomers coexist [11, 12].

TABLE 5.8

Melting points of sugar alcohols.

ALCOHOL	MELTING POINT
Allitol	150°
D-mannitol	166°
Galactitol	189°
D-iditol	74°
D-altritol	88°
D-glucitol	97°
Xylitol	94°
Ribitol	102°

Other physical parameters that have been correlated with conformation include melting point, solubility behavior, chromatographic mobilities, refractive index, infrared, and nuclear-magnetic-resonance spectra. In a general way, it may be stated that properties that depend on the symmetry of the molecule, such as melting point, will correlate with what would be predicted on the basis of configuration.

The melting point may be considered that temperature necessary to disrupt the crystal lattice and overcome the energetically favorable crystalline array in favor of the more entropic liquid state; the sharp transition observed can be ascribed to the tight geometrical criteria that have to be satisfied for lattice formation to occur. In a qualitative sense, we may visualize that symmetric molecules are more easily accommodated in such a lattice structure than are asymmetric ones. Although this may seem intuitive, the correlation is substantiated by examination of the melting points of the sugar alcohols, illustrated in Table 5.8 [13].

The dissolution of a crystal structure by a solvent will occur when the forces interacting between solvent and solute exceed those between solute molecules. Considerations similar to those above suggest that more symmetric compounds will have lower solubilities than their "less ordered" counterparts. By similar reasoning, it may be surmised that conformationally unstable forms will be highly soluble and difficult to crystallize. The effort required to induce recalcitrant carbohydrate syrups to crystallize is legendary. Table 5.9 lists pertinent solubility data [14].

TABLE 5.9

Solubility and melting points of several sugars.

SUGAR	SOLUBILITY[a]	MELTING POINT
α-D-galactose	0.65	164°
α-D-glucose	4.5	146°
β-D-mannose	13.0	132°
β-D-fructose	27.4	103°

[a] Grams per 100 ml in 80 percent aqueous ethanol at 20 degrees.

Parameters that depend largely on conformer stability, such as chromatographic behavior and refractive index, will be more directly related to the amount of instability present in any single form.

The chromatographic behavior of carbohydrates has been extensively discussed in several specialized treatises; qualitative considerations emphasize the following points: (1) Conventional partition systems have an aqueous stationary phase and an organic mobile phase. (2) Stable conformers have very great affinity for the hydroxyl groups of the water, whereas open chain forms or those with fewer OH groups (anhydro sugars, lactones, and others) have less and will therefore have higher mobility.

The refractive index of a medium is the ratio of the speed of light in a vacuum to its speed in the medium. The greater the polarizability of the molecules in the medium, the greater is the electromagnetic field induced in opposition to the applied field (that of the incident light) and accordingly, the higher the refractive index. As illustrated in Table 5.10, this correlates with conformer instability even though the relationship to polarizability is still obscure [15].

A general discussion of infrared and nuclear-magnetic-resonance spectra has given. Gross applications to conformation problems can be indicated in the sense that one conformer for any given sugar will have a characteristic absorption behavior. These have been largely determined on the basis of empirical studies, although several general relationships have been proposed.

TABLE 5.10

Refractive indices of methyl tetra-*O*-methyl
pyranoside sugars.

SUGAR (PYRANOSIDE) METHYL TETRA-*O*-METHYL	n_D^{20}
β-D-glucose	1.4399
α-D-glucose	1.4444
β-D-galactose	1.4467
α-D-mannose	1.4478
β-D-mannose	1.4517
α-D-altrose	1.4520
β-D-idose	1.4504
β-D-xylose (trimethyl)	1.4368
α-D-xylose	1.4408
α-D-lyxose	1.4438

The application of optical rotatory methods to the determination of carbohydrate *conformation* has been largely restricted to rotatory dispersion measurements.[5] (See Chapter 4.) However, attempts have been made to provide a more rigorous structural basis for several of the empirical rotation rules mentioned previously. The following discussion is based primarily on the studies of Brewster and Whiffen [16, 17].

Rotatory dispersion measurements that show the location, sign, and magnitude of Cotton effects, furnish the *most direct* method for identifying the rotatory contribution of individual centers of optical activity. It is assumed that the molar rotational contribution M of a given asymmetric center can be expressed as

$$M = \frac{k}{\lambda^2 - \lambda_0^2} \tag{5.3}$$

where λ_0 is the wavelength of the optically active absorption band forming part of the center of optical activity. The *sign* of M will therefore depend on the wavelength chosen for measurement, λ. It is also assumed that complex contributions can be expressed as the sum of several individual components. Thus, the total contribution of two adjacent centers of asymmetry, as illustrated in Figure 5.15, may be expressed as the sum of 9 terms, each of which is a rotational contribution for a different combination of substituents (UC-CX, UC-CY, UC-CZ, VC-CX, and so on). Solvent effects may be important especially when solvent interaction with the chromophoric groups is significant. Temperature and concentration effects are known but no quantitative treatment has been offered.

---

[5] Measurement of optical rotation as a function of wavelength. Unusual rotational changes are usually exhibited at or near the absorption maxima of chromophores which coincide or are adjacent to asymmetric centers. This phenomenon, termed the Cotton effect, has been of considerable utility in conformational studies on steroids and alkaloids.

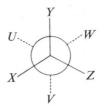

FIGURE 5.15   A schematic representation of two adjacent asymmetric carbons with substituents as indicated. Looking along the carbon–carbon bond a total of nine possible rotational contributions can be formulated as indicated in the text.

   A center of optical activity will have an asymmetric screw pattern of polarizability. A right-hand screw pattern is defined as one which, when rotated in a *clockwise* direction, moves *away* from the observer.

   If X is the asymmetric center in Figure 5.16, and the Fischer projection is as indicated, then this configuration has a *left*-handed screw pattern *when* the order of polarizability of the groups is $A > B > C > D$.

FIGURE 5.16   Projection formula of a compound with asymmetric center X and the groups arranged in order of decreasing polarizability. $A > B > C > D$.

   In this view, the relevant property of the molecule (atoms or groups) under consideration is the electron polarizability; the more "asymmetric," the larger the effect.

   In order to calculate the rotatory contribution of a center such as that depicted above, three coordinate axes are established, each of which bisects a pair of opposite edges of the regular tetrahedron made up by the atoms A, B, C, and D. The projections along these axes correspond to Figure 5.17.

   In (1), edges AC and BD are successively encountered by a light wave passing down a projection axis perpendicular to the plane of the paper. If A and B are high polarizability ends, a thread connecting these two, when turned clockwise, moves away from the observer.

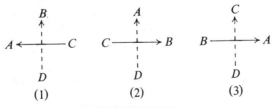

FIGURE 5.17

The contribution of A and C in the above are opposite and can be expressed as some function of $(A - C)$; a similar expression holds for B and D. The expression for the A and C contribution can be written

$$M_{A,C} = k(A - C)\frac{(B - D)}{(B + D)} \qquad (5.4)$$

Expressions for the other contributions are similar. It can be assumed that all centers having a like arrangement of polarizable groups will contribute to the optical rotation in the same way. The above configuration has a positive contribution.

Some information is available about the relative polarizability of groups. The approximate order for functional groups encountered most often in carbohydrate studies is Br, SH, CO_2H, CH_3, NH_2, OH, H. Whenever hydrogen bonding occurs or the asymmetric atom is in a *flexible chain*, the above rules may not apply.

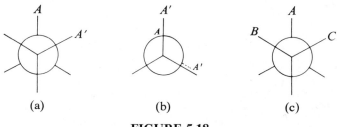

(a)   (b)   (c)

FIGURE 5.18

Several simplifying rules have been proposed to aid in calculations of rotational contributions:

1. Effects are additive in conformations such as shown in Figures 5.18(a) and 5.18(b).
2. Figure 5.18(c) is not allowed when all groups are larger than hydrogen.
3. All other conformations are equiprobable.

Rules 2 and 3 are both oversimplifications, yet the predicted values agree quite well with experimental ones for hydrocarbons.

The cyclohexane system has alternating dextro and levo contributions from the ring atoms so the rotation will be a function of the substituents. An isolated equatorial substituent has a slight effect, and an isolated axial substituent has an equal and opposite effect on the two centers concerned. Adjacent hydroxyl functions have a contribution of about +45 degrees when the one farther from the observer is rotated +60 degrees. The tetrahydropyran ring, however, unlike cyclohexane, does have an axis of polarizability because of the presence of the oxygen in the ring. An axial hydroxyl at position 1 with H at C_5 has a positive contribution. Table 5.11 lists the rotational contributions *estimated* for the indicated groupings.

Optical rotatory dispersion measurements make it possible to distinguish between axial and equatorial glycosides, D- and L-sugars, and in cases with marked conformational instability, the presence of other ring forms can be noted. One interesting facet of dispersion studies is that sugars exhibiting a

TABLE 5.11

Rotational contributions of indicated groupings.

GROUPING	CONTRIBUTION
(O—H)(O—H)	+45
(C—H)(O—H)	+50
Axial C_1OH	+100
Axial C_2 or C_4OH	+60
CH_2OH at C_5	+25
Equatorial OCH_3 at position 1	−105

considerable amount of free aldehyde form in aqueous solution show little or no Cotton effect, probably because the free aldehyde is completely hydrated in solution. The realization that optical rotation is a function of conformation must be emphasized. Despite the above efforts, our general understanding of optical rotation as a physical phenomenon is limited, theoretical considerations are largely quantum mechanical, and have not yet solved the multicenter problems presented by most carbohydrates. Accordingly, the expansion of empirical yardsticks will almost certainly continue.[6]

5.4 *Rules of Carbohydrate Conformation*

The following general statements about carbohydrate conformations are largely empirical but will assist in predicting likely conformations for most sugars.

1. The chair form is preferred to any boat form whenever possible and whenever secondary steric restrictions, such as fused ring systems, have not been imposed on the molecule. It is not possible with information presently at hand

---

[6] An analogous situation prevails in the development of antibiotics. Since the discovery of penicillin and streptomycin, literally hundreds of organisms have been screened in a hit-or-miss fashion for their ability to provide new "miracle" drugs. Confronted with the criticism that this is distressingly unscientific, the reply is invariably: "No one yet knows how an antibiotic works. Since we cannot design them on theoretical grounds, we will continue to search. Besides, the current methods work!"

to decide between chair forms and alternate half-chair or skew conformations in all cases. The simple sugars follow this rule satisfactorily and most observed experimental data is consistent with the assumption that a given chair form will predominate. The nomenclature proposed for the two possible chair forms of the tetrahydropyran ring is not entirely satisfactory. The most commonly employed terms are C1 and 1C, or normal and reverse. The latter terminology seems more suitable because it is less likely to introduce confusion with position 1 of the carbohydrate and acknowledges the broader natural distribution of D-sugars.

2. Any hydroxyl substituent that is axial confers one instability unit on the conformer under consideration. The unit is a relative one and energetic approximations range from 1.5–2.5 kcal. Naturally, the bulk and polarity of the substituent group will have an effect. It is a well-known technique in studies on cyclohexane to freeze or fix groups in an equatorial position by putting a large substituent group, such as *t*-butyl, in the appropriate equatorial position. However, such transformations are not possible in the carbohydrate field and accordingly restrict our ability to quantitate these differences.

3. An instability rating of $2\frac{1}{2}$ units is assigned to an axial CH_2OH grouping. This appears to be extremely rare in the carbohydrate field, and, in fact, the only well-documented example of this is in the idose series, wherein unusual conformational behavior is the rule rather than the exception.

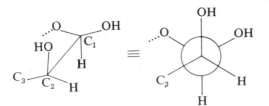

FIGURE 5.19   Representation of the delta-2 effect as typified in β-D-mannose.

4. There is an additional consideration for axial hydroxyl groups which involves the transannular interactions when hydroxyls are on the same side of the ring. Thus, if C-3 is axial, an axial hydroxyl at C-1 will introduce $\frac{1}{2}$ instability unit. Similarly, if C-4 is axial, an axial hydroxyl at C-2 introduces $\frac{1}{2}$ instability unit. This is termed the *Hassel-Ottar effect* [18].

5. The delta-2 rule states that if the oxygen on carbon 2 is axial and the oxygen substituent at carbon 1 is equatorial, then $2\frac{1}{2}$ instability units are present. As can be seen from Figure 5.19, the C-2 oxygen bisects the dihedral angle between the substituent at carbon 1 and the ring oxygen. This interplay of these three oxygens appears to be quite unfavorable but the assigned value is probably somewhat high. Mannose derivatives furnish the most common examples. Crystalline β-D-mannose glycosides have always been difficult to obtain and, in fact, β-D-mannose itself is rather rare, the α form being the one

almost always crystallized. Nevertheless, the mutarotation equilibrium suggests that the energetics are not so unfavorable, since 30 percent of the β form appears to be present.

The above rules make little effort to assign any energy content to these instability units. It is obvious that deoxy groups, other substituents, polar

TABLE 5.12

Instability factors and preferred ring forms for common sugars.[a]

SUGAR	C1 (NORMAL)	1C (REVERSE)	PREFERRED
α-D-arabinose	1,2,3	4	1C
β-D-arabinose	Δ2,3	1,4	1C
α-D-lyxose	1,2	3,4	C1, 1C
β-D-lyxose	Δ2	1,3,4	C1
α-D-ribose	1,3	Δ2,4	C1
β-D-ribose	3	1,3,4	C1
α-D-xylose	1	Δ2,3,4	C1
β-D-xylose	none	1,2,3,4	C1
α-D-allose	1,3	Δ2,3,4,5	C1
β-D-allose	3	1,2,4,5,H	C1
α-D-altrose	1,2,3	4,5	C1
β-D-altrose	Δ2,3	1,4,5,H	C1
α-D-galactose	1,4	Δ2,3,5,H	C1
β-D-galactose	4	1,2,3,5,H	C1
α-D-glucose	1	Δ2,3,4,5,H	C1
β-D-glucose	none	1,2,3,4,5,H	C1
α-D-gulose	1,3,4	Δ2,5	C1
β-D-gulose	3,4	1,2,5,H	C1
α-D-idose	1,2,3,4	5	1C
β-D-idose	Δ2,3,4	1,5,H	1C
α-D-mannose	1,2	3,4,5,H	C1
β-D-mannose	Δ2	1,3,4,5,H	C1
α-D-talose	1,2,4	3,5,H	C1, 1C
β-D-talose	Δ2,4	1,3,5,H	C1, 1C

[a] The numerical representation indicates an axial hydroxyl or hydroxyl-methyl group at a given position. H refers to transannular hydroxyl repulsion, or Hassel-Ottar effect. The preferred conformer in cases of marked instability may depend on a specific derivative. However, facile ring interconversion is not likely.

interactions, and the like all play a significant role. It is also clear that these rules are based on an ideal model wherein the bond angles do not significantly deviate from those to be expected from tetrahedral orientation and bond distances are also not significantly distorted. Inherent is the assumption that model chairs predominate for all sugars.

Nevertheless, these rules serve as a satisfactory working guide if the above discussion is kept in mind. With these as a basis, it is possible to construct a table for the two possible chair forms which could be expected to be theoretically present for any given carbohydrate (Table 5.12). Keep in mind in viewing the table that the ring conformation is *normal* for a D-sugar and *reverse* for an L-sugar. β-D-glucose serves as the standard reference compound with all substituent groups equatorial in the *normal* conformation (Figure 5.20). Thus, any

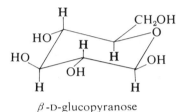

β-D-glucopyranose

FIGURE 5.20 Preferred conformer for β-D-glucopyranose.

epimer of β-D-glucose may be visualized as having an axial substituent at that locus. If all centers are epimerized, the all axial form is obtained (β-L-glucose), which in turn is the standard reference compound for the reverse ring conformer with all groups equatorial (Figure 5.21).

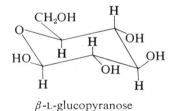

β-L-glucopyranose

FIGURE 5.21 Preferred conformer for β-L-glucopyranose.

It is commonly stated that conformational instability is anticipated whenever the difference between forms is less than 1½ instability units. In addition, if any given form has more than 2½ total instability units, then some conformational instability is expected. It is not clear, however, that *conformer equilibrium* occurs between alternative ring forms. The activation energy required to overcome such a barrier may be very large, because even for a halogen-substituted ethane, this is 15 kcal per mole. Although the driving force required to overcome the eclipsed configuration required for ring interconversion to take place is substantial, the transition skew or half-chair form may still occur to a significant extent under normal laboratory conditions, and specific reactions may go by this pathway. Most sugars that have been examined which display conformer instability appear to exist in either one ring form or the other. It has been noted that β-D-glucose is a slightly stronger acid than is α-D-glucose. Whether this relates to an effect of the ring oxygen or to a change of entropy on ionization is not clearly established, and the relation of hydroxyl ionization to configuration (axial or equatorial) at position 1 is unknown.

PART 2
Reactions

CHAPTER 6

Carbohydrate Reactions

6.1 Reactions at Carbon 1

A survey of carbohydrate reactions may be organized in any number of ways. Reaction type, reagent employed, survey of glucose, then galactose, and so on, all form convenient categories for subdivision. In an attempt to treat reactions in a fairly uniform way, keeping in mind such conformational information as is available, transformations will be discussed according to the position at which they are taking place.

The next section shall be concerned primarily with those reactions in which the hemiacetal or reducing carbon is featured. Most of the examples are drawn from the aldose sugar series and shall concern themselves either with the reactions that take place with the hemiacetal (most prevalent form), or with that small percentage of the free aldehyde form of the carbohydrate that exists in solution.

A partial listing includes oxidation, reduction, esterification, halogen substitution, addition, alkylation, arylation, glycoside synthesis or full acetal formation, and several specialized kinds of elimination reactions.

Oxidation

Consider the various types of oxidations that may take place at carbon 1. These will include conversion of the aldonic acid (CHO → COOH), to the aldoniclactone

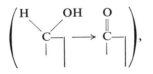

and removal of C-1 as carbon dioxide.[1]

The utilization of the reaction rates of equatorial or axial groups toward

---

[1] The use of nonstoichiometric oxidants such as cupric ion or ferricyanide in alkaline solution is restricted to analytic purposes and will be discussed in Chapter 14.

such oxidizing agents as an indication of conformational stability and hydroxyl accessibility has been previously described. The most common conditions for carrying out such a reaction for preparative work utilize iodine as the oxidizing

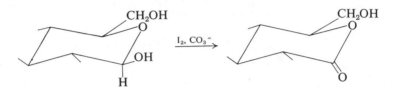

FIGURE 6.1 Oxidation of aldopyranose with iodine. The ring form of the lactone is distorted to accommodate the carbonyl group and is not a typical chair.

agent and a solvent such as methanol or aqueous buffer, usually carbonate. A typical reaction is illustrated in Figure 6.1. Syntheses are also conveniently carried out in alcohol in the presence of a base such as potassium hydroxide, whereupon the salt of the aldonic acid is precipitated directly from the reaction medium (Figure 6.2).

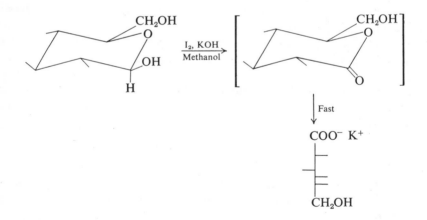
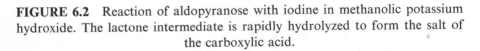

FIGURE 6.2 Reaction of aldopyranose with iodine in methanolic potassium hydroxide. The lactone intermediate is rapidly hydrolyzed to form the salt of the carboxylic acid.

The use of oxidizing agents to react specifically with aldose sugars and to convert them to aldono lactones or aldonic acids is well known and forms the basis of several analytical methods.

The quantitative measurement of the amount of aldose sugar present in a solution is carried out most conveniently by running the reaction in the dark and in carbonate buffer, utilizing iodine as the oxidizing agent [1]. At various time intervals aliquots are withdrawn; they are acidified with sulfuric acid to convert all hypohalite to free halogen and also to stop the oxidation reaction. The residual iodine is then titrated in the usual manner and the amount consumed is estimated by the difference from zero time. The failure of keto sugars to react under these conditions makes this a particularly useful technique. In addition, in contrast to most assays for reducing sugar, the consumption of oxidant in this reaction is strictly stoichiometric.

Stoichiometry is as follows:

$$RCHO + I_2 \xrightarrow{OH^-} RCOO^- + 2I^- + H_2O$$

Excess I_2 is titrated with thiosulfate in the usual way.

$$RCHO \xrightarrow[CO_3^=]{Cu^{++}} \text{MIXED products, up to 5 moles of oxidant consumed}$$

$$RCHO \xrightarrow[CO_3^=]{Fe(CN)_6^{\equiv}} \text{MIXED products, up to 5 moles of oxidant consumed} \tag{6.1}$$

Therefore, within the limits of the amounts of material available and the sensitivity of the titration, this provides a direct measure of molecular weight (moles of end group per unit weight of sample), although practical problems prevent this from being a true micro method.

The initial product of the reaction is the lactone corresponding to the parent hemiacetal (Figure 6.1). When the reaction is carried out in the presence of a

TABLE 6.1

Composition of halogen solutions in
water as a function of *p*H.

*p*H	Cl_2	HOCl	OCl^-
1	82	18	
2	31	69	
3	4	96	
4	0.4	99.6	
6	$\cdots$	96	4
7	$\cdots$	73	27
8	$\cdots$	21	79
9	$\cdots$	3	97

strong base, the lactone is rapidly hydrolyzed and the product isolated is the salt of the aldonic acid (Figure 6.2) [2]. Should the isolation of the lactone itself be desired, then careful control of *p*H during the reaction is essential.

The halogen ion species present in a solution of a halogen in water is very much dependent on *p*H, as illustrated in Table 6.1. At acid *p*H, the hypohalous acid (hypochlorous acid, *p*K 7.5) is the predominant species, whereas at alkaline *p*H, this dissociates and only the ion is present. Because the actual oxidizing species is the *hypohalite ion*, the reaction is most efficient when the hydrochloric acid is removed or when the *p*H is maintained at a sufficiently high level [3].

The first step of this oxidation, which forms the aldonolactone as the primary product, presumably involves an attack on the oxygen of the hemiacetal hydroxyl. The mechanism is consistent with the experimental data and receives substantiation from the knowledge that carbohydrates with equatorial hydroxyl groups are much more rapidly attacked than those containing axial OH groups (Figure 6.3).

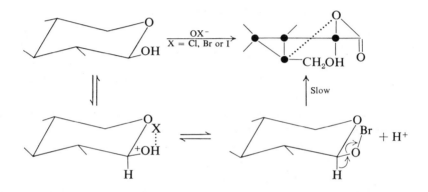

FIGURE 6.3   Mechanism of oxidation of aldoses by halogen.

Several other oxidizing reagents commonly employed in the carbohydrate field are nitric acid, nitrogen tetraoxide, chromium trioxide, and molecular oxygen. These are generally far less specific in their mode of action; they attack both C-1 and the terminal hydroxymethyl group at comparable rates, and in addition, they react with chain hydroxyls. One exception is the oxidation of glucose by oxygen in the presence of alkali to yield formic acid (from carbon 1) and D-arabonic acid as products [4]. In several cases, the oxidation at C-6 is more rapid and the product may be uronic acid rather than the desired aldonic acid.

The removal of carbon 1 as carbon dioxide is a degradative reaction most effectively carried out by microorganisms or enzymes and appreciably less so by chemists. The most common chemical reaction involves treating the calcium salt of an aldonic acid with hydrogen peroxide in the presence of ferrous ion (Figure 6.4) [5].

This reaction sequence, the so-called Ruff degradation, has been employed for preparative and analytic purposes for some time. Because the yields are rather low, this has largely been supplanted by more suitable techniques.

The general problem of enzymic oxidations, both of the hemiacetal form and of the aldonic acid, is discussed in Chapter 13. The single feature, which serves both as the primary advantage and major drawback, is the high specificity of these reactions. Nevertheless, both analytic and preparative uses are made.

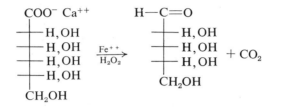

FIGURE 6.4 Reaction of calcium salt of an aldonic acid with ferrous ion in the presence of hydrogen peroxide.

Reduction

The converse reaction to oxidation—reduction—is of classic importance both from the standpoint of conversion of lactones to hemiacetals and in their subsequent transformation to polyols.

The reducing agent employed by Fischer in most of his studies was sodium amalgam, which will carry out the reduction of an aldonic acid lactone to the corresponding hemiacetal without significant formation of the polyol [6] (Figure 6.5). The reduction is generally carried out under acidic conditions

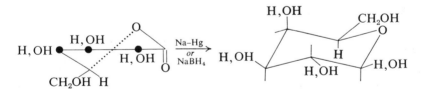

FIGURE 6.5 Reduction of sugar lactone with sodium amalgam or sodium borohydride.

which are necessary to prevent hydrolysis of the lactone to the resistant carboxylate ion. The most common buffers employed are the relatively insoluble benzoic and oxalic acids which provide smoother pH control than does the periodic addition of strong acid.

Although metal hydrides are currently the most commonly employed reagents for this specific reduction, both catalytic reduction and hydride reductions have frequently been employed (Figure 6.6). In the case of hydride reductions, considerable precaution must be exercised. Problems of *p*H and temperature control and reduction to the polyol are the major concerns. Carbohydrates that do not have marked conformational instability, such as gluconolactone, reduce smoothly with sodium borohydride, forming the aldose (glucose) in high yields. However, where marked conformational instability is present in the aldose product, hydride reduction of the lactone is considerably more difficult. Conditions employed for the reduction of L-idono-lactone either do not suffice to reduce the lactone to any significant extent or else the considerably larger amount of the open chain form of the product aldose is rapidly reduced by the hydride to the polyol. Although careful quantitative studies have not been carried out, kinetic factors are obviously important; the ease with which a ring form is converted to the open chain form may determine the over-all course of the

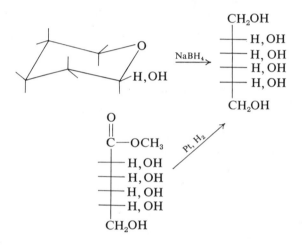

FIGURE 6.6   Reduction of aldose or methyl esters of aldonic acids to sugar alcohols with either sodium borohydride or platinum-hydrogen.

reduction. Because this energy barrier will be less where more ring strain is present, the above results are not surprising. Sugars with moderate instability (1–2 instability units) are best reacted with a slight excess of reductant under good temperature and *p*H control. It is also desirable to assay reducing sugar formed during the course of the reaction.

Because compounds such as sodium borohydride are unstable at acid *p*H, the reaction must be carried out under slightly alkaline conditions. If the solution becomes too alkaline, the rate of hydrolysis of the aldonolactone becomes substantial and, as a result, the yields in the reduction become very low. If the solution is kept too acidic, the half-life of the hydride is considerably shortened and again the yields are correspondingly low. Most reactions are carried out at approximately *p*H 8 in borate buffer, thereby avoiding the introduction of a different ionic species into the reaction mixture. The hydride is smoothly destroyed by the addition of acid, cations removed by resin, and borate removed by repeated distillation with methanol under acidic conditions. Final deionization is usually accomplished by means of ion-exchange resins.

Hydrogenation with Raney nickel and with platinum catalysts has also been employed for reductions [7]. These conditions are more commonly used when the desired end product is the polyol starting from the ester. When reduction of the hemiacetal to the polyol is desired, then reagents such as sodium borohydride are preferred.

The course of the reduction under consideration obviously introduces some steric problems. Because the starting aldonolactone does not contain an asymmetric carbon at C-1, whereas the final hemiacetal does, there will probably be some steric effect[2] on the nature of the final product. In most cases, because the reaction is carried out in aqueous solution, a mixture of anomers results with the final composition of this mixture being determined by thermodynamic considerations. However, the initial product is probably formed by addition of hydrogen to give the C-1 hydroxyl, which is equatorial rather than axial, with subsequent equilibration taking place. Careful kinetic studies have been carried out on these reductions; typical results are illustrated in Figure 6.7.

The other functional groups present in the molecule, primarily hydroxyl, are not susceptible either to sodium amalgam or hydrides. Therefore, the side reactions are confined to those taking place at carbon 1. However, when other functional groups are present, as for example, blocking groups which are sensitive to hydrogenolysis, or a second carbonyl group which may be reduced by the hydride, then additional precautions must be observed. The decision is primarily one of choice of reagents[3] with sodium amalgam still being the most specific and mildest reducing agent, followed by the hydrides and, lastly, catalytic methods. When the carbohydrate is highly substituted and reducing agents such as lithium aluminum hydride are employed, then appropriate care must be taken to assure that no other sensitive groups are present, because these will almost certainly be affected at the same time. For example, blocking functions such as toluenesulfonyl are cleaved by hydrogenolysis.

It is convenient to monitor reactions by either polarimetric or reducing sugar assays. Polarimetry is commonly employed because, in the usual case, the

---

[2] Asymmetric induction is another term frequently employed to explain the results obtained when a new asymmetric center is introduced by chemical means into an already optically active molecule. Because the parent compound will have a preferred spatial orientation, attack by the reducing agent is expected to be nonrandom, thus favoring one of the two possible final products. This may be by as much as 20/1 and can frequently be controlled by an appropriate choice of reducing agent. There are numerous examples in the steroid field where very rigid stereochemistry is present.

[3] With other reducible groups, such as carbonyl, suitable blocking methods must be employed. See Chapter 7.

over-reduction product (sugar alcohol), has a very low optical rotation, whereas the rotation of the hemiacetal form of the carbohydrate is usually sufficiently different from that of the starting lactone such that ready kinetic data can be obtained. Alternatively, a rapid reducing sugar assay may be employed to follow the course of the reduction. Some quantitative studies employing hydrides under carefully controlled conditions have been reported. The consumption of hydride in a given reaction may be used as a measure of the amount of potentially reducible groups and has also been used as a molecular weight technique in certain specialized cases.

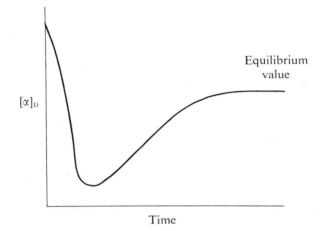

FIGURE 6.7   Change in optical rotation during the reduction of an aldono lactone to an aldopyranose. The initially lower rotation suggests that the β anomer is predominantly formed in the reduction and that equilibration with the α form takes place subsequently.

Additions

The reaction that was of classic importance in the development of carbohydrate structure and which led to considerable work on the problem of lactone reduction, is the addition of cyanide to the potential free carbonyl group present in a carbohydrate [8]. This is the Fischer-Kiliani synthesis and was used extensively by Fischer in his demonstration that simple carbohydrates were configurationally related to one another and that higher carbon sugars could be derived by successive applications of this synthesis to shorter chain precursors. The typical reaction sequence is

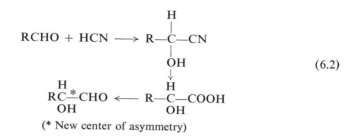

$$(6.2)$$

(* New center of asymmetry)

The stereochemistry of the cyanide addition is of some interest. As is apparent from the reaction, a new center of asymmetry appears at carbon 2 and, in light of previous comments, equimolar mixtures of products are not expected. Early studies demonstrated that when D-arabinose was carried through this procedure, the main product of the reaction was not D-glucose but rather D-mannose. This might occasion some question because it is clear that the structure of D-glucose is thermodynamically favored over D-mannose because it does not have an axial hydroxyl group at the 2 position. However, consideration of the stereochemistry of the *initial adduct* where the asymmetry of carbon 2 is developed, reveals that the controlling factor is not the position of the hydroxyl group at carbon 3, but rather that at carbon 4. As illustrated in Figure 6.8, the

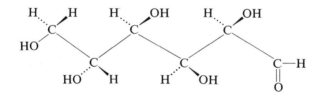

FIGURE 6.8 Zigzag arrangement of the open chain form of a carbohydrate.

folded or zigzag chain arrangement, which is prevalent for open chain compounds, has the position of closest approach of two hydroxyl groups not on adjacent carbons but rather on carbons one removed from each other. Thus, in the addition of cyanide to D-arabinose, the hydroxyl group on position 2 prefers to be *trans* to *that on carbon 4* and, thus, the final product has the D-manno rather than the D-gluco configuration. This general rule is applicable to all such additions.

This reaction has been studied in considerable detail by chemists at the National Bureau of Standards [9]. Their primary problem was concerned with the synthesis of isotopically labeled sugars, particularly those specifically labeled at carbon 1. The normal technique for carrying out this synthesis is to use radioactive cyanide in the addition step with the remainder of the sequence as above. However, because glucose is by far the most commonly employed carbohydrate for biological tracer studies, the low yields of this isomer afforded in the cyanide addition reaction led to very low isotope yields. It was found that by careful control of pH, temperature, and order of addition of reactants, the yield of the gluco isomer could be maximized to 50 percent or better. The reaction conditions are described in a series of publications by Isbell and co-workers [9].

The resulting addition product is usually hydrolyzed with alkali, and the salt of the aldonic acid subsequently lactonized by heating under slightly acidic conditions with a high boiling solvent such as toluene. In some cases, dilute hydrochloric or sulfuric acid may be used to effect the lactonization directly. Alternatively, the cation (sodium or potassium) may be exchanged for hydrogen by means of an ion-exchange resin (Figure 6.9), and the resulting

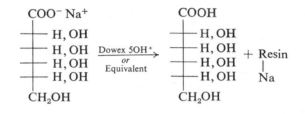

FIGURE 6.9   Conversion of the salt of an aldonic acid to the free acid form by treatment with ion-exchange resin.

aldonic acid lactonized by heating concentrated solutions under slightly dehydrating conditions with a catalyst such as toluene sulfonic acid. The resulting lactone can be freed from starting material and other products by deionization using ion-exchange resins and then reduced to the hemiacetal as described above. The over-all yields in reaction sequences of this type range from 20–50 percent.

The functional specificity of the cyanide addition, that is, restriction to potential reducing groups rather than to any other functional groups normally present in carbohydrates, has led to its employment in quite a different context although the fundamental reaction is the same.

This restriction of the reaction has led to its utilization as a method for measuring molecular weights of intermediate size oligosaccharides [10]. The procedure employed is as follows: The addition of cyanide is carried out with C-14 labeled starting cyanide of known specific activity[4] under slightly alkaline conditions. After the addition reaction is complete (and this is by no means easy to assess), the residual cyanide is removed by acidification and aeration, by dialysis, by gel filtration chromatography, or by hydrolysis, and the radioactivity that has been bound to the carbohydrate moiety is then measured. A calculation

[4] Usually defined as disintegrations per unit time per mole.

of the number of moles of cyanide added per mole of carbohydrate then gives a direct measure of the number average molecular weight.

Nitromethane and 2-Nitroethanol Additions

The ability of nitroparaffins to react with aldehydes has been known for some 70 years and proceeds as indicated in the equation below [11]:

$$RCHO + R'CH_2NO_2 \longrightarrow RCHOH—CHR'NO_2$$

$$\downarrow Na^+$$

$$\begin{array}{c} R' \\ | \\ RCHOH—C{=}NO_2 \\ Na^+ \end{array} \qquad (6.3)$$

Although basic catalysts are generally employed (sodium methoxide in methanol) the reaction may be reversed by strong alkali so that some control of conditions is important.

The application of this reaction to the carbohydrate field was made feasible by the discovery that treatment of the nitro product with cold dilute acid caused hydrolysis to the aldehyde [12]:

$$\begin{array}{ccc} R' & & R' \\ | & \xrightarrow{H^+} & | \\ RCHOH—C{=}NO_2 & & RCHOH—C{=}O + N_2O \\ Na^+ & & \end{array} \qquad (6.4)$$

$$R'{=}H \text{ or } CH_2OH$$

Reactions are generally carried out in solvents such as methanol or water, and partially substituted carbohydrates are frequently employed as starting materials. As is the case with the cyanohydrin addition, a new center of asymmetry is generated at carbon 2. (Figure 6.10.) Similar considerations to those above predict that the OH at C-2 will prefer to be *trans* to that on C-4; this is observed experimentally. The major advantage of this procedure over the cyanohydrin route arises when the epimeric nitro adducts are readily separated in contrast to the lactone analogs arising from a cyanohydrin sequence. L-glucose is most conveniently synthesized from L-arabinose by this method.

The second major utility of this procedure has been in the synthesis of higher carbon ketoses by the addition of 2-nitroethanol to aldoses [13].[5] The reaction sequence is illustrated in Figure 6.11.

In this case, the ketose products are epimeric at carbon 3; we might predict that the configuration at C-5 would be controlling. The few studies that have

---

[5] The known explosive behavior of this reagent or byproducts in its preparation has severely curtailed the use of this procedure.

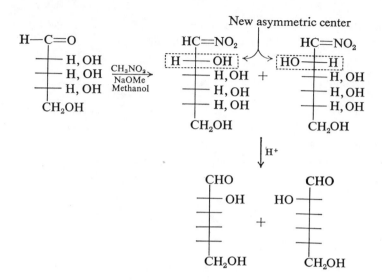

FIGURE 6.10 Schematic representation of the nitromethane synthesis as applied to a 5-carbon sugar.

been carried out are equivocal as far as application of this rule is concerned. It seems possible that the effects of asymmetric induction will vary depending on the location in the chain and that the adjacent nitro group may also play a role.

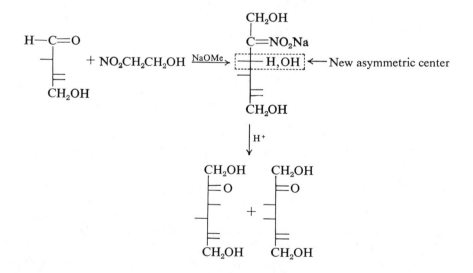

FIGURE 6.11 Schematic representation of the 2-nitroethanol synthesis to yield a pair of asymmetric ketoses.

6.2 *Condensations at Carbon 1*

The small percentage of free aldehyde form present in an aqueous solution of an aldohexose, for example, can nevertheless undergo several condensation reactions that are more or less typical of a carbonyl function.

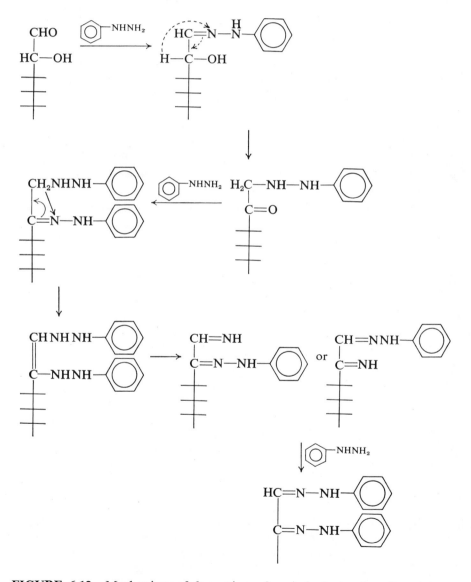

FIGURE 6.12 Mechanism of formation of carbohydrate phenylosazones.

The best known of these is the formation of phenylhydrazones and phenyl-osazones initially described by Fischer. The stoichiometry of the formal reaction is (see Figure 6.12):

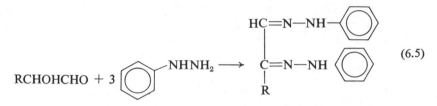

$$\text{(6.5)}$$

Note that the formation of the initial product, which is a Schiff base, proceeds to completion only because the second reaction is essentially uni-directional as written. This is especially true in the presence of large excesses of reagent. Should the Schiff base be readily hydrolyzed, such as that formed by the reaction with leucofuchsin dye, then a multiple equilibrium is set up and the composition of the equilibrium mixture is determined both by the equilibrium constant of the second reaction as well as the amount of free aldehyde form present in the initial reaction (the equilibrium for the reaction between ring and open chain forms of a sugar, Figure 6.13).

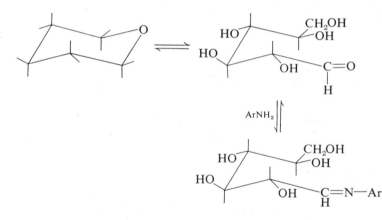

FIGURE 6.13   Formation of Schiff base on treatment of a carbohydrate with an aromatic amine. The amount of Schiff base present will be determined by equilibrium constants of the reactions indicated and will be substantial when there is a significant amount of open chain form initially present.

This multiequilibrium system can be utilized to good advantage in estimations of sugars that have a considerable amount of the free aldehyde form present in solution, and in addition, where the equilibrium constants of the two reactions are such that the Schiff base is formed to a significant extent from a conformationally unstable sugar but to an insignificant extent from sugars that have only a very small percentage of open chain form. This is the basis of the well-known Schiff reaction for deoxyribose and also the basis of the periodic acid-Schiff stain for glycogen and periodate susceptible polymers in tissue sections (Figure 6.14).

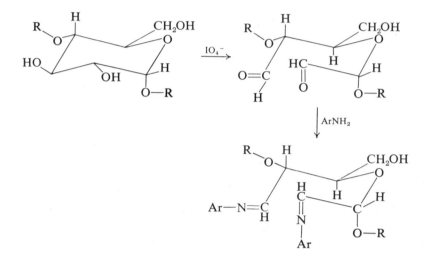

FIGURE 6.14 Reaction of periodate with a substituted carbohydrate (polysaccharide) wherein adjacent hydroxyl groups are present. The dialdehyde form is then condensed with an aromatic amine to form a colored product.

Examination of the mechanism of phenylosazone formation as written would lead us to wonder why the reaction ceases at the phenylosazone stage, and why still further oxidation does not take place along the carbohydrate chain. In fact, although the yields of phenylosazones are not spectacular, they themselves are quite readily oxidized, extremely difficult to recrystallize, have very poorly defined melting points, and in many respects are poor crystalline derivatives for characterization purposes. That they are still widely used, especially in teaching laboratories, is a tribute to tradition as well as a comment on education.

There has been considerable controversy regarding the correct structure for the carbohydrate phenylosazones. The noninteracting structure depicted above is almost certainly incorrect due to the strong probability of hydrogen-bond formation and chelation. Based largely on theoretical considerations, Fieser and Fieser proposed two alternate, open chain chelate structures illustrated in Figure 6.15. These could be stabilized by their ability to exist as tautomers, as shown. A series of studies on osazones and formazans (see Section 4.8) by Mester provided chemical evidence in support of structure 1 although definitive proof was lacking [14]. Recently, several attempts have been made to resolve this problem by the use of nuclear-magnetic-resonance spectroscopy. The data,

Stabilized by:

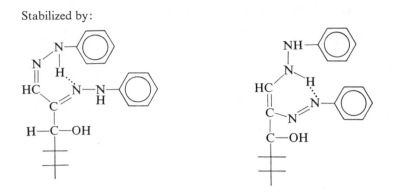

FIGURE 6.15   Stabilization of a carbohydrate phenylosazone by formation of chelate structure.

which are discussed in detail in Chapter 4, strongly favor structure 1 and its tautomer. This has received additional support from x-ray diffraction studies which show that the 6-membered chelate ring is nearly planar and coplanar with the two benzene rings [15]. The bond angles are approximately 120 degrees,

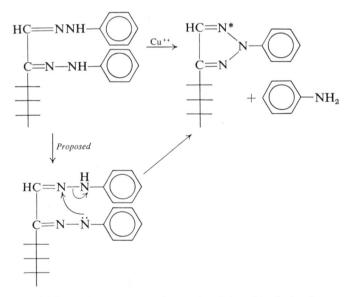

* If the C-3 hydroxyl is on the right, this derivative will have a positive rotation.

FIGURE 6.16   Conversion of carbohydrate phenylosazone to a phenylosatriazole by oxidation with copper.

which is in the expected range for 6-membered aromatic systems, and the stabilization energy of the chelated sugar osazones is about 10 kcal per mole higher than that for the corresponding methyl phenylosazones, which are incapable of chelate ring formation. This high value is attributed to a combination of resonance and chelation.

The current utility of the phenylosazone derivatives largely rests on their oxidation with cupric ions in the presence of phenylhydrazine to form a phenylosatriazole derivative, as illustrated in Figure 6.16 [16]. These crystalline compounds have excellent physical properties and as such have been extensively used as intermediate derivatives in isotopic degradations of sugars. The mechanism suggested for their formation, although likely, has not been experimentally confirmed.

Despite the generally poor behavior of carbohydrate hydrazones, several specific reagents have been employed to prepare derivatives for individual sugars. Thus, fructose may be identified as a parachloro phenylhydrazone, arabinose as the diphenyl hydrazone, and so on [17] (Table 6.2).

TABLE 6.2

Melting points and optical rotations of selected carbohydrate derivatives.

COMPOUND	DERIVATIVES	MELTING POINT	$[\alpha]_D$
L-Arabinose	Diphenylhydrazone	174	−14.6
D-Ribose	p-Bromophenylhydrazone	204	15
D-Xylose	Benzylphenylhydrazone	95	−20.3
D-Galactose	Benzylphenylhydrazone	158	−14.3
D-Mannose	Phenylhydrazone	200	34
D-Fructose	2,5-Dichlorophenylhydrazone	154	5.3
L-Sorbose	2,5-Dichlorophenylhydrazone	117	−33
L-Fucose	Benzylphenylhydrazone	178	15

Formazans

The reaction of carbohydrate phenylosazones with diazo compounds to yield formazans is one that has been known for a great many years, but only recently has been employed both for identification and for preparative purposes [18]. The formazans themselves react with salts of heavy metals to give well-characterized crystalline compounds, and these have been widely used in analytical chemistry for metal determination and chelation. More recently, formazan complexes, particularly those of copper, have been utilized in preparation of tetrazolium dyes. These are used for determining reducing sugars and as electron acceptors in biological oxidation-reduction systems.

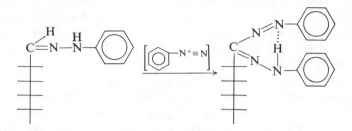

FIGURE 6.17   Formation of a formazan by reaction of a carbohydrate phenyl-hydrazone with an aryl diazonium compound.

The reaction of an aldose phenylhydrazone with a typical diazo compound in pyridine proceeds as illustrated in Figure 6.17. The structure of the formazan as depicted does not disturb the stereochemistry of any center (other than carbon 1) and thus derivatives obtained from glucose and mannose, for example, are different compounds and, unlike the osazones, somewhat better behaved. It is also possible to carry out acetylation of the carbohydrate moiety of these formazans with acetic anhydride and pyridine to yield red pentaacetates which are usually readily crystallized.

The formazan sugar derivatives show typical properties which include a

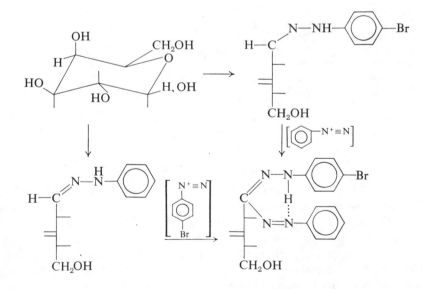

FIGURE 6.18   Proof of structure of carbohydrate formazans by use of sub-stituted phenylhydrazine. See text for details.

brilliant red color, complexing with heavy metals, and oxidation under rather mild conditions to colorless compounds.

As was the case with the phenylosazones, there has been some uncertainty regarding the actual structure of formazans. In an attempt to resolve ambiguities, D-galactose was first condensed with parabromophenylhydrazine and then with diazotized aniline, to yield a monobromodiphenylformazan. The same derivative was also prepared by initial condensation with phenylhydrazine followed by reaction with diazotized para bromoaniline. Because the products obtained were identical, the proposed structure involving disubstitution at the aldol carbon was strongly substantiated [19] (see Figure 6.18). The intermediates in the above sequence, in common with the phenylhydrazones, undergo ready oxidation to yield a variety of compounds of unknown structure; and on prolonged standing, quite a large number of degradation products are formed.

The rate of reaction of the diazotized aromatic derivative with the phenylhydrazone of the sugar is rather slow. For example, the formation of glucosediphenylformazan is not complete even after 40 hours. There is apparently a substantial effect of stereochemistry on the rate of the reaction and also some solvent effects as well, but the relation of these to structural isomerization or configurational effects has not been fully worked out.

The application of the formazan reaction to periodate oxidized glycosides, oligosaccharides, and polysaccharides has been employed and the resulting chromogenic derivatives have been used as an assay for periodate reactive sites in these molecules.

Benzimidazoles

Condensation reactions at carbon 1 are not restricted to the formation of hydrazones although these are most common. The condensation of carbonyl compounds with O-phenylene diamine is well known and was first utilized in

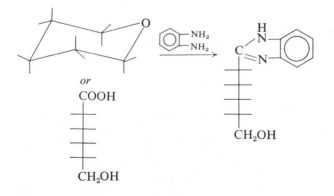

FIGURE 6.19   Condensation of aldose or aldonic acid with orthophenylenediamine to form a carbohydrate benzimidazole.

the carbohydrate field by Moore and Link [20]. This reaction results in the formation of a benzimidazole derivative according to the scheme shown in Figure 6.19. As indicated, the reaction proceeds either from the aldonic acid or from the aldose, although in the latter case, an oxidizing catalyst must be added. The initial studies of this reaction utilized prior oxidation of the aldose to the aldonic acid, isolation of this product, and subsequent condensation. More recently, it was ascertained that the entire sequence could be carried out in a single step if cupric ion was present during the condensation reaction. Presumably, the first step is still an oxidation but the mechanism of the condensation has not been worked out in any detail.

The polyhydroxy alkyl benzimidazoles possess several desirable properties and have been extensively used in degradation of isotopically labeled sugars. A typical sequence is illustrated in Figure 6.20.

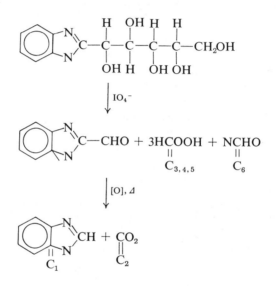

FIGURE 6.20 Degradation of carbohydrate benzimidazole. See Chapter 13.

Oximes, Semicarbazones, and so on

The reaction of carbonyl compounds with nitrogen-containing reagents (in addition to those discussed above) is a common method of identification in organic chemistry. However, the utility of reagents such as hydroxylamine, semicarbazide, hydrazine, and others, in the carbohydrate field is extremely limited. This is primarily due to the reversibility of these condensations in aqueous systems, and to solubility problems, although several specialized derivatives have been reported. In particular, the condensation between aldoses and hydroxylamine to yield oximes and between ketoses and primary amines to yield ketosylamines have been studied. However, both of these reactions form part of a more extensive synthetic or degradative sequence.

The oximes have one property of some interest and that is the phenomenon of mutarotation. Inspection of the structural formula of a typical oxime does not readily permit decision between *syn* and *anti* or ring forms. Obviously, the equilibrium exhibited may be that between open chain and ring forms (Figure 6.21). Acylation of the remaining hydroxyl groups produces two derivatives,

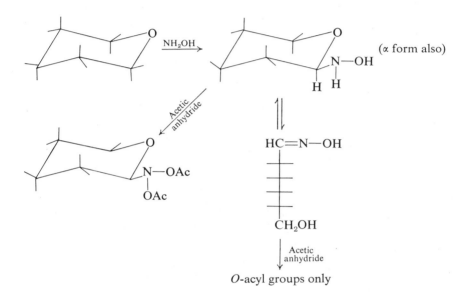

FIGURE 6.21 Reactions of carbohydrate oximes.

one of which contains an *N*-acyl and the other only *O*-acyl substituents. This is strong supporting evidence for the existence of the cyclic form [21].

6.3 Substitution at Carbon 1

In order to carry out substitution reactions of any type at carbon 1, it is generally necessary to introduce an activating group, which is most often halogen, although several addition reactions can be performed with derivatives having a double bond between positions 1 and 2. The subsequent replacement of halogen can be carried out with a wide variety of reactants; these reactions have several general features in common. The majority of reactions that take place at carbon 1 of carbohydrates proceed by mechanisms that are primarily ionic, as illustrated in Figure 6.22. Thus, in the attack of a nucleophile on carbon 1 of a halogen sugar, the rate determining step would be dissociation of the halogen to form a carbonium ion intermediate which is then attacked by the free electron pair on the nucleophile. Assuming that this type of mechanism is operative, the expectation would be that mixtures of products will invariably result. A logical extension of the same reasoning would predict that the primary control of product would be the stereochemistry of the parent, although in specifically substituted derivatives, the stability of the intermediate oxonium ion is also a consideration. Because most reactions will take place with the ring form of the carbohydrate, the position of the group at carbon 2, the greater stability of equatorial substituents and the possible interaction of polar residues with the ring oxygen are all contributing factors.

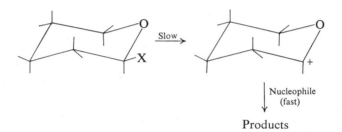

FIGURE 6.22   Schematic representation of reactions of halogen substituted carbohydrate. In most cases the rate-determining step is the dissociation of the halogen to form the cyclic carbonium ion which then reacts with a nucleophile to give products.

The above generalizations, when examined superficially, appear to explain many of the stereochemical results observed in carbohydrate systems. However, relatively little careful kinetic study has been made of most reactions and the observed results do not always agree with those that would be predicted from thermodynamic and steric considerations alone. An accurate appraisal of mechanism, especially where dealing with asymmetric (predisposed) molecules, requires isolation of all products, study of solvent effects, careful rate data, and so on. Even though a given reaction may proceed by an ionic mechanism (that is, the rate determining step is the formation of a charged intermediate), the different stabilities of the parent carbohydrate coupled with differing polar and steric effects on incoming groups render predictions quite difficult.

In many reactions, it is apparent that the polar effect of the ring oxygen has had an effect on substitution at carbon 1 and in several reactions, it has been demonstrated that the group departing from carbon 1 exerts a shielding effect such that it serves to direct the stereochemistry of the incoming nucleophile.

A very common effect is exerted when the constituent at carbon 1 is an acyloxy group; most data have been obtained with acetoxy groups [22]. In this case, the interaction between the oxygen of the carbonyl and the ring oxygen is such as to favor the axial substituent at C-1 rather than the equatorial. This is termed the anomeric effect and has been documented for glucose, mannose and galactose acetates, phosphates, and some halogeno derivatives. Under suitable conditions, the axial and equatorial acetates exist as an equilibrium mixture; the data for the composition at equilibrium is indicated in Table 6.3. The equilib-

TABLE 6.3

Composition of the equilibrium mixture of α and β-D-glucose pentaacetates. (See page 168.)

STARTING MATERIAL	PERCENT α (FINAL)	PERCENT β (FINAL)
β-D-glucose pentaacetate	88, 90[a]	12, 10
α-D-glucose pentaacetate	90, 87.5	10, 12.5

[a] Ac_2O—H_2SO_4 or Ac_2O—$HClO_4$ catalysis.

rium for the gluco-isomers is attained whether we approach it from a pure α or pure β-D-glucose pentaacetate; the equilibrium is approximately 90 percent α, 10 percent β. This corresponds to an energy difference of about 1000 calories per mole. Because the normally favored equatorial position is approximately 1 kcal per mole more stable than the axial (for hydroxyl), the carbonyl oxygen-ring oxygen interaction should be in the neighborhood of 2 kcal per mole. This "anomeric effect" has been attributed to the dipole–dipole interaction between the ring oxygen and the substituent at carbon 1. The magnitude of the effect varies with the dielectric constant of the medium and the electronegativity of the substituent at position 1. When the group at carbon 1 is hydroxyl, the inter-action is estimated to be 0.55 kcal per mole; in aqueous methanol, the percentage of α-D-glucopyranose present in solution reaches about 50 as compared to 35 percent in water. Accurate calculations of this sort of interaction are difficult to assess and have only been extensively studied for the gluco analogs.

It has also been suggested that the p orbital of the ring oxygen which has an axial orientation is better able to participate in delocalization of the developing charge at the anomeric center than is the equatorially oriented p orbital. Axial attack at the anomeric center by negatively charged ions is preferred.

There appear to be relatively few examples of reactions that take place at carbon 1 of carbohydrates by means of SN_2 displacement, and most reactions that appeared to follow this type of mechanism have been shown to proceed by ionic or shielded-ion mechanisms. The major exception to this occurs when the functional group at carbon 2 (occasionally at carbon 6) participates in an in-ternal displacement of the group at C-1. This type of neighboring group reaction is fairly common but clearly not the conventional type of displacement.

One example of a reaction which was initially thought to be SN_2 in nature but which, on further study, has been demonstrated to be more complex, is that described by MacDonald for the synthesis of aldosyl-1-phosphates [23]. This reaction involves the condensation of the β-pentaacetate of a carbohydrate with anhydrous phosphoric acid (Figure 6.23). The isolated product

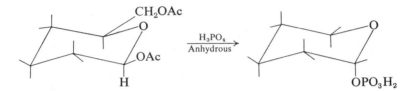

FIGURE 6.23   Reaction of peracetylated carbohydrate with anhydrous phosphoric acid. The reaction does not go exclusively by inversion.

appeared to be exclusively the α-1-phosphate, and this result, coupled with the fact that relatively low yields of the β-phosphate were obtained from the α-acetate (which, as would be expected, was rather unreactive), led to the suggestion that the mechanism was that of a simple displacement reaction. However, careful examination of the reaction products revealed the presence of both anomers in both reactions, thus making an SN_2 mechanism untenable [24]. The rather complex mixtures of products frequently obtained in carbohydrate reactions plus difficulty in separation and crystallization has seriously hampered mechanistic studies. Failure to isolate small yields of "minor" products can easily lead to an incorrect postulate as to a given mechanism; as a result, much laboratory practice is empiric in nature.

Glycosides and Glycosyl Halides

The synthesis of carbohydrate derivatives substituted at C-1 will generally involve activation of either the sugar or the condensing reactant. The ideal activating group forms easily isolable derivatives, acts as a good leaving group, and has properties that permit steric or kinetic control of the reaction. Obviously, such paragons are rare; the compromise adopted by most practicing chemists is to employ halogen substituted carbohydrates.

There are several procedures available for replacing a group at the C-1 position by halogen. The most frequently employed involves the reaction of the fully acylated carbohydrate with an anhydrous solution of the hydrogen halide in glacial acetic acid–acetic anhydride (Figure 6.24) [25]. Liquid hydrogen fluoride is used to prepare the glycosyl fluorides; and Lewis acid reagents, such as phosphorus pentachloride, titanium tetrachloride, and aluminum chloride, have been used for glycosyl chloride syntheses. Under certain conditions, acetyl chloride or acetyl bromide can be reacted directly with the carbohydrate to yield the fully acetylated glycosyl halide directly. This latter reaction is somewhat difficult to control and is not widely used.

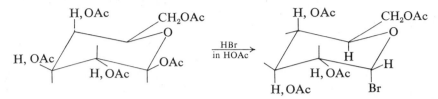

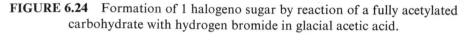

FIGURE 6.24 Formation of 1 halogeno sugar by reaction of a fully acetylated carbohydrate with hydrogen bromide in glacial acetic acid.

The general problem regarding the conformation of the halogenated product is readily solved utilizing previously developed information. Interaction with the ring oxygen is significant and the anomeric effect will strongly favor the axial product. The anomerization of 2,3,4,6 tetra *O*-acetyl D-glucopyranosyl chloride has been studied in acetonitrile [26]. The reaction is first order in chloride ion and presumably proceeds by nucleophilic attack of chloride at the anomeric center. The conversion of the α anomer to the β could be rapidly achieved using tetraethyl ammonium chloride as the displacing agent; the anomeric effect for chloride was estimated at 2 kcal per mole. In cases where an axial hydroxyl group is present at carbon 3, the transannular repulsion between this group and the halogen favors the equatorial conformer at position 1 but these latter halides are almost unknown. These considerations must also be modified due to the presence of an acyloxy group at carbon 2. In contrast to the (relatively) nonparticipating hydroxyl function, an acetoxy residue readily behaves as a neighboring group and internal displacement of the C-1 acetoxy may occur (Figure 6.25).

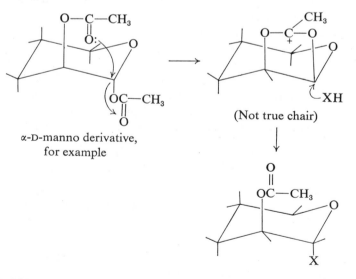

FIGURE 6.25 Stereochemistry of reactions of acetylated carbohydrates when neighboring group participation is possible.

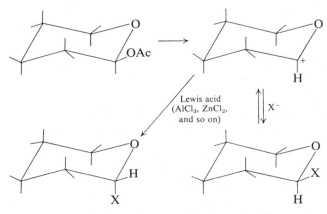

Note: Mechanism of anomerization may be more complex than illustrated. Equilibrium will still favor axial halogen with the exception noted in the text.

FIGURE 6.26   Schematic formulation for anomerization leading to the formation of the axial halogen as the predominant although not necessarily initial product.

This will be most prevalent when a *trans* diaxial conformation exists at C-1 C-2, but *trans* diequatorial acetates may also react in a similar fashion.

Because the product halides undergo anomerization quite readily, especially in the presence of Lewis acid catalysts, the axial anomer is almost always the exclusive product although it is not necessarily the *initial product*. This reaction is illustrated in Figure 6.26.

There are two other side reactions that must be considered. These are halogen substitution at positions other than C-1 and epimerization of adjacent centers.

The former reaction is minor when the hydrogen halide is employed, although bromine replacement at C-6 has been noted with extended reaction times. When phosphorus pentachloride is employed, however, ready chlorine substitution takes place on the methyl group present at C-2 (Figure 6.27) [27].

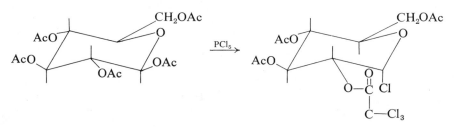

FIGURE 6.27   Reaction of β-D-glucose pentaacetate with phosphorus pentachloride to form the 1-chloro-2-trichloroacetyl derivative.

The resulting derivative has certain advantages because the group now present at

C-2 $\left(\begin{array}{c} O \\ \| \\ -C-C-Cl_3 \end{array}\right)$ has been deactivated by the electron withdrawing halogens.

The epimerization reaction is apparently confined to disaccharide acetates and the mechanism is still obscure. Treatment of cellobiose or lactose acetates with phosphorus pentachloride proceeds according to the scheme shown in Figure 6.28 [28].

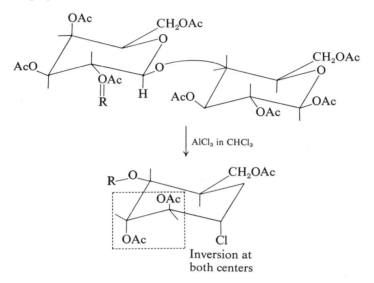

FIGURE 6.28 Reaction of lactose with aluminum chloride in chloroform.

This is probably the most convenient way to prepare allose. The extension of this to other sugars has not been reported.

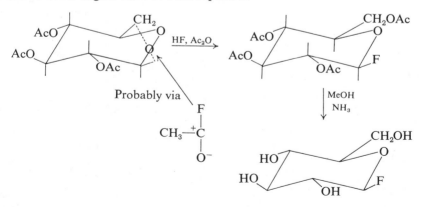

FIGURE 6.29 Reaction of 2,3,4-tri-*O*-acetyl 1,6-anhydro-β-D-glucopyranose with hydrogen fluoride.

6.4 Glycosyl Fluorides

Treatment of 2,3,4 triacetyl 1-6-anhydro-β-D-glucopyranose with hydrogen fluoride and acetic anhydride yields the 2,3,4,6-tetraacetyl β-D-glucosyl fluoride (Figure 6.29) [29]. Unlike the chloro and bromo compounds, it is possible to

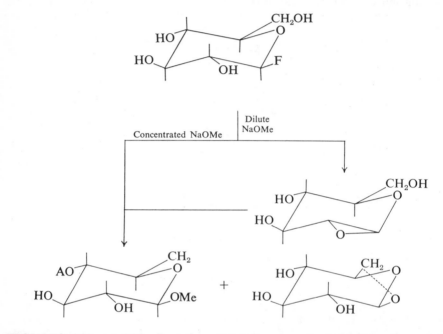

FIGURES 6.30 and 6.31 Reaction of β-1-fluoro-D-glucose with sodium methoxide to form the 1,2 epoxide sugar; the β-methyl glycoside and the 1,6-anhydro sugar.

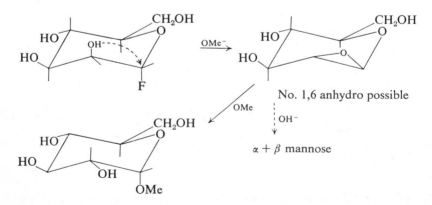

FIGURE 6.32 Mechanism of reaction of glycosyl fluorides with methoxide.

prepare the fluorides of the free sugars (Figure 6.30). The reactions that these derivatives undergo are quite different from those displayed by the other halogeno carbohydrates. Treatment of 1-fluoroglucose with sodium methoxide in methanol yields a mixture of products as illustrated in Figure 6.31 [30].

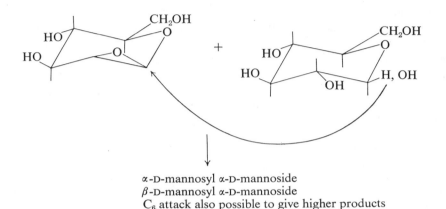

α-D-mannosyl α-D-mannoside
β-D-mannosyl α-D-mannoside
C₆ attack also possible to give higher products

FIGURE 6.33 Reaction of mannose epoxides leading to the formation of dimannosides and higher products.

α-mannosyl fluoride, on treatment with base, gives the 1,2 epoxide or a mixture of α and β mannose (Figure 6.32). The free sugar can then attack the epoxy sugar to give disaccharide products (Figure 6.33) [31].

Reactions of the fluoro sugars are generally slow but the increased electro-negativity of the halogen will permit the hydroxyl at C-2 to attack C-1.

6.5 Glycosyl Azides

Azide derivatives at carbon 1 can be prepared by the reaction of the appropriate halogeno sugar with silver azide (caution!) (Figure 6.34). These are extremely stable and undergo reactions similar to those of the fluorides under alkaline conditions [32].

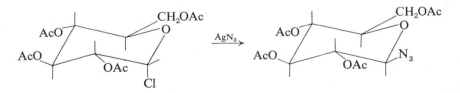

FIGURE 6.34 Formation of carbohydrate azides by treatment of an appropriate halogeno sugar with azide.

6.6 Glycoside Synthesis

The synthesis of glycosides both from a theoretical and from a practical viewpoint is of very considerable interest. The simple methyl and ethyl glycosides are of utility in studies of optical rotation phenomena. Model substrates such as paranitrophenylglycosides are employed for the study of glycosidases; substituted glucosides such as thiophenylgalactosides which themselves do not act as enzyme substrates, are used as inducers of enzyme synthesis in microorganisms; and the synthesis of specific disaccharides is still an active area of work.

The classic method of glycoside formation involves the reaction of the dry carbohydrate with an alcohol in the presence of a catalyst, usually hydrogen chloride (Figure 6.35) [33]. This is the procedure employed by Emil Fischer and

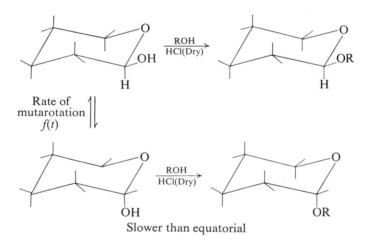

FIGURE 6.35 Formation of carbohydrate glycosides by direct reaction of the sugar with an alcohol in the presence of dry hydrogen chloride.

is most often carried out with hydrogen chloride and methanol. As in any reaction of this type, a mixture of anomeric glycosides is obtained which is not an equilibrium mixture but rather reflects the species present at the start of the reaction, mutarotation rates, and the relative reactivities of the axial and equatorial hydroxyls at carbon 1. In order to obtain the axial glycoside, for example, it is necessary to start with the axial sugar and keep the reaction conditions such as to minimize mutarotation rates since the equatorial hydroxyl is much more reactive.

The treatment of fully acetylated glycosyl halides with alcohols is still one of the most common methods for glycoside synthesis (Figure 6.36). In most cases, the fully acetylated bromide is employed; however, these sometimes prove difficult to handle, and for acetyl amino sugars, the chloride has been used with some success. The initial work carried out by Koenigs and Knorr did not employ an acid acceptor or silver salt to facilitate the reaction [34]. Thus, the dissociation of the C-1 halogen bond was not promoted and the yields of glycoside were quite low. Silver oxide, silver perchlorate, mercuric cyanide, and several

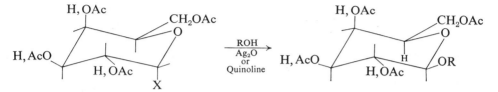

FIGURE 6.36 Reaction of halogeno-substituted carbohydrate with alcohol in the presence of a halogen acceptor such as silver oxide or quinoline. The bromide is the derivative most usually employed and although the product is depicted as the equatorial isomer it is definitely not formed exclusively.

organic bases are currently used. Good yields are obtained when mercuric bromide–mercuric oxide is used. If an organic base such as quinoline is employed as the acid acceptor, a mixture of anomeric products results with the β still predominating.

The stereochemistry of the substitution proceeds with apparent inversion at carbon 1, yielding the β-glycoside from the α-halide[6]; this may be a case of shielding of carbon 1 by the departing halide although the accessibility of the equatorial position to attack by the oxygen of the alcohol is also a factor (Figure 6.37).

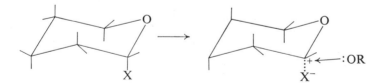

FIGURE 6.37 Schematic representation of the effect of the departing halogen on the stereochemistry of attack by the incoming nucleophile. The electronegative halogen may hinder the approach of the electron pair on oxygen to the positively charged center. In any case some axial product is always formed.

It should be emphasized that few, if any, of these syntheses have been shown to proceed *exclusively* with inversion and that adequate kinetic studies have not been

---

[6] The anomeric effect discussed previously is greatly enhanced if a bulky, highly polar halogen is present. In addition, the handling of the highly reactive equatorial halogen is quite difficult. As a result, halogen sugars are almost always axial at carbon 1 (equatorial fluorides are the major exception).

carried out. These reactions almost certainly occur by ionic mechanisms although the failure to isolate the minor (axial) product might suggest the operation of a displacement (SN$_2$) mechanism. The fully benzoylated glycosyl halides react rapidly in the absence of any acceptor and, in this case, the configuration of the

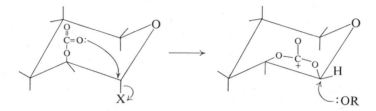

FIGURE 6.38 Formation of axial glycosides due to the participation of a neighboring benzoyl group. The ring is more nearly planar than that depicted due to the restraint imposed by the formation of the 5-membered ring intermediate.

product is largely determined by steric hindrance [35]. Those groups that have a benzoxy group at carbon 2 *trans* to the halogen react without inversion, while those having a *cis* relationship at C-1, C-2 react with inversion at carbon 1. This result is most easily understood if it is assumed that the group at carbon 2, when *trans* to the halide at carbon 1, acts as a neighboring group by the mechanism shown in Figure 6.38. Thus, double displacement with retention of configuration at carbon 1 occurs, whereas in the second case, the shielded ion mechanism yields predominantly inversion at carbon 1.

Direct condensation of aromatic phenols with fully acetylated sugars in the presence of Lewis acid catalysts has also been carried out. This reaction is similar to the condensation of fully acetylated sugars with anhydrous phosphoric acid and the yield of anomeric products is determined by the nature of the catalyst and also by the possibility of participation by the group at carbon 2. In

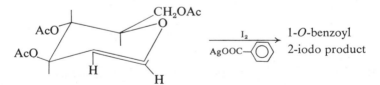

FIGURE 6.39 Reaction of D-glucal triacetate with silver benzoate and iodine.

most cases, the equatorial acetate is the most reactive and if conditions are such so as to favor rapid anomerization, then mixed products will be obtained. The composition will largely be determined by the rate at which anomerization occurs. However, where this reaction is slow compared to the substitution, the yield of products may be determined by thermodynamic considerations. Catalysts that have been employed in this reaction include sulfuric acid, zinc chloride, toluene sulfonic acid, and polyphosphoric acid [36].

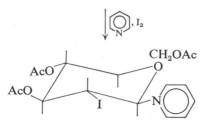

FIGURE 6.40 Reaction of D-glucal triacetate with iodine and pyridine.

Glycosides may also be synthesized by reactions involving addition to the double bond present in compounds such as D-glucal triacetate (Figure 6.39) [37]. Treatment of D-glucal triacetate with silver benzoate and iodine produces the 1-benzoyl 2-iodo adduct with both β-gluco and α-manno configurations being obtained. Similar reactions can be carried out in methanol with chlorine or bromine to yield the 2-halo methyl glycosides. When a nitrogenous base is used as the acid acceptor in such a reaction, *N*-glycoside formation may occur as well (Figure 6.40). This can be prevented by use of a sterically hindered base such as collidine. It is interesting to note that 2,3,4,6 tetraacetyl pyridinium *N*-α-D-glucopyranoside apparently has the reverse ring conformation because of the strong tendency for the quaternary nitrogen to be equatorial; this may be a type of reverse anomeric effect.

6.7 *Thioglycosides*

Sulfur-containing derivatives of sugars, particularly thioglycosides, are very widespread in plant sources. The reaction of a carbohydrate with a mercaptan in the presence of a Lewis acid catalyst, such as zinc chloride or dry hydrogen chloride, proceeds with the formation of the dithioacetal which in many

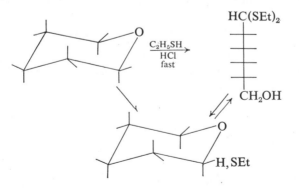

FIGURE 6.41 Reaction of a carbohydrate with ethyl mercaptan in the presence of hydrogen chloride.

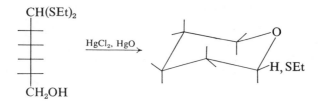

FIGURE 6.42 Conversion of the diethyl mercaptan of a carbohydrate to the thioglycoside.

cases may be isolated as a crystalline derivative (Figure 6.41) [38]. However, under these conditions, further exposure of the dithioacetal to the mercaptan leads to an equilibrium mixture containing the dithioacetal and the α and β thioglycosides (Figure 6.42). The configuration of the 1-thio derivative is dependent on the ability of the group at carbon 2 to participate. The course of the

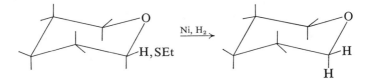

FIGURE 6.43 Removal of the thioglycoside group by Raney nickel and hydrogen leading to the formation of an anhydro sugar alcohol.

reaction of fully acetylated sugars with an alkyl mercaptan in the presence of zinc chloride will depend on the rate of C-2 participation and on the rate of anomerization of the acetoxy function at carbon 1 as opposed to the rate of displacement by the highly nucleophilic sulfur. It is also possible to convert the dithioacetal to the 1-thioglycoside and thence to the aldose, removing the thio function with reagents such as mercuric chloride. A deoxy function may be synthesized by subsequent hydrogenolysis (Figure 6.43). Thioglycosides may

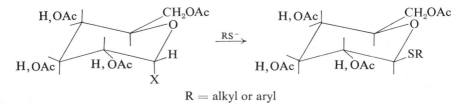

R = alkyl or aryl

FIGURE 6.44 Formation of thioglycosides by reaction of an appropriate sulfide with an acetohalogen sugar. It should be noted that the D-mannohalide is unreactive.

also be synthesized in good yields by reaction of acetohalogen sugars with RS-type compounds (Figure 6.44). Potassium thioacetate, thiourea, or potassium sulfide in the presence of base yield the free 1-thioaldose (Figure 6.45) [39].

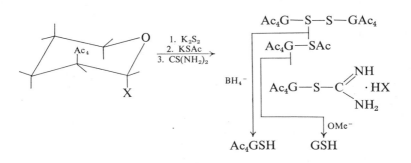

FIGURE 6.45 Formation of thioacetates, thiourea, and disulfide derivatives of carbohydrates by reaction of the acetohalogen sugar with the indicated reagent.

As might be expected, the thioglycosides are appreciably more resistant to acid hydrolysis than are the corresponding oxygen analogs. This is due to the fact that the nucleophilic sulfur is not as readily protonated as is oxygen. The cyclic carbonium ion which is an intermediate for glycoside hydrolysis is therefore more difficult to form.

The thioglycosides may be oxidized with peroxide or per acids to sulfones.

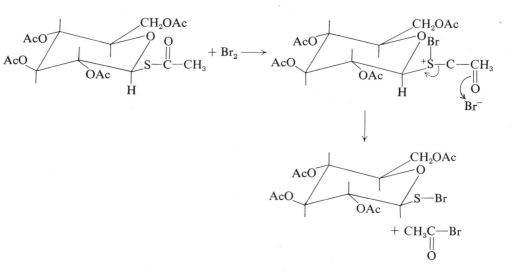

FIGURE 6.46 Bromination of the 1-thioacetyl function in 1-thioacetyl 2,3,4,6-tetraacetyl β-D-glucopyranose.

These have not been extensively studied synthetically but corresponding sulfone derivatives have been employed as intermediates in carbohydrate degradations (see Chapter 14).

It is possible to brominate the sulfur function with bromine in ether or to effect replacement by acetoxy by using bromine in acetic acid. The mechanism of this interesting reaction is shown in Figure 6.46 [40].

The free thiosugars are typical reducing sugars and can be estimated by most of the conventional reducing sugar methods. They are readily oxidized to disulfides by iodine and this has been made a basis of their quantitative estimation (Figure 6.47) [41].

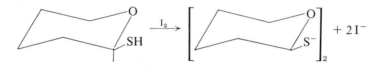

FIGURE 6.47   Oxidation of thio sugars by iodine.

Anomerization of Acetates

The anomerization of carbohydrate acetates has been extensively studied by Bonner, Lemieux, and their co-workers [42–44]. In the initial studies carried out by Bonner, the acid catalyzed anomerization of glucose pentaacetate was

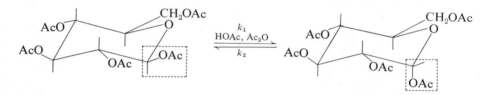

FIGURE 6.48   Equilibration between α and β-D-glucose pentaacetate.

followed by polarimetric methods, using Hudson's rate expression for the reaction (Figure 6.48):

$$k_1 + k_2 = \frac{2.303}{t} \log \frac{\alpha_0 - \alpha_e}{\alpha_t - \alpha_e} \tag{6.6}$$

α_0 = rotation at time zero
α_t = rotation at any time t
α_e = rotation at equilibrium

A calculation of $k_1 + k_2$ gave a figure of 0.0097 at 35 degrees and 0.03 at 45 degrees, using zinc chloride as a catalyst and acetic anhydride as the solvent. However, in the presence of sulfuric acid, there was a nearly linear dependence of the anomerization rate on the concentration of the acid. Thus, an additional factor had to be introduced into Hudson's expression that corrected it for the concentration of the sulfuric acid. It was found that the properties of the sulfuric acid catalyst were variable and depended upon how long the solution of acetic anhydride and sulfuric acid was allowed to stand before adding the sugar acetate. This was attributed to the formation of sulfoacetic acid by the reaction of sulfuric acid with the acetic anhydride. Because there was little or no salt effect on the reaction, it was suggested that the sulfuric acid ionized completely in the acetic anhydride according to the following equations:

$$H_2SO_4 + Ac_2O \longrightarrow Ac_2OH^+ + HSO_4^- \tag{6.7}$$

$$H_2SO_4 + AcOH \longrightarrow AcOH_2^+ + HSO_4^- \tag{6.8}$$

Lithium bisulfate alone catalyzed the anomerization only to a very small degree, and therefore the bisulfate ion is not dissociated to an appreciable extent in this solvent. The effect of varying the solvent composition on the reaction was also examined using solvents containing progressively higher percentages of glacial acetic acid. The rate fell off rapidly at first but was still substantial even in 100 percent glacial acetic acid. However, the reaction products in this case were not satisfactorily characterized. Acetic acid was apparently a nonreactive species although a protonated form of acetic anhydride might be involved in the reaction.

For any mechanistic interpretation to be made under such reaction conditions, it is necessary to show that only the anomeric center is undergoing reaction. The specific rotation of the equilibrium mixture of α and β pentaacetates, which would obtain starting either with the α or with the β fully acetylated sugar, showed a final composition of approximately 84 percent α and 16 percent β. Synthetic mixtures made up to these proportions gave identical properties to those obtained from the equilibrium mixture. The stability of the other ester linkages was examined by observing the reaction of tetraacetyl β-D-glucopyranosides with propionic anhydride in the presence of sulfuric acid. Neither mutarotation nor acyl interchange took place, indicating that the ester linkages at secondary hydroxyls and at the C-6 hydroxymethyl grouping were not participating in the reaction to any significant extent. The following mechanism was therefore proposed wherein the first step involves the reaction of sulfuric acid with acetic anhydride according to the following equation:

$$
\begin{array}{ccc}
\underset{\displaystyle \overset{O}{\|}}{CH_3C}-O-\underset{\displaystyle \overset{O}{\|}}{C}-CH_3 + H_2SO_4 \longrightarrow & CH_3-\underset{\displaystyle \overset{+OH}{\|}}{C}-O-\underset{\displaystyle \overset{O}{\|}}{C}-CH_3 \\
\end{array}
$$

$$
\begin{array}{c}
OH \\
| \\
CH_3-\underset{+}{C}-O-\underset{\|}{C}-CH_3 \\
\overset{\|}{O}
\end{array}
\qquad\qquad + \qquad HSO_4^-
\tag{6.9}
$$

The second step, which was thought to be rate determining, involves the formation of a 6-membered cyclic intermediate (Figure 6.49). There is a significant probability that attack by the ester oxygen rather than the carbonyl oxygen of the acetoxy group could take place to give a cyclic intermediate. However, no attempt was made to differentiate these two possibilities. The only substantiating feature for this over-all proposal resided in the stability of the 6-membered ring as opposed to other possible intermediates.

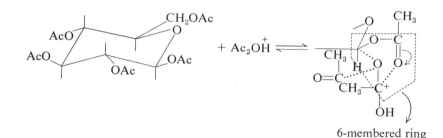

6-membered ring

FIGURE 6.49   Reaction of α-D-glucose pentaacetate with acetonium ion to form a 6-membered ring intermediate.

Further studies on the mechanism of this reaction were carried out using perchloric acid as the catalyst [45]. As previously found, an appreciable rate of anomerization occurred in pure acetic acid, and crystalline products were obtained. On the basis of rate data obtained in the perchloric acid system, a mechanism was proposed involving the intermediates shown in Figure 6.50. A

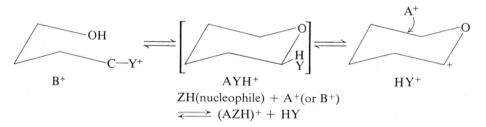

$$ZH(\text{nucleophile}) + A^+(\text{or } B^+)$$
$$\rightleftharpoons (AZH)^+ + HY$$

FIGURE 6.50   Reaction of ionic species with formation of cyclic carbonium ion.

nucleophile, not designated, can react with either of the cationic species to give the intermediate shown which would involve elimination of HA and recyclization in the case of B. The rate laws that would govern this particular mechanism may be derived by assuming that the conjugate acid of the sugar acetate is formed as the initial step after the reaction of acetic anhydride with the catalyst (Figure 6.51).

$$\text{GOAc} + \text{AcOH}_2{}^+ \underset{}{\overset{k_1}{\rightleftharpoons}} \text{GOAcH}^+ + \text{AcOH}$$
(Sugar acetate)

$$\text{GOAc} + \text{Ac}_2\text{OH}^+ \underset{}{\overset{k_2}{\rightleftharpoons}} \text{GOAcH}^+ + \text{Ac}_2\text{O}$$

$$\text{GOAcH}^+ \underset{k_{-3}}{\overset{k_3}{\rightleftharpoons}} \text{G}^+ + \text{AcOH}$$

FIGURE 6.51 Breakdown of anomerization reactions into several discrete kinetic steps.

This can dissociate a carbonium ion and, in the case where acetic acid is the solvent, anomerization is simply the reverse of this dissociation reaction. In the presence of acetic anhydride, however, the carbonium ion forms and the anomerization step is as below. The over-all rate equation is as follows:

Anomerization step:

$$\text{G}^+ + \text{Ac}_2\text{O} \underset{k_4}{\overset{k_4}{\rightleftharpoons}} \text{GOAc}_2{}^+$$

Rate in HOAc:

$$k_3(\text{GOAcH}^+) = k_3 K_1 [\text{GOAc}]\left(\frac{\text{AcOH}_2{}^+}{\text{AcOH}}\right) \tag{6.10}$$

Rate in Ac$_2$O:

$$k_3 K_2 (\text{GOAc}) \frac{[\text{Ac}_2\text{OH}^+]}{[\text{Ac}_2\text{O}]} + k_4 [\text{GOAc}_2{}^+]$$

The introduction of isotopic techniques permitted Lemieux and co-workers to investigate this reaction from the standpoint of acetate exchange. The carbonyl carbon of the C-1 acetoxy group was labeled as C-14 and it was observed that the α–β inversion rate and the rate of exchange of the labile acetoxy group with the solvent (in this case 1:1, acetic acid:acetic anhydride) were identical (Figure 6.52). It was also shown that the β–α inversion rate was about *5 percent as rapid*

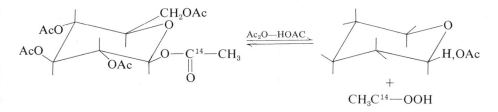

FIGURE 6.52 Acetate anomerization as studied by ^{14}C acetate exchange.

as the C-1 acetoxy turnover. Because the C-1 oxygen bond is much more acid labile than the $O^{14}C$ bond, it was assumed that radioactive interchange was measuring essentially only acetoxy interchange. The apparently stoichiometric relationship between acetoxy exchange and anomerization rate is consistent with a bimolecular displacement mechanism and would seem at first to rule out the ionic mechanism discussed above. However, there are numerous examples where ionic intermediates participate in reactions which proceed with virtually complete inversion. In this case, the double bond character given to the carbon 1-oxygen bond as illustrated below may play a role; thus, the ion has a much greater tendency to form the inverted product.

In the case of the β–α transfer, participation by the C-2 acetoxy group to form a cyclic carbonium ion intermediate may also take place (Figure 6.53).

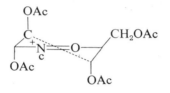

FIGURE 6.53   Skew-form representation of hypothetical ionic intermediate in the anomerization reaction.

The probability of this cyclic intermediate or, in general, of participation by the C-2 acetoxy group, was further substantiated by an examination of the effect of progressive chlorine substitution in the C-2 acetoxy group. The trichloro acetoxy derivative undergoes anomerization approximately 400-fold slower than does the parent compound; this is strongly indicative of participation by the group at carbon 2 in the nonchlorinated analog. It is extremely unlikely that steric considerations alone would give rise to an effect of this magnitude. The electron withdrawing effect of the chlorine with the resultant reduction of the nucleophilic character of the C-2 acetoxy group lowers the tendency to form this cyclic intermediate and would thus appreciably slow down the anomerization rate. A similar study carried out on the α–β anomerization led to a 50-fold reduction, which could be rationalized by inductive effects without the necessity for participation.

Although the possibility of participation by the C-6 acetoxy group has been suggested, the fact that 1,2,3,4-tetra-*O*-acetyl-6-deoxy-D-glucopyranose undergoes anomerization at substantially the same rates as does pentaacetyl D-glucopyranose makes this rather unlikely.

It is still not resolved as to whether the initial reaction is with the conjugate acid of the acetic anhydride and the anomer or with acetic anhydride and the conjugate acid of the aldose. The fact that C-1 acetoxy exchange in *trans* acetylated aldoses may be an intramolecular SN_2 process not related to anomerization is supported by the change in ratios as more and more chloro groups are introduced into the C-2 acetoxy function. Finally, in a recent paper by Bonner, it was concluded that all of the data could still be explained by an ionic SN_1 mechanism with the stoichiometric exchange-anomerization data for the α acetate being explained by the rather selective ionic intermediate form [46]. The participation by the C-2 acetoxy group in this reaction was further eliminated by examination of the anomerization rate of 1,3,4,6-tetraacetyl-2-deoxy-D-glucopyranose. The exchange to inversion ratios for this compound are between 2 and 4 rather than unity as found for the pentaacetate, and thus an SN_2 mechanism is extremely unlikely. Further substantiation was given by a steady-state treatment of the SN_1 mechanism which permitted accurate predictions of anomerization rates for a variety of acetylated aldoses.

The mechanism of glycoside anomerization catalyzed by Lewis acid catalysts has not been as extensively studied as has been the anomerization of acetoxy sugars. The ease of anomerization and the extent to which it takes place to give an equilibrium mixture is a function not only of the stability of the glycoside but of steric and electronic factors as well. A mechanism that will involve a carbonium ion will involve some ring distortion and, as a result, if there are particularly bulky substituents brought into opposition, a considerable energy barrier will be present. Those studies that have been carried out indicate that some open chain intermediate is formed, since orthoacetate type derivatives are present at the end of such reaction sequences. Figure 6.54 depicts a suggested mechanism for glycoside anomerization [47].

A summary of reactions of fully acetylated carbohydrates and acetylated glycosyl halides leads to the following conclusions.

1. Because in almost every case the axial halogen is favored, the stereochemical course of the reaction will be determined largely by the ability of the group at C-2 to participate. If, as in the case of sugars of the gluco configuration, this is *cis* to the functional group at C-2, then the predominant mechanism will be ionic to give the thermodynamically favored glycoside. Inversion proceeds probably not by an SN_2 mechanism, but rather by what may be termed a shielded ion mechanism to give the product with the *trans* configuration at carbon 1 and carbon 2.

2. The reason that the SN_2 mechanism seems unlikely for most reactions at the glycosidic carbon is, that in the absence of a suitable catalyst such as silver carbonate or quinoline, which may be envisioned as facilitating dissociation of the C-1 halogen, these reactions are very sluggish indeed. Had they been simply SN_2 displacements, then a choice of suitable solvent to promote nucleophilic attack on the carbon at position 1 would have permitted the reaction to go rather smoothly.

3. Where the group at carbon 2 is *trans* to the axial halogen, as in the case of sugars such as mannose and talose, then active participation by the

axial acetoxy function may be expected. In these cases, the extent of participation and the extent of neighboring group displacement is a function of the
solvent to a certain extent, but in most polar or semipolar solvents, this is the
predominant mechanism. Thus, replacements in the manno series go predominantly by retention at carbon 1 via a double displacement mechanism.

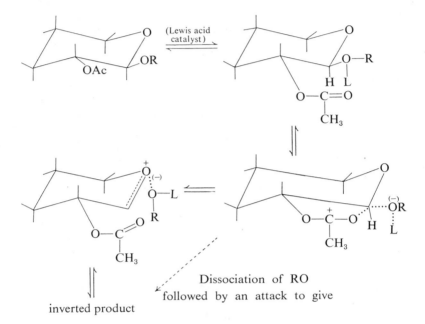

FIGURE 6.54 Anomerization of glycosides in the presence of a Lewis acid
catalyst. The dissociation of the :OR group may be facilitated by the acetoxy
group present at carbon 2 and followed by reattack of :OR to give the inverted
product.

    4. The extent of participation by the acetoxy group at C-2 can be reduced
by deactivating this functional group so that the carbonyl oxygen is much less
of a nucleophile. This has been most effectively accomplished by a substitution
of the methyl carbon of the C-2 acetoxy function by chlorine (reaction with
phosphorous pentachloride). The resulting trichloroacetoxy derivative with its
strongly electron withdrawing halogens is essentially nonparticipating and
approximately as inert as hydroxyl, if not more so. In addition, the rather bulky
nature of the halogens makes participation of this group unlikely. A similar
group, trifluoroacetyl, has been utilized in the synthesis of glycosides of 2-amino
sugars. When feasible, the nitrate ester of the hydroxyl at position 2 also serves
as a deactivating group; amino groups may be protected by the formation of
nonparticipating Schiff bases.

5. Under suitable conditions, reactions of acetohalogen sugars with water can be used to prepare derivatives in which the C-1 group has a free hydroxyl. This is carried out in the presence of a catalyst which can form a complex ion with the halogen and thus render it inactive in the solution. A typical sequence involves preparation of 2,3,4,6-tetraacetyl-D-glucopyranose by treatment of 2,3,4,6-tetraacetyl-α-D-glucopyranosyl bromide, with water in the presence of mercuric bromide [48] (Figure 6.55). This reaction may be more complex than initially realized because treatment of 2,3,4,6-tetraacetyl-β-D-glucopyranosyl chloride with silver acetate in acetic acid yields 1,3,4,6-tetraacetyl-β-D-glucopyranose as the initial product. This reaction apparently proceeds by neighboring group participation of the C-2 acetoxy function (displacement of the *trans* halogen at C-1) followed by ring opening to give the indicated product. The 1,3,4,6-tetraacetate on standing in an aqueous solvent slowly rearranges to the 2,3,4,6-tetraacetate which is apparently more stable.

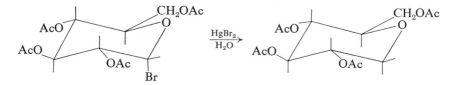

FIGURE 6.55 Formation of 2,3,4,6-tetraacetyl-D-glucopyranose by reaction of α-bromo 2,3,4,6-tetra-*O*-acetyl-D-glucopyranose with mercuric bromide in aqueous solution.

6. In the absence of a halogen function at C-1, replacements will be largely determined by the accessibility of the group at C-1 to attack either internally or by external reagents. Ionic intermediates may still prevail in reactions of β-D-glucose-pentaacetate, but the accessibility of the equatorial oxygen function at C-1 to attack by any number of reagents (whether they be protonating or otherwise) renders this compound far more reactive than the corresponding α anomer. However, if dissociation of the carbon–oxygen bond is not the rate determining step, then steric or other considerations may come into play. There are very few examples known where this has been shown not to be the case. In other words, most reactions that take place at C-1 can be envisioned as having a slow step which involves dissociation of the bond between C-1 of the carbohydrate and the atom to which it is attached, whether this is the oxygen of an acetoxy function or halogen or some other functional group.

7. The reactions of ketoses are not comparable, and the synthesis of ketose glycosides presents problems that are quite different from those found in the synthesis of aldose glycosides. One point needs to be mentioned in connection with the above discussion: the ability of the C-1 acetoxy group of a ketose acetate to participate in reactions taking place at the ketal carbon (Figure 6.56).

Ketose may be represented as:

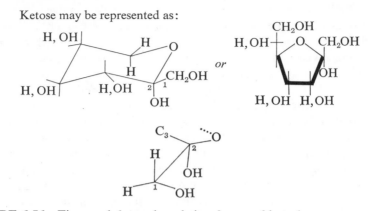

FIGURE 6.56 Five- and 6-membered ring forms of keto hexose sugars. Rotation of the carbon–carbon bond between carbon 1 and carbon 2 will permit attack on carbon 2 by the groups substituted on the hydroxyl of carbon 1.

This is possible under all circumstances due to the fact that the group at C-1 is exocyclic whether the ketose is in the furanoside or pyranoside ring form. There is relatively unrestricted rotation about the C-1–C-2 bond, and thus participation of an acetoxy function present at C-1 in attack at C-2 is always possible. Stereospecific ketoside syntheses are relatively rare.

      8. The rate of oxidation of the hydroxyl group at C-1 correlates with the ease of attack and thereby with the relative steric hindrance. The equatorial, β-hydroxyl is much more readily attacked by reagents such as hypohalite ion, whereas axial hydroxyls are more readily oxidized by oxygen in the presence of platinum catalyst. The latter case may be a function of adsorption to the catalyst surface or may involve direct attack on the carbon bound proton rather than the hydroxyl.

Glycoside Hydrolysis

      Some of the factors controlling the rate of glycoside hydrolysis have been briefly discussed previously. It is clear that no single factor can be adduced to account for all of the known features of glycoside hydrolysis. There are inductive, steric, participating, and ring strain effects that contribute both to the rate and mechanism of hydrolysis for an individual glycoside. In general, some of the differences that have been observed can be attributed to changes in the energy of activation. For example, the energies of activation for the hydrolysis of methyl, benzyl, and phenylglycosides successively decrease. Inductive effects are very clear in the case of fully methylated glycosides which have a slower rate of hydrolysis than do the free hydroxyl analogs. The effect of the chain hydroxyl groups is quite marked and at least partly cumulative. It is particularly noticeable in the case of the 2 position because the rate of hydrolysis of 2-deoxy-glycosides is several hundred times faster than comparable compounds containing an oxygen function at C-2. Glycoside hydrolysis is generally facilitated by electron repelling groups in the aglycon; this is also consistent with the nature of the hydrolysis process.

Most mechanistic studies of the cleavage process show that cleavage takes place between the carbon of C-1 and the oxygen of the glycoside, and that the intermediate is the carbonium ion of the sugar. One exception to this general rule is found in the hydrolysis of tertiary butyl glycosides which proceeds with cleavage between the glycosidic oxygen and the carbon of the *t*-butyl group; this is consistent with the recognized stability of the *t*-butyl carbonium ion [49].

The studies that have been carried out on anomeric methyl pyranosides indicate that conformational stability correlates very strongly with the rate of hydrolysis. In all cases, the equatorial glycosides are more rapidly hydrolyzed than the axial, presumably because of the greater accessibility of the glycosidic oxygen to attack by proton. In cases where considerable conformational instability is present, the rate differences between α and β glycosides are not quite as marked as they are in the case of glucose. The rates of hydrolysis are generally somewhat faster than those for the more stable sugars. It is not clear whether there are actually different transition states or different transition conformations present or whether the initial conformation of the carbohydrate determines the concentration of the rate controlling species. Thus, if common ionic intermediates are present for all glycoside hydrolyses, then it must be concluded that the differences would be largely in the energy of activation with the more highly strained sugars having higher initial energy states. However, if transition states are nonidentical, then other mechanisms may be operable. It is also possible that the greater reactivity of equatorial substituents may be due to the dipole effect of the ring oxygen. The nonbonding orbitals of this oxygen have their dipole closer to the equatorial substituent than to the axial one; repulsion by the electron pairs is greater for the equatorial group and thereby facilitates its departure.

A recent article on relative hydrolysis rates of a large number of glycosides has correlated several findings [50]. There is a direct relationship between the rate of hydrolysis and the freedom of rotation about the C-2, C-3 and C-5, C-4 bonds. An effect of transannular interactions was also demonstrated.

As indicated in Table 6.4 the rate of hydrolysis is decreased by increasing opposition of the substituent on C-2 relative to that on C-3 when rotation is in such a direction as to eclipse the equatorial group. This same phenomenon is true when looking along the axis from C-5 to C-4.

In the case of strong acid catalysis, the rate of glycoside hydrolysis is approximately parallel to the acidity, and cyclic C-1 carbonium ions have been proposed as intermediates. The formation of a cyclic C-1 carbonium ion under

TABLE 6.4

Newman projections of indicated hydroxyl groups in various sugars compared with the relative rate of hydrolysis of their methyl glycosides.

METHYL PYRANOSIDE	C_2–C_3	C_5–C_4	RELATIVE RATE
β-D-xylose	HO, HO (Newman projection)	OH (Newman projection)	9.1
β-D-ribose	HO, OH (Newman projection)		12.3
β-D-glucose	HO, HO, OH (Newman projection)		1.9
β-D-mannose	HO (Newman projection)	CH_2OH, OH (Newman projection)	5.7
2-deoxy-β-D-glucose	HO (Newman projection)		5125
β-D-glucuronic acid		CO_2H, OH (Newman projection)	0.62
β-D-galactose		OH, CH_2OH (Newman projection)	9.2

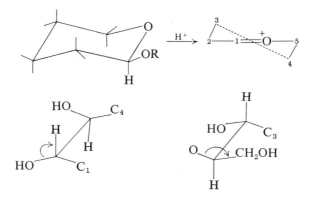

FIGURE 6.57 Projected intermediate for the hydrolysis of glycosides as compared with the rotation of the bond necessary to achieve the near planar form.

such circumstances requires distortion of the normal chair into a half-chair conformation (Figure 6.57). As indicated in the figure, this will involve counterclockwise rotation about C-2, C-3, and C-5, C-4, respectively. The conformation or configuration at C-1 may be strictly planar (trigonal rather than tetrahedral) but this has not yet been established.

The nature of the aglycon group also has been shown to have a marked effect on hydrolysis rates because increasing the electronegativity of this group enhances the rate of hydrolysis. There are two opposing effects that need to be considered. One is the equilibrium concentration for conjugate acid and the second is the rate of its breakdown. The problem of C—C bond rotation in relation to this latter effect was examined in a study of the hydrolysis rates of cellobiuronic acid and pseudocellobiuronic acid (Figure 6.58). In this case, the former compound in which the glycosidically substituted carbohydrate residue contains a carboxylic group at C-6, and thus has impeded rotation about C-5, C-4, has a much lower rate of hydrolysis than does the latter (pseudocellobiuronic acid), wherein the normal CH_2OH function is present on the glycosidically substituted residue and the carboxyl is in the aglycon. The resistance to "eclipse" effect is apparently larger than any inductive effect that the carboxyl group may have. These results are apparently offset by the lesser stability of *n*-butyl, neopentyl, and cyclohexyl glucuronides as compared to the corresponding glucosides. The uronides have a lower entropy of activation for the hydrolysis process and thus may be cleaved by a different (bimolecular?) mechanism. In any case, the substituent at position 5 has both a polar and a conformational effect on glycoside hydrolysis.

In sugars with marked conformational instability such as in β-mannose glycosides or in substituted glycosides where bulky axial groups are present, the attainment of suitable half-chair conformations may involve considerable ring strain. Table 6.5 lists hydrolysis constants for selected glycosides examined

TABLE 6.5

Relative rates of hydrolysis of selected glycosides. Note that the hydrolysis of the *t*-butyl β-D-glucopyranosides proceeds via the *t*-butyl carbonium ion and the remarkable difference in rate indeed suggests that the mechanism for this reaction is different from that of the other glycosides.

COMPOUND	RELATIVE RATE	CONDITIONS	
		ACID	TEMPERATURE C degrees
Methyl pyranoside of			
α-D-glucose	1.0	0.5 N HCl	75
β anomer	1.9		
α-D-galactose	2.4	0.5 N HCl	75
β anomer	5.7		
α-D-xylose	5.2	0.5 N HCl	75
β anomer	9.2		
α-L-arabinose	13.1	0.5 N HCl	75
β anomer	9.0		
α-D-glucuronic acid	0.47	0.57 M H_2SO_4	75
β anomer	0.62		
Pyranoside			
Ethyl β-D-gluco	2.1	0.5 M H_2SO_4	60
n-propyl-β-D-gluco	2.5	0.5 M H_2SO_4	60
t-butyl-β-D-gluco [a]	1960	3.3 M $HClO_4$	25
p-nitrophenyl-β-D-gluco	3.2	0.1 N HCl	60
Phenyl-β-D-gluco	8.0	1.0 N HCl	60
Phenyl-β-D-galacto	28.2	1.0 N HCl	60
Phenyl-β-D-xylo	93.7	1.0 N HCl	60

[a] Via *t*-butyl carbonium ion.

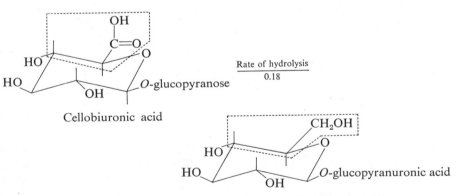

Cellobiuronic acid

Pseudocellobiuronic acid

FIGURE 6.58 Cellobiuronic acid and pseudocellobiuronic acid. The rate constant for the hydrolysis of the latter is some 35 times as great as that of the former.

under identical conditions. The correlation with the above conclusions is very good.

Alkylation and Arylation of Carbohydrates at the Anomeric Center

The possibility of direct carbon–carbon bond formation by treatment of suitably substituted derivatives under either Friedel-Crafts or Grignard reaction conditions has been known for some time [51, 52]. Early studies involving the reaction of aluminum chloride with acetylated carbohydrates under anhydrous conditions revealed the rather unusual epimerization reaction mentioned previously. The reaction of tetraacetyl glucosyl chloride with benzene and anhydrous aluminum chloride leads to arylation of carbon 1 and the formation of C-phenyl derivatives (Figure 6.59). Both mono and disubstituted derivatives are formed and the mono-substituted derivative still retains asymmetry at carbon 1 so that two isomers are possible. The disubstituted aryl derivatives can be obtained not only with benzene but also with toluene and several substituted benzenes but not with condensed systems such as naphthalene. It is also possible to carry out subsequent substitution of the aromatic moiety after linking it to the carbohydrate; para nitro derivatives of C-glycosides have been made in this manner [53].

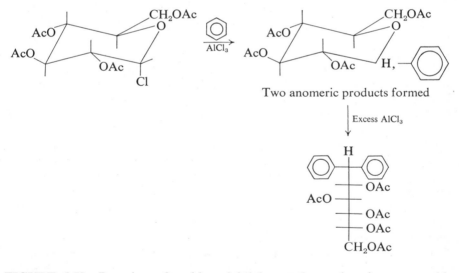

FIGURE 6.59   Reaction of α-chloro-2,3,4,6-tetra-*O*-acetyl-D-glucopyranoside with benzene and aluminum chloride.

These rather unusual compounds are not unknown and a wide variety of C-glycosides of natural occurrence have been described. These are predominantly of the flavone type although several have been described that have anthracene or similar aromatic substituents (Figure 6.60). All of these are polyhydroxylated in the ring as well, and in general, the carbohydrate residue is

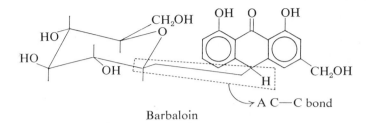

Barbaloin

FIGURE 6.60 A naturally occurring C-glycoside. The three-dimensional structure of this compound and many related C-glycosides have not as yet been elucidated.

attached directly to an aromatic ring. There have been few biochemical studies carried out in this area and the mechanism of formation of this particular type of carbon–carbon bond is currently unknown. It may be suggested that following the general mechanism of carbon–carbon bond synthesis, a good leaving group on the carbohydrate or one that makes the anomeric carbon a nucleophile is probably a prerequisite for the formation of such compounds. Both glucose and xylose have been demonstrated to be present in compounds of this type.

The reaction of substituted carbohydrates with Grignard reagents was described some time ago. The initial studies were complicated by the fact that the derivatives chosen for reaction were acetylated and, as might be expected, the Grignard reagent also reacted with the ester function to give the appropriate tertiary alcohol. Accordingly, before alkyl carbohydrate derivatives could be satisfactorily synthesized, it was necessary to employ very large molar proportions of the organometallic reagent. The derivatives most commonly studied have been the tetraacetyl aldonic acid lactones which, on reaction with aryl or alkyl magnesium halide, yield the substituted sugar alcohol. There is simultaneous cleavage of the ester bonds with the formation of quantitative yields of tertiary alcohol. Typical reactions are formulated in Figure 6.61. Support for the formulated structures came from independent synthesis of the aromatic derivatives by the Friedel-Crafts procedure described above.

The occurrence of branched chain carbohydrates in cardiac glycosides and several unusual 'nucleotides found in microorganisms has led to renewed interest in methods for their synthesis. The most convenient procedure for formation of a branched chain is to condense an appropriately protected carbonyl compound with a Grignard reagent, usually methyl magnesium iodide. Because most branches consist of a C-methyl group, many steric complications are avoided. Although it is obvious that the reaction will generate two isomers (new asymmetric center), it is generally found that the methyl group prefers the equatorial orientation.

It is also possible to carry out reaction of the Grignard reagent with the aldehydo form of the sugar acetates. The products expected from such a reaction are illustrated in Figure 6.62.

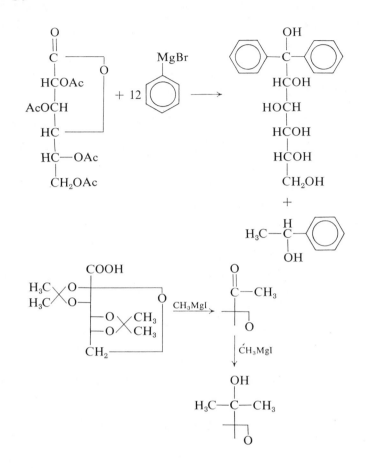

FIGURE 6.61 Grignard reaction of an acetylated carbohydrate lactone, or isopropylidene aldonic acid.

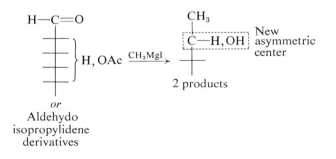

FIGURE 6.62 Grignard reaction with the aldehydo form of a carbohydrate to form a new asymmetric center.

The reaction of organo cadmium and other organometallics with acyl glycosyl halides has been studied [54]. In this case, the reaction is somewhat less extensive than with the corresponding Grignard reagents and only the replacement of the halide is observed. Thus, treatment of tetraacetyl-α-D-glucopyranosyl bromide with diphenyl cadmium yields tetraacetyl-β-D-gluco-pyranosyl benzene. As might be expected, the comparable α-mannose derivative yielded the corresponding α-D-mannopyranosyl benzene. However, employment of dibenzyl or dibutyl cadmium under similar conditions gave mixed acetals at carbon 1 and carbon 2 according to the reaction in Figure 6.63. In this case the reaction mechanism is somewhat more complicated than appears at first

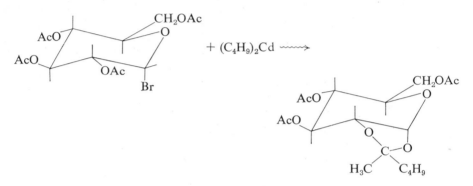

FIGURE 6.63   Reaction of α-bromo 2,3,4,6-tetraacetyl-D-glucopyranose with dibutyl cadmium.

glance. Because the halide and acetate on carbon 1 and 2 repel one another, the acetate would not normally be expected to participate as a neighboring group in this reaction as it does in the case of the α-manno compounds. The following mechanism is possible in which the first step involves ionization of the halide to give the C-1 carbonium ion, followed by attack of the carbonyl oxygen on this ion to give a cyclic intermediate, which in turn is alkylated on carbon by the alkyl organometallic (Figure 6.64).

The normal coupling reaction would predominate if the attacking R group was highly electronegative such as in diphenyl cadmium. However, with a less localized reagent, the second path might be followed although this might be a matter of the kinetic control of the various part reactions. The stereochemical support for this is rather weak. In the ionization step, it is possible that the species merely acts as an electron deficient carbon; otherwise, the coupling of the base should certainly give a mixture of anomers. The attack from underneath would give the observed β-phenyl product but even with the expected asymmetric induction, there should still be some appearance of the α anomer. These reactions have not been nearly as carefully worked out as have the comparable glycoside syntheses in which, although inversion predominates, careful work has shown the other anomer to be present as well. The reactions

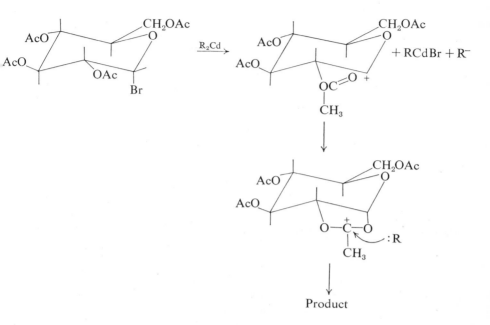

FIGURE 6.64 Mechanism of the reaction of dialkyl cadmium with aceto-bromoglucose.

with the dibenzyl and dibutyl cadmiums which presumably proceed through a cyclic carbonium ion may also undergo C substitution by addition of the entering anions from the top or the bottom of the plane. There is no obvious preference but only one isomer has been reported.

Lobry de Bruyn Transformation and Isomerase Reactions

The Lobry de Bruyn transformation, named after the investigator who first observed the reaction, is what is termed an isomerase type of reaction. This was first observed to occur when glucose was treated with alkali and the subsequent formation of fructose and mannose noted (Figure 6.65). Many other C-2 epimerizations of this general type and, in particular, aldose-ketose isomerizations and ketose C-3 epimerizations have been subsequently reported. In a general sense, these are classified as Lobry de Bruyn transformations and this label has been applied to isomerizations of α-hydroxy-aldehydes and ketones where the supposed common feature is the formation of an enediol intermediate. At least fifty such nonenzymatic reactions and several enzymatic reactions have been described. The marked similarity of the types of reactants and products suggests that the mechanism that prevails for the nonenzymatic transformations probably prevails for the enzymatic ones with the latter proceeding through a path with lower activation energy.

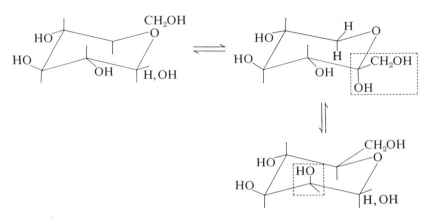

FIGURE 6.65   Schematic representation of the Lobry de Bruyn transformation.

As would be predicted, the nonenzymatic transformations are far less specific with respect to catalytic agents and conditions than are the enzymatic ones. Most of the chemical transformations are carried out in the presence of bases, such as calcium hydroxide or pyridine, although phosphate buffer, formate, acetate, and salts of alkaline earth metals have also been shown to catalyse the transformation. Different carbohydrates undergo the reaction to quite different extents, with the isomerization of uronic acids requiring more vigorous conditions than does the isomerization of the corresponding aldoses.

The nature of the reaction in the nonenzymatic systems results in less specificity with regard to product formation, and aldol condensations, and formation of metasaccharinic acids are common side reactions. In the presence of carboxyl groups, the anticipated lability of the hydrogen on the carbon α to the carboxyl may lead to epimerization at a center considerably removed from the potential reducing group as in the case of the C-5 epimerization of D-glucuronic acid.

The mechanism of this reaction has been intermittently investigated with developments in isotope techniques facilitating recent studies. Both kinetic analyses and exchange reactions have been employed to study this transformation. These will be briefly summarized.

Generic analyses of nonenzymatic transformations of this type have generally been difficult because of the relative lack of assay specificity and because of the prevalence of side reactions.

The treatment of 2,3,4,6-tetra-*O*-methyl-D-glucose with limewater yields 2,3,4,6-tetra-*O*-methyl-D-mannose but no methylated ketose is observed [56]. The reaction mixture shows a higher iodine absorption or reducing capacity than can be accounted for by the presence of aldoses alone, but upon acidification, the iodine uptake correlates with the amount of aldose present. The suggested formation of an intermediate with a double bond between carbon

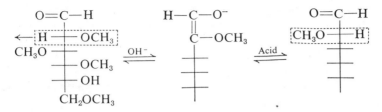

FIGURE 6.66 Reaction of 2,3,4,6-tetra-*O*-methyl-D-glucose with mild alkali
to form 2,3,4,6-tetra-*O*-methyl-D-mannose.

1 and 2 was shown to be incorrect (Figure 6.66). The 2,3,4-tri-*O*-methylated
pentoses, xylose, and arabinose behave analogously to the tetramethylglucose,
but upon acidification of these reaction mixtures, furfuraldehyde derivatives
were formed.
    In 1956, Tenner and Richards demonstrated the loss of the β-methyl group

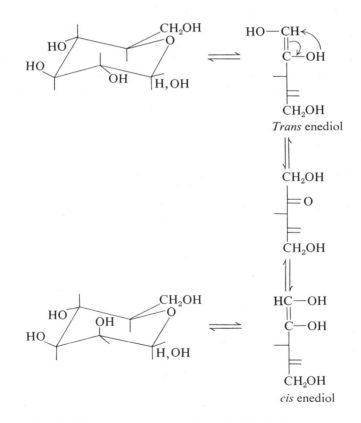

FIGURE 6.67 Proposed mechanism of the Lobry de Bruyn transformation
involving *cis* and *trans* enediol intermediates.

of 2,3-di-*O*-methyl-D-glucose in the presence of calcium hydroxide [57]. The intermediate product formed had a double bond between carbon 2 and carbon 3 and had apparently undergone β elimination.

D-glucose was found apparently to undergo no significant hydrogen exchange when reacted in deuterium oxide saturated with calcium hydroxide even though a 27 percent yield of ketose was observed. Upon increasing the temperature to 40 degrees, appreciable quantities of carbon bound deuterium were found in the product. A recent study by Topper reported the presence of 1.55 atoms of deuterium in the fructose isolated from a similar reaction mixture [58]. These two results are obviously incompatible but the latter finding was substantiated in another laboratory and is probably correct. Because exchange probably takes place to an extent greater than 1 deuterium atom per molecule, an additional carbon–hydrogen bond is labilized besides the one at carbon 1. Topper and Stetten also reacted D-glucose-1-D in H_2O and found that the product mannose contained 44 percent of the deuterium whereas the fructose retained 94 percent [59]. Accordingly, they postulated the mechanism illustrated in Figure 6.67. The intermediate enediol formulation had been suggested intermittently for some number of years, although several inconsistencies were not explained (particularly the epimerization of the tetra-*O*-methyl glucose).

The isomerization of DL-glyceraldehyde to dihydroxy acetone and of DL-glyceraldehyde to pyruvaldehyde in acetate buffers has been studied. The products were analyzed by periodate oxidation and the results were consistent

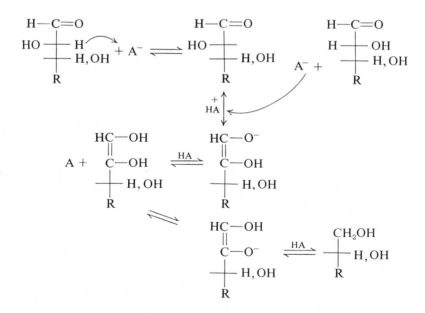

FIGURE 6.68   Preferred mechanism for the Lobry de Bruyn transformation which overcomes most of the objections present in the earlier formation.

with first-order kinetics with respect to acetic acid and acetate anion when glyceraldehyde was used as a starting material. Both calcium and barium ions catalyzed the reaction and were implicated in the rate expression. The equilibrium ratio was found to be 17 to 1 in favor of the ketose. The general mechanism shown in Figure 6.68 was postulated.

A further consideration of the mechanism is most profitably accomplished by reviewing some studies on enzymatic transformations of a similar type. The enzymic reactions exhibit rather remarkable specificity in that such enzymes are able to distinguish between the two protons on the 1-carbon atom of the reacting ketose (Figure 6.69) [60]. Studies using tritium-enriched water demonstrated that muscle aldolase catalyzes the replacement of one of the carbinol hydrogen atoms of dihydroxy acetone phosphate, whereas triosephosphate isomerase catalyzes the replacement of the other carbinol hydrogen (Figure 6.70)[61]. Similarly, in a study with phosphoglucose isomerase, it was shown

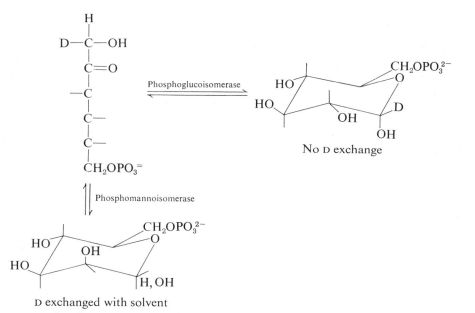

FIGURE 6.69 Enzymatic Lobry de Bruyn transformations. The enzymatic reactions are highly stereospecific as indicated by the ability of the enzyme to discriminate between the two proton substituents at position 1 of the ketose phosphate.

that D-glucose-1-D-6-phosphate suffered no loss of deuterium to solvent, but in the presence of phosphoglucose isomerase *and* phosphomannose isomerase, exchange did occur. A *cis* and *trans* enediol mechanism similar to the one proposed for the nonenzymatic transformation was proposed for the last reaction

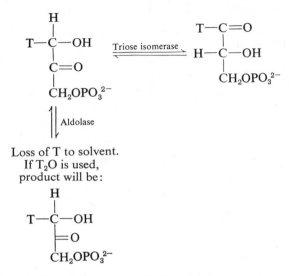

FIGURE 6.70 Ability of enzyme to distinguish between two protons present at carbon 1 of a triose sugar. In one case, the tritium is lost to the solvent whereas, in the other case, it is retained in the glyceraldehyde product. Aldolase catalyzes the condensation of dihydroxy acetone phosphate with quite a number of different aldehydes.

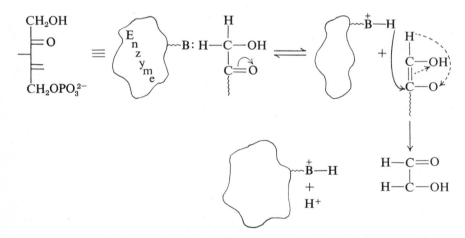

In large solvent pool, H^+ is lost by this mechanism.

FIGURE 6.71 Schematic representation of the Lobry de Bruyn transformation as it may take place in the surface of an enzyme.

but did not specify which intermediate might go with which reaction. This mechanism has been strongly criticized (in part on insufficient grounds although the critique is probably generally valid) because the C-2 epimerization of 2,3,4,6-

tetra-O-methyl glucose is incompatible with such a mechanism. It is also true that neither epimerizations nor isomerizations require such *cis* and *trans* enediol intermediates. Based on studies with isotopically labeled carbohydrates, a proposed conjugate acid-enzyme-enediol substrate mechanism was suggested (Figure 6.71). According to this proposal, both exchange and transfer of the hydrogen are accounted for and the ratios of exchange and transfer are independent of both substrate and enzyme concentration. When the log of the exchange transfer ratio is plotted against the reciprocal of the reaction temperature, a straight line is obtained, and therefore, the ratio is probably reducible to a ratio of constants as would be expected from the above mechanism. At most, only one in six atoms of hydrogen exchange in the phosphoglucose isomerization and there is no mixing of the proton with even one other proton on the enzyme. Several proposals have been advanced to implicate groups on the enzyme surface as potential proton acceptors. It is interesting to note that very

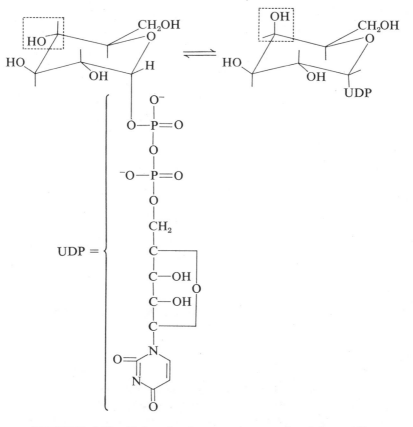

FIGURE 6.72   Epimerization reaction catalyzed by uridine diphosphoglucose-4-epimerase.

few of the studies of this reaction have made any attempt to rationalize the reactions on the basis of the cyclic forms of the carbohydrate. This seems rather strange particularly since several carbohydrate epimerizations are known to take place wherein the open chain form is not present and other mechanistic considerations must apply. In particular, consider a simple epimerization such as that catalyzed by uridine diphospho-D-glucose-4-epimerase (Figure 6.72). Removal of a proton from carbon 4 of the glucose derivative will yield an intermediate which, although enolic in form, can also exist as a dihydropyran-type ring structure. Should this intermediate occur, the carbons involved in the double bond would be planar or very nearly planar. Therefore, without the necessity to invoke ionization of an enol or formation of a free carbonyl group in the carbohydrate, it would be possible for the proton to be returned to the substrate via a route that will produce the opposite stereochemistry at the center involved (Figure 6.73). A very pertinent study of this reaction has recently

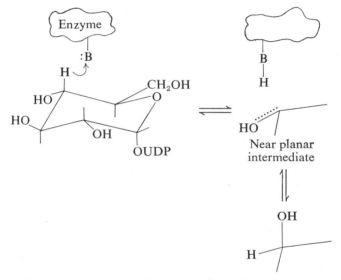

No exchange occurs. Entire reaction takes place on enzyme surface.

FIGURE 6.73 Schematic representation of the epimerase reaction on the enzyme surface.

been carried out using glucose specifically tritiated at the 4 position [62]. In this study it was shown that tritium was *not lost from the 4 position* during the over-all enzymatic reaction. Accordingly, it is not possible to envision mechanisms wherein exchange of this proton is mandatory, although exchange that occurs in similar nonenzymatic reactions may still occur due to the nature of the intermediates. It was also shown that tritium is removed from position 4 *during the course of the enzymatic reaction*, perhaps by attachment to the pyridine nucleotide present on the enzyme surface. However, *this same tritium is returned to the identical carbon* so that no net exchange is noted even though a planar intermediate has been formed. In a similar way, a mechanism can be proposed for the Lobry de Bruyn transformation which does not necessarily require the formation of open chain forms, as postulated by several workers. Naturally, the isomerization of trioses and tetroses will go in the open chain form since the ring forms are not present in such structures. Nevertheless, the labilization of hydrogen in the 6-membered ring and the formation of planar intermediates will satisfactorily account for much of the data that has been obtained.

The possible participation of histidine residues or pyridine nucleotide on the enzyme surface seems likely. The ability of these compounds to catalyze the nonenzymatic transformations is unknown, but the participation of imidazole compounds in charge transfer reactions is well known and particularly pertinent

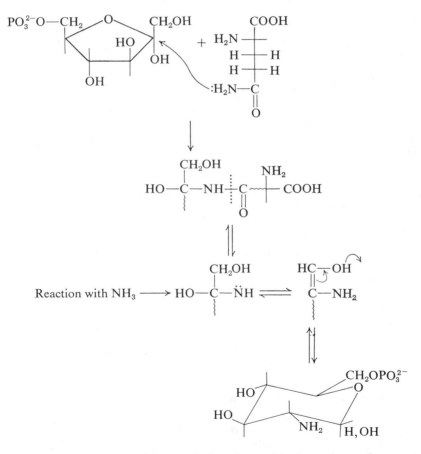

FIGURE 6.74 Reaction of fructose-6-phosphate with glutamine and suggested mechanism.

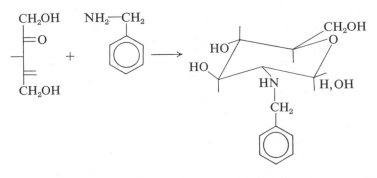

FIGURE 6.75   Reaction of fructose with benzylamine to form
N-benzylglucosamine.

in the chemistry of pyridinium ring compounds. Their reactions as ion pairs
may serve to explain the role of the pyridine nucleotide in the enzymatic transformation. Whether these types of reactions are pertinent to the epimerization
of carbohydrates generally or could serve as more appropriate models for the
Lobry de Bruyn transformation has not been established at the present time.

A slightly different example of this type of reaction is in the enzymatic
synthesis of glucosamine-6-phosphate from fructose-6-phosphate and ammonia in one case or from fructose-6-phosphate and glutamine in the other [63].
The proposed mechanisms for these reactions are indicated in Figure 6.74. In
the first case, with no driving force (hydrolysis of glutamine) present in the
reaction, the equilibrium is far in favor of ketose formation, whereas the second
reaction is essentially irreversible in favor of hexosamine formation. The condensation of fructose with benzylamine followed by treatment with acetic acid
leads to the formation of *N*-benzylglucosamine in good yields (Figure 6.75)
[64]. A mechanism similar to the ammonia reaction above might be expected.

CHAPTER 7

Reactions of Chain Hydroxyls

7.1 Introduction

The types of reactions that can be carried out at the chain hydroxyl functions include esterification, etherification, oxidation, reduction, cyclic derivative formation, and replacement (generally displacement) of the hydroxyl group by other functional groups.

As is the case with much of organic chemistry, the reactions can be roughly subdivided into two broad groups, those primarily concerned with synthetic problems and those employed for structural analysis. The similarity of the functional groups (all hydroxyl) frequently requires selective masking or blocking of several of these so that appropriate or desired transformations may be carried out at a specific locus. By the same token, structural analysis frequently depends on a knowledge of reaction path given that one or another position is substituted.

The general type of information desired can be summarized as follows:

1. Suitability of a given derivative in view of contemplated subsequent reactions. For example, acetoxy groups are relatively acid stable, tosyloxy groups are good "leavers," that is, leaving groups, and are easily displaced; benzyl ethers may be cleaved by hydrogenolysis, and so on.

2. Choice of conditions for carrying out a given reaction. Possible steric and mechanistic control.

3. Relative reactivities of hydroxyl groups toward a given reagent. Possible selectivity of substitution.

4. Ability of groups already present (including the ring oxygen) to influence (steric, electronic) incoming substituents.

5. Likelihood of neighboring group participation and methods of controlling (either promoting or inhibiting) this.

6. In a practical sense, problems of yield, ease of isolation and purification, control of byproduct formation, and so on, are all serious considerations. Hopefully, proper design of the reaction sequence will reduce these to readily manageable proportions.

TABLE 7.1 Summary of ester blocking groups employed in carbohydrate reactions.

REACTION	REAGENT AND CONDITIONS	SOLVENT	CATALYST	SELECTIVITY
Esterification[a]	Ac$_2$O, reflux	None	NaOAc	Equatorial anomer predominant.
	Ac$_2$O, 0°	Pyridine	None	Configuration at C-1 retained.
	Ac$_2$O, 0–30°	HOAc	Lewis acid (ZnCl$_2$, H$_2$SO$_4$)	Axial anomer predominant.
	$\overset{O}{\overset{\|\|}{CH_3C}}$—Cl, 20°	Pyridine	None	1 halo sugar formed.
	$CH_3\overset{O}{\overset{\|\|}{C}}$—Br	Pyridine	None	1 halo sugar formed.
	CH_3OSO_2Cl	Tertiary amine (Pyridine)		All positions react.
	H_3C—⟨C$_6$H$_4$⟩—OSO$_2$Cl	Tertiary amine (Pyridine)		Selectivity for C-6 possible under controlled conditions.
	C$_6$H$_5$—$\overset{O}{\overset{\|\|}{C}}$—Cl	Tertiary amine (Pyridine)		Selectivity for C-6 possible under controlled conditions.
	(F$_3$C—CO)$_2$O	Tertiary amine (Pyridine)	NaOH	Very readily removed group.
	$\overset{O}{\overset{\|\|}{Cl-C}}$—$\overset{O}{\overset{\|\|}{C}}$—Cl	Tertiary amine (Pyridine)	NaOH	Cyclic ester product. Sterically determined.
	C$_2$H$_5$—O—$\overset{O}{\overset{\|\|}{C}}$—Cl, 0°	Pyridine	or NaOH	All positions react.
	CS$_2$ (xanthate)		NaOH	Position 2 favored.
	N$_2$O$_5$ or H$_2$SO$_4$·HNO$_3$, 0°	CCl$_4$	...	Anomeric configuration retained, all positions react.
	P$_2$O$_5$ or H$_3$PO$_4$·P$_2$O$_5$	None		All positions react.
	HOSO$_2$—Cl	CHCl$_3$	Pyridine	All positions react.
	(C$_2$H$_5$)$_3$N—SO$_3$	CHCl$_3$	Pyridine	C-6 selectivity possible.

[a] Occasional equatorial selectivity possible; bulky reagents can generally be made to react preferentially at C-6 using stoichiometric amounts of

TABLE 7.2 Ether forming reactions.

REACTION	REAGENT AND CONDITIONS[a]	SOLVENT	CATALYST	SELECTIVITY[b]
Etherification	$(CH_3)_2SO_4$, cold	NaOH	...	All positions react. Steric hindrance common. Protection of C-1 desirable common for polysaccharides.
	CH_3I, reflux	CH_3OH	Ag_2O	C-1 protection necessary. All positions react.
	CH_3I, reflux	CH_3OH	$TlOH$ or $TlOC_2H_5$	All positions react.
	CH_3I, Room temperature	NH_3, then inert solvent	$NaNH_2$	Good for polyols.
	CH_3I, Room temperature	$(CH_3)_2S \rightarrow 0°$	BaO	Current method of choice for simple sugars and derivatives.
	$(C_6H_5)_3$C—Cl, Room temperature	$CHCl_3$ pyridine	Pyridine	Selective for C-6; very easily removed.
	$C_6H_5CH_2Cl$, Room temperature	Inert	Pyridine NaOH or NaH	Selective for C-6; very easily removed.
	CH_2N_2, 0°[c]	Ether	Pyridine NaOH	Partial methylation of most sugars.
	H_3C—C_6H_4—OSO_2OH (dihydropyran derivative)	$CHCl_3$	NaOH	Ether adduct. Equatorial preferred. Base stable.

[a] Several specialized etherifying agents are utilized in the derivatization of cellulose for commercial use. Others that should be useful but have been little studied include t-butyl and trimethylsilyl (widely used in gas-liquid chromatography but not extensively employed in synthetic work).

[b] As usual, equatorial sites are more reactive. Even for these steric hindrance may assume considerable proportions. Thus, the C-3 hydroxyl in cellulose is quite difficult to methylate.

[c] A highly polar, nonsolvating solvent.

197

TABLE 7.3 Summary of oxidation reactions.

OXIDATION	REAGENT AND CONDITIONS	SOLVENT	CATALYST	SELECTIVITY
C—C cleavage	HIO_4, dark, 0° Room temperature	Aqueous	None	1,2 diols: α-OH aldehydes or ketones, active CH_2 groupings, and so on. See detailed discussion.
C—C cleavage	$Pb(OAc)_4$ 60°	HAc	...	Similar to above. Rate more sensitive to stereochemistry. See detailed discussion.
$\underset{\vert}{\overset{\vert}{H-C-OH}} \rightarrow \overset{\vert}{C}=O$	CrO_3 · (pyridine)	Pyridine		Yields low. Little steric data available.
$\underset{\vert}{\overset{\vert}{H-C-OH}} \rightarrow \overset{\vert}{C}=O$	Pt, O_2, 30–80°	Alcohol, aqueous	Pt	Axial OH (attack on equatorial hydrogen).
$\underset{\vert}{\overset{\vert}{H-C-OH}} \rightarrow \overset{\vert}{C}=O$	Enzymatic	Aqueous	Enzyme	Axial OH (attack on equatorial hydrogen) (cyclitol only).
$CH_2OH \rightarrow COOH$	Pt, O_2	Aqueous	Pt	C-1 protection necessary. Axial ring OH also susceptible.
$CH_2OH \rightarrow COOH$	N_2O_4 or HNO_3	Inert	...	Used to prepare oxidized celluloses or dicarboxylic acids.
$CH_2OH \rightarrow COOH$	DPN^+, Enzymatic	Aqueous	Enzymatic	High specificity. Best known is UDP-glucose dehydrogenase.

198

TABLE 7.4 Summary of reactions leading to cyclic derivative formation.

CYCLIC DERIVATIVE	REAGENT AND CONDITIONS	SOLVENT	CATALYST	SELECTIVITY
Epoxide (3-membered ring)	OCH_3 or OH on suitable ester or halide (latter generally C-6 only)	CH_3OH	...	Glucoside necessary; favorable stereochemistry—*trans* diaxial. *Trans* diequatorial exocyclic or adjacent carbons.
Anhydro (5- or 6-membered ring)	HNO_2 on 2-amino aldose, aqueous	H_2O	...	2,5 anhydro sugars via ionic mechanism through diazo intermediate.
Anhydro (5- or 6-membered ring)	H_2SO_4, heat: alditols	Acid	Acid	Dehydration and ring closure.
Anhydro (5- or 6-membered ring)	Alkali on suitable derivative (6-tosylate most common)	CH_3OH or similar	Base	3,6 anhydro sugars. 1,6 anhydro from base catalyzed hydrolysis of phenylglycosides.
Acetal	CH_3CHO ⟨C$_6$H$_5$CHO⟩	Inert	Acid	Adjacent *cis* OH; 5-membered ring favored. See detailed discussion.
Acetal		Inert	Acid	4,6 acetal most common.
Carbonate	$O{=}CCl_2$	$CHCl_3$ or pyridine	Tertiary amine	5-membered ring acetal most common.
Thiocarbonate	CS_2	...	$Ba(OH)_2$	5,6 cyclic furanosides or *cis* adjacent OH.
Quinone adduct	⟨phenanthrenequinone structure⟩	Inert	*hv*	Adds to double bonds. Remove by ozonization, transesterification.

199

TABLE 7.5

Relative efficiency of nucleophiles.

DISPLACING AGENT[d]	COMPOUND	REMARKS
$\begin{array}{c} O \\ \parallel \\ C-O^- \end{array}$ (benzene ring) in DMF[a]	Methyl-2,3-di-*O*-benzoyl 4,6-di-*O*-(*p*-tolylsulfonyl)[b] α-D-galactopyranoside	Inversion at C-4 (endocyclic) as well as displacement at C-6.
$\begin{array}{c} O \\ \parallel \\ C-O^- \end{array}$ (benzene ring) in DMF	1,2,4,6-tetra-*O*-benzoyl 3-*O*-tosyl β-D-glucopyranoside	Allose derivatives; furanose analog unreactive.
NH₂NH₂	Methyl-2-*O*-tosyl 3,5,6 tri-*O*-benzoyl α-D-glucofuranose	Reduction with Raney-Nickel-H₂ and hydrolysis yield 2-deoxy 2-amino D-mannose.
OAc⁻ in MeOCH₂CH₂OH	Methyl 3-deoxy 3-acetamido 2,4 di-*O*-(methanesulfonyl)[c] D-xylopyranoside	Inversion at C-2 *and* C-4 due to participation of acetamido group.
NaN₃ in DMF	Methyl 2,3,6 tri-*O*-benzoyl 4-*O*-mesyl α-D-galactopyranoside	Reduction of azide product produces 4-amino glucose derivative.
Heat (internal)	Methyl 3,5,6 tri-*O*-benzoyl 4-*O*-mesyl 2-*O*-methyl D-gluconate	C-4 mesyl displaced by carbonyl oxygen to give galactonolactone derivative.

[a] Dimethyl formamide.
[b] Tosyl.
[c] Mesyl.

[d] Anions such as $CH_3\overset{\displaystyle O}{\overset{\displaystyle \parallel}{C}}\!-\!S^-$, 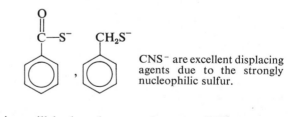 CNS⁻ are excellent displacing agents due to the strongly nucleophilic sulfur.

The subsequent discussion will be based, as much as possible, on general principles with specific illustrative examples.

Tables 7.1–7.5 summarize pertinent reactions. Those with specific steric requirements are indicated. The choice of reagents will depend not only on possible mechanism control, but ease of removal, other groups present, and so on.

7.2 General Properties of Displacement Reactions

The displacement of a group, which is usually termed the leaving group, from a carbon atom due to the attack of a nucleophile on that carbon may be represented by the formulation in Figure 7.1. In many cases, it is not necessary

$$A: + C:L \longrightarrow A:C + :L$$

When a catalyst is present (E for electrophilic catalyst)

$$A: + C:L + E \xrightarrow{\text{slow}} (A: \cdots C \cdots L: \cdots E)$$

$$\downarrow \text{fast}$$

$$\text{Product}$$

FIGURE 7.1 Schematic representation of a bimolecular displacement reaction in the presence and absence of catalysts.

for this reaction to be catalyzed because either the departing group has a sufficiently low affinity for the carbon, or the attacking nucleophile is a sufficiently electronegative agent so as to provide enough driving force for the displacement to take place. It is frequently necessary, however, to add some catalyst which itself is electrophilic and serves to assist or facilitate the departure of the leaving group. The over-all driving force of the reaction under such conditions is a combination of the ability of the nucleophile to attack the carbon center and the ability of the electrophilic catalyst to assist dissociation of the group originally present. Catalysts that are most commonly employed in the carbohydrate field include polar solvents, Lewis acids, heavy metal ions, and tertiary amine bases.

Numerous attempts have been made in the field of organic chemistry to correlate the rate of a given reaction with the properties of the entering and the leaving group and with the "pulling" ability of the electrophile present. An empirical relationship has been described which is shown as follows [1]:

$$\ln \frac{K}{K_0} = nS_n + eS_e \tag{7.1}$$

In this expression, K is the rate of the reaction and K_0 is the rate in some standard state or standard conditions of solvent and temperature. The terms n and e depend on the nature of the nucleophile and the electrophile, respectively, and the terms S_n and S_e relate to the push and pull of the nucleophile and the electrophile. Thus, the right-hand side of the equation contains four parameters which serve to define the system in a reasonably complete manner.[1] The parameters are assigned arbitrary values for the so-called standard system and

---

[1] Four parameters probably permit any conditions to be satisfied but this many are frequently necessary to fit experimental data to "theory."

whereas these may be in considerable error from any absolute assignment, the equation is quite useful for predicting the effects of changes in any of these on the reaction rate. According to the terms, in reactions where the nucleophile is very strong, this factor is large compared to that involving the electrophile. Under such conditions it could be expected that the reaction will proceed with second-order kinetics or by a bimolecular mechanism, and that inversion will take place at the carbon under consideration. Therefore, for a given substrate the rate will be primarily dependent on the nucleophilicity of the entering group and not nearly so dependent on the nature of the solvent and the possible addition of a facilitating catalyst.

The reverse of the above is true where a poor nucleophile is employed as the displacing agent. In this case, the requirement is that the electrophilic pull must be large for the reaction to proceed at a significant rate. Under these conditions, first-order kinetics may apply, the control of stereochemistry may not be so great and suitable choice of both solvent and catalysts are probably necessary in order to insure that the reaction goes at a reasonable speed. The nucleophilic constants for several systems are listed in Table 7.6. The constant is

TABLE 7.6

Relative efficiency of nucleophiles.

NUCLEOPHILE	n
OAc^-	2.7
Cl^-	3.0
Br^-	3.9
N_3^-	4.0
OH^-	4.2
SCN^-	4.8
I^-	5.0
$SO_3^=$	5.1
HS^-	5.1
$S_2O_3^=$	6.4

related to a standard where S is 1.0 for methyl bromide in water [2]. Examination of the table reveals several useful features:

1. There is a very considerable difference in nucleophilicity between anions.

2. Many sulfur-containing anions are very good nucleophiles, particularly those of anionic nature.

3. Iodide and azide are also very strong nucleophiles.

This table can be used as a relative assessment of the ability of groups to interact; those with higher nucleophilic constants might reasonably be expected to displace those with lower ones.

The transition state theory for nucleophilic displacements demands a relatively planar intermediate wherein the entering nucleophile and the leaving group are coplanar and backside attack is mandatory, as depicted in Figure 7.2. This will result in a Walden inversion of the carbon atom, and during the transition state, the crowding of the atoms or molecules together becomes very great. Therefore, if particularly bulky or polar groups are present at R_1, R_2, or R_3 as depicted in the diagram, it is to be expected that displacements at such a

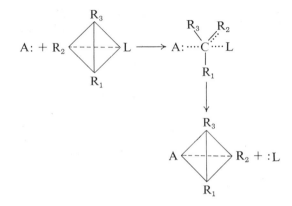

FIGURE 7.2   Stereochemical representation of a bimolecular displacement reaction.

carbon will be correspondingly more difficult. It is also true that as substituents on carbon increase, the tendency is for ionic mechanisms to predominate. This is at least partly due to the additional stability of tertiary carbonium ions as opposed to primary or secondary carbonium ions.

One of the features that will make the departing group a good leaving group relates to the *pK* of its conjugate acid, which should be as low as is practicable. In this case, the ion that is generated is stable and the polarizability of the ion or of the leaving group permits effective charge separation in the transition state. The possible energy to be derived from solvation of the leaving group may also assist in lowering the energy barrier needed to achieve the desired transition state. This is well illustrated in the relative displacement order of halogens where iodine is better than bromine which in turn is better than chlorine; the highly polarizable iodine is the best leaving group. The most commonly encountered functional group in the carbohydrate field, hydroxyl, is not readily displaced (*pKa* of water is 15.7) but conversion of the hydroxyl to a tosyl or mesyl ester results in formation of a good leaving group because the resultant anion has a low *pK*. Substitution of the aromatic ring with electron-withdrawing groups such as bromo or nitro make these even better leaving groups than the parent.

It is possible in carbohydrate systems to draw some distinction between displacement reactions carried out at the primary alcohol position (C-6) and those carried out at secondary positions. These distinctions are not only steric with considerations of the interference by the ring itself but will also reflect the relative crowding around the individual atoms with reactions much more readily effected at the primary position than at the secondary positions. A cursory inspection of leaving group potential might suggest design of synthetic sequences requiring the introduction of halogen into the molecule. However,

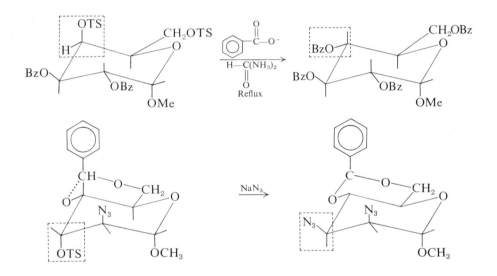

FIGURE 7.3 Displacement of a tosyloxy group by benzoate ion or by sodium azide in dimethyl formamide. Both displacing agents are good nucleophiles.

the replacement of a secondary hydroxyl by halogen in the chain or in the ring is extremely difficult and accordingly these are rarely employed especially since a suitable sulfonate ester usually provides a satisfactory derivative. It is also true that displacements at secondary hydroxyls require not only good leaving groups but very effective nucleophiles due to the additional crowding imposed both by the ring and by the adjacent carbon atoms. The requisite transition state in any case is going to depend upon the flexibility of the ring system. Because near planarity is required in this step, if fused rings are present or if the geometry of the molecule is such that the transition state cannot be accommodated without excessive distortion, then these displacements will either not take place or will take place with concomitant rupture of other sensitive bonds. When other routes are not available, it may be necessary to use severe forcing conditions, high boiling solvents, and so on. It is not to be expected that high yields of product will result. Successful displacements by azide and benzoate ions have been carried out at secondary hydroxyls and a consideration of the relative nucleophilicity of these groups would predict (post-facto) these results. Typical reactions are illustrated in Figure 7.3 [3, 4].

As might be expected from Equation (7.1), the nature of the solvent has a very considerable effect on the outcome of such reactions. The primary effect usually is in lowering of the activation energy, and thus, the over-all rate of the reaction increases. The theory originally proposed states that the rate of bimolecular displacement or SN_2 reactions is only slightly affected by a change of solvent and is retarded by changes or increases in ion solvating power. This is certainly valid when relatively protic solvents or those containing dipoles such

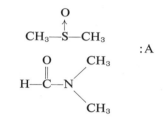

as opposed to

FIGURE 7.4   Highly polar nonsolvating solvents, dimethyl sulfoxide and dimethyl formamide.

as water or alcohol are present. However, when polar nonprotic solvents are considered, the solvent theory is not in agreement with observed reaction rate increases. This is particularly true for solvents such as dimethyl formamide and dimethyl sulfoxide. Solvents such as acetonitrile and nitromethane can also be appreciably "faster" than protic solvents especially if the nucleophile is small and of relatively low polarizability. The explanation of this effect is that the entering ion or anion is relatively poorly solvated even though the dipole moment of the solvent may be extremely high (as in the case of dimethyl sulfoxide). The poor solvation may be due to steric resistance because the bulky dipoles present simply may not be able to surround the nucleophile (Figure 7.4). As a result of this, steric repulsion of the entering nucleophile is appreciably lessened because the "solvent shell" does not accompany the ion. Such a nucleophile will exist in a relatively higher energy state than the corresponding nucleophile in a solvating or protic solvent and thus the reaction may proceed by a path with a lower activation energy. A particularly useful solvent that has been employed in the steroid series to effect displacements by acetate, azide, bromide, chloride, or fluoride at carbon 3 and carbon 17 is 1-methyl 2-pyrrolidinone (Figure 7.5). This solvent is particularly effective (it is obviously related

FIGURE 7.5 1-methyl 2-pyrrolidinone, a highly polar solvent not yet
extensively employed in the carbohydrate field.

to dimethyl formamide) because it does not have a sensitive amide group which
may be involved in side reactions. The possible utility of this solvent in the
carbohydrate field has not as yet been extensively investigated.

The general advantages of displacement reactions that can be mechanisti-
cally controlled to some extent are immediately obvious in the carbohydrate
field, where control over stereochemistry is desirable whenever possible. Al-

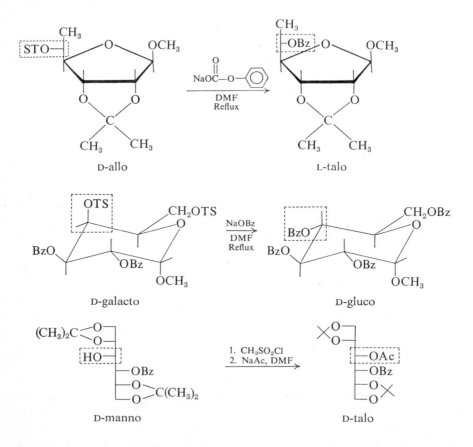

FIGURE 7.6   Selected displacement reactions utilizing benzoate or acetate as
the displacing agents.

though contemporary separation techniques now make the resolution of epimeric mixtures generally a practicable achievement, failure to exert such control may result in high yields of unwanted isomers or particularly annoying separation problems. At the same time, the ability to control the steric course of the reaction permits selection of optimal synthetic routes to relatively rare or unavailable sugars on the basis of predictable reaction sequences.

$$\text{CH}_2\text{OTS} \xrightarrow{\text{KSAc}} \text{CH}_2\text{SAc}$$

Primary or exocyclic tosyl best

FIGURE 7.7 Displacement of tosyloxy function by thioacetate.

There are numerous examples of this type of steric control. These include negative ones, such as the addition of cyanide to arabinose resulting in the predominant formation of the manno rather than the gluco isomer. This is readily understood and predictable now although perhaps somewhat unexpected when the original reactions were carried out. Some specific examples of positive steric control are illustrated in Figure 7.6 [5].

The introduction of sulfur into the ring is generally accomplished by means of displacement reactions. Tosyl groups are displaced by thioacetate in refluxing dimethylformamide (Figure 7.7) [6]. Secondary tosyls can also be displaced using particularly nucleophilic sulfur derivatives such as S-benzyl compounds. Epoxide rings can be opened with the usual *trans* diaxial stereochemistry predominating. Treatment of 2,3 anhydro 4,6 benzylidene methyl α-D-altro-pyranoside with NaSMe yields the 2-S-methyl derivative (Figure 7.8) [7]. The

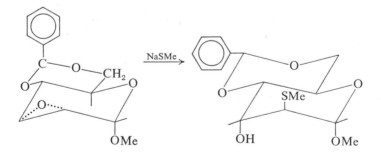

FIGURE 7.8 Reaction of an epoxide with sodium thiomethylate.

treatment of similar epoxides with thiourea proceeds with inversion; the converse of this reaction also takes place (Figure 7.9).

The thiourethane function has been used as a neighboring group particularly in the presence of nitrogen substituents which appear to facilitate participation (Figure 7.10) [8].

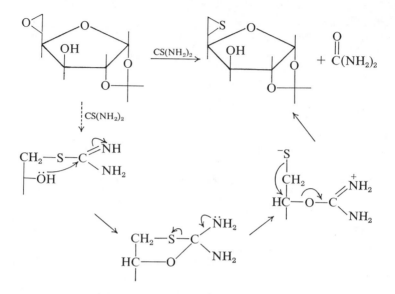

FIGURE 7.9   Reaction of epoxides with thiourea.

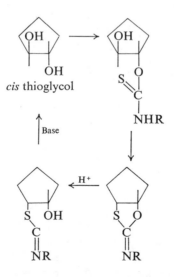

FIGURE 7.10   Use of the thiourethane function as a neighboring group.

7.3 Acyl Migrations and Neighboring Group Reactions Leading to Anhydro Sugars

The observation that treatment of partially acetylated sugars with acid catalysts resulted in migration of acyl groups was made initially by Emil Fischer. He was primarily concerned with intramolecular transesterification and demonstrated that this type of acyl migration could occur. A typical reaction is illustrated in Figure 7.11. The possibility of migration of acyl groups during

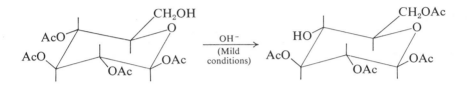

FIGURE 7.11   Reaction of 1,2,3,4-tetra-*O*-acetyl-β-D-glucopyranose with alkali under mild conditions permitting migration of the acetoxy group from carbon 4 to carbon 6.

either acid catalyzed glycoside formation or during attempts to block free hydroxyls using acid catalysis has been extensively investigated. There are several common features for all such internal transesterifications and most mechanisms that have been proposed involve the formation of cyclic intermediates of the orthoester type as illustrated in Figure 7.12 [9].

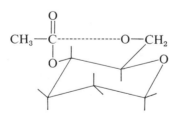

FIGURE 7.12   Closed cyclic intermediate involved in acetyl migration.

Migrations generally occur in the direction of the primary hydroxyl group, should this be free. This is particularly true for acetyl migrations although examples of benzoyl migrations during removal of isopropylidene blocking groups from the primary alcohol position have also been recorded. A satisfactory synthesis of 6-benzoyl 1,2 isopropylidene glucofuranose can be carried out by this means (Figure 7.13).

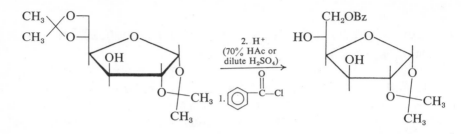

FIGURE 7.13   Synthesis of 6-benzoyl 1,2 isopropylidene D-glucofuranose via an acyl migration sequence.

If the proposed mechanism is correct, then for migration to take place, the formation of the cyclic orthoester must proceed with little or no steric . strain. This is feasible when there is a *cis* relationship between the acyloxy

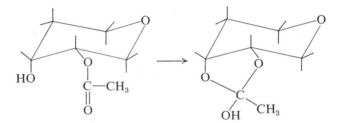

FIGURE 7.14   Formation of 5-membered ring intermediate by the reaction of an acetoxy function with a cis hydroxyl on an adjacent carbon.

group that is migrating and the neighboring hydroxyl (Figure 7.14). If there is a *trans* relationship, a neighboring group reaction may occur with internal displacement by intramolecular attack of the carbonyl oxygen of the acyl function

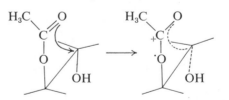

FIGURE 7.15   Rear attack of the carbonyl oxygen of the acetoxy function leading to the displacement of the group present on the adjacent carbon.

leading to inversion at that particular center (Figure 7.15). Several examples of this type of displacement reaction are known and include reactions leading to anhydro sugar formation.

The synthesis of anhydro sugars having ethylene oxide type rings is of considerable interest because of the versatility of these derivatives as intermediates for the synthesis of amino sugars, thio sugars, methylated sugars, and so on. Typical reactions are illustrated in Figure 7.16. The well-defined stereochemistry of the opening of the epoxide ring, which leads to a *trans* configuration of the hydroxyl and incoming group (Fuerst-Plattner rule), has permitted synthesis of several rare sugars [10].

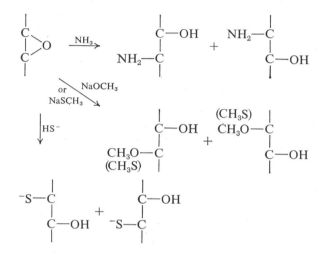

FIGURE 7.16   Ring openings reactions of the epoxides.

Several examples of participation reactions that lead to the formation of epoxide rings may be given. The most common method of epoxide formation involves substitution of an accessible hydroxyl by what we have previously termed a good leaving group. The reagent most commonly employed for this type of substitution prior to elimination reaction has been *p*-toluenesulfonyl (tosyl) chloride (Figure 7.17). This reagent combines the advantages of ease of reaction and ready displacement of the product ester. The general concepts of group participation suggest that hydroxyl groups are relatively poor neighbors. However, the proximity of the oxygen to the adjacent carbon, coupled with the substitution which renders that carbon particularly electron deficient, provides very favorable conditions for internal attack. Treatment of tosylated sugars in alkali leads to a dissociation of the proton from the hydroxyl function and attack by the oxygen on the positive carbon bearing the tosyloxy substituent (Figure 7.18). The replacement generally goes quite smoothly to yield the epoxide in crystalline form. In cases where apparent choice between 3 and 5 or 6-membered rings exist, we might predict that formation of the larger ring would predominate. However, the rate of formation of the 3-membered ring is appreciably faster than that of the 5- or 6-membered ring; this is the initial product. If the reaction conditions or stereochemistry are such as to facilitate ring

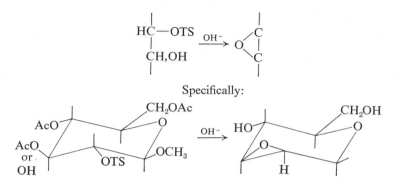

FIGURE 7.17 Formation of epoxides by treatment of a tosylates with alkali.

opening or internal attack of the epoxide, then the 5- or 6-membered ring form may be the prevalent final product.

The formation of 3-membered rings of the ethylene oxide type requires planarity for the 3-membered ring and, in situations where such a configuration is prohibited, 3-membered ring formation will generally not take place. In the case of 5,6 anhydro 1,2 isopropylidene α-D-glucofuranose, there is relatively little tendency for the C-3 hydroxyl to attack the anhydro ring (Figure 7.19). However, the 5,6 ditosyl compound on treatment with alkali undergoes elimination of the tosyloxy group via displacement from the C-3 hydroxyl to yield the 3,6 anhydro derivative [11]. It is probable that the reaction course in this case involves some steric restriction. It seems reasonable that the relatively free rotation of the tosyloxy groups which are exocyclic may contribute to a favorable conformation for the displacement reaction. Certainly, it could not be argued that the hydroxyl group itself is a very efficient displacer although the tosyl group is a good leaver.

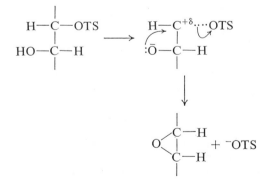

FIGURE 7.18 Mechanism of epoxide formation by tosyl displacement.

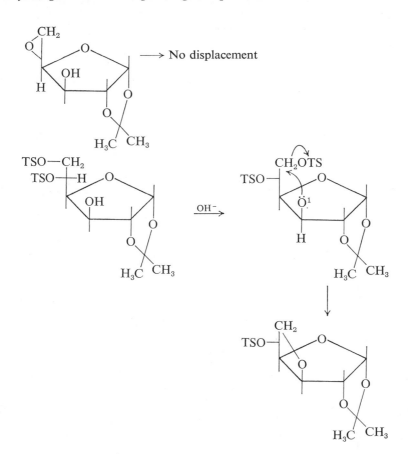

FIGURE 7.19 Formation of a 3,6-anhydro sugar produced by displacement of a primary tosyloxy group by the hydroxyl group at carbon 3.

The alkaline degradation of phenyl β-D-glucopyranosides is also accompanied by an elimination reaction of the phenyl group to yield an anhydro sugar product. One mechanism suggested involves an attack by the primary hydroxyl group (carbon 6) on the asymmetric center at C-1 with internal displacement of the phenyl group yielding a 1-6 anhydro sugar (Figure 7.20) [12].

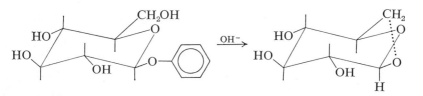

FIGURE 7.20 Formation of 1,6-anhydro sugars in hydrolysis of aryl glucosides.

Nevertheless, although this mechanism seems reasonable and does account for the nature of the final product, it is quite possible that participation by the C-2 hydroxyl may take place, facilitating the departure of the phenyl group (Figure 7.21). From the above, it is clear that this can only occur when the hydroxyl at C-2 is *trans* to the phenyl group at C-1.

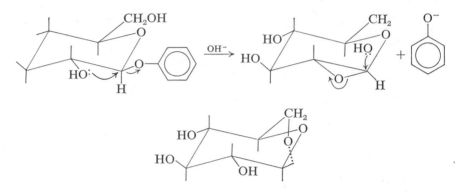

FIGURE 7.21   Mechanism of formation of 1,6-anhydro sugars involving participation of the hydroxyl group at carbon 2.

Although most glycosyl halide reactions take place by ionic mechanisms (discussed in Chapter 6), the reactions of glycosyl fluorides are somewhat different. Treatment of β-fluoroglucose with sodium methoxide yields initially the 1,2 epoxide by displacement of the fluoro group by the hydroxyl at carbon 2 (Figure 7.22). The 1,2 epoxide can react further by addition of methoxide to

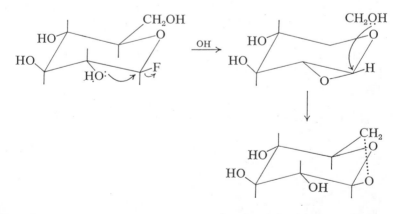

FIGURE 7.22   The reaction of equatorial fluoride in the presence of alkali leading to the formation of 1,2 epoxide and subsequently (Figure 7.23) the formation of a 1,6-anhydro sugar.

form the methyl glycoside with net retention of configuration, or by attack of the C-6 hydroxyl on the epoxide to yield a 1,6 anhydro sugar, also with net retention of configuration at both carbon 1 and carbon 2 (Figure 7.23) [13]. Apparently the C-1 carbon has been rendered sufficiently electron deficient so that the rate of internal displacement supersedes the rate of dissociation of the C-1 halogen bond.

7.4 Selective Reactivity

Introduction

The differential reactivity of the various hydroxyl positions can be of considerable use in preparing suitably substituted derivatives for use as intermediates in synthetic sequences. The general rules of conformation as it influences reactivity will be followed.

1. Equatorial hydroxyl groups are more reactive, easier to esterify and etherify, substituents are more susceptible to cleavage and to attack by hydrolytic agents than are those on axial hydroxyl groups.
2. The primary alcoholic group on C-6 being essentially exocyclic, is far more reactive than any of the chain hydroxyls and in several cases can be uniquely substituted without the necessity for blocking other functional groups.
3. The presence of particularly bulky substituent groups can render adjacent hydroxyls relatively unreactive even when they are in equatorial conformation. In cellulose, for example, the substitution of the C-4 hydroxyl of the glucose residues by glucose makes complete methylation difficult to achieve due to the fact that the 3-hydroxyl, even though equatorial, is quite unreactive (Figure 7.24).

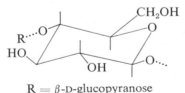

R = β-D-glucopyranose

FIGURE 7.24 Schematic representation of a carbohydrate unit in a typical polysaccharide chain with linkage occurring at position 4.

Reactions at the Primary Alcohol

The use of triphenylmethyl chloride to selectively etherify primary alcohols is perhaps the best illustration of selective reactivity[2] (Figure 7.25). Other

---

[2] In a sense this is disappointing because we would expect the primary alcohol function to be easily distinguished. We would like to have similar selectivity for the secondary hydroxyls but this is rare.

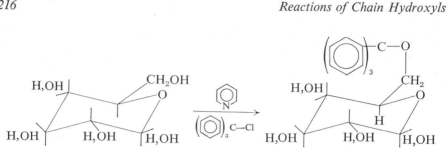

FIGURE 7.25   Selective esterification of primary alcohol function.

etherification or esterification agents are not quite as specific although selective substitution by tosyl or benzoyl groups can be carried out. The synthesis of 6-tosyl glucose by reaction of D-glucose with tosyl chloride proceeds under controlled conditions utilizing a stoichiometric amount of tosyl chloride. Similarly, reaction of 1,2 isopropylidene α-D-glucofuranose with a stoichiometric amount of benzoyl chloride yields exclusively the 6-benzoyl derivative in yields approaching 80 percent (Figure 7.26) [14]. The rate of substitution at

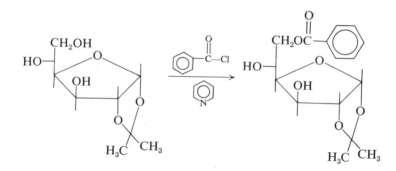

FIGURE 7.26   Selective benzoylation of the primary alcohol function in 1,2-*O*-isopropylidene D-glucofuranose.

the primary hydroxyl is undoubtedly faster than that at secondary hydroxyls for any reaction, but except for those cases noted above, these rates are not sufficiently different to permit selective substitution at the C-6 position.

Secondary Hydroxyls

The tosylation of secondary hydroxyls in a specific manner has been achieved in several cases. The reaction of exocyclic secondary hydroxyls with tosyl chloride has been successfully used to specifically substitute carbon 5 of glucose (Figure 7.27) [15]. This intermediate is well suited to subsequent

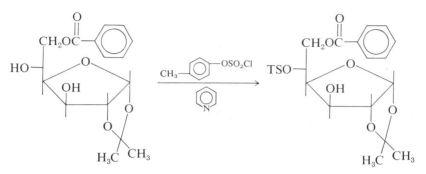

FIGURE 7.27 Selective tosylation of the exocyclic hydroxyl in 6-*O*-benzoyl 1,2-isopropylidene D-glucopyranose.

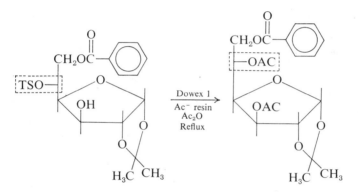

FIGURE 7.28 Displacement of the exocyclic tosyl function by acetate yielding a derivative of the L-ido configuration.

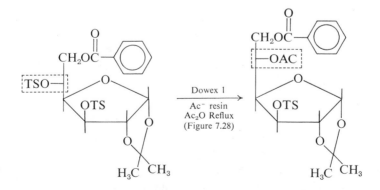

FIGURE 7.29 Selective displacement of exocyclic rather than endocyclic tosyloxy group yielding a derivative with the L-ido configuration. The removal of the endocyclic tosyloxy group is extremely difficult.

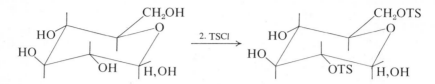

FIGURE 7.30 Preferred reaction of 2 moles of *p*-toluene sulfonyl chloride with D-glucose. The second substitution occurs at position 2.

displacement reactions and provides the best route to sugars with the ido configuration (Figure 7.28) [16]. The use of excess tosyl chloride in the first step of the above sequence yields a 3,5 ditosyl derivative which can still be selectively displaced at carbon 5 (Figure 7.29). It should be noted that removal of endocyclic tosyl groups does not proceed readily. Similarly, in a study of the direct

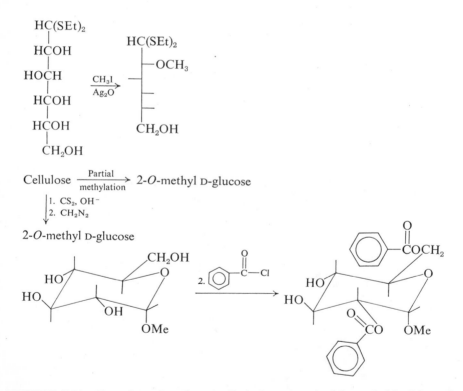

FIGURE 7.31 Reaction of D-glucose diethylmercaptal with methyl iodide and silver oxide. If stoichiometric amounts are employed the primary product is 2-*O*-methyl derivative. Partial methylation of cellulose as indicated also yields the 2-*O*-methyl D-glucose product. Benzoylation of methyl α-D-glucopyranoside will yield a 2-6-di-*O*-benzoyl derivative.

tosylation of D-glucose, it was found that a second mole of tosyl chloride was introduced at position 2 of the glucose moiety with relatively little substitution occurring at positions 3 or 4 (Figure 7.30) [17]. The primary reason for this is that the electronegativity of the ring oxygen makes substitution at the neighboring hydroxyl more likely than at either position 3 or position 4. This is a general effect of the ring oxygen on reactions carried out at the C-2 hydroxyl. Several examples are given in Figure 7.31.

It can be predicted that where electron deficiency will promote a given reaction, the C-2 hydroxyl is more reactive than the chain hydroxyls at C-3 and C-4. Failure to achieve complete hydroxyl substitution when such is desired is most likely due to preferential reaction at C-2 followed by steric hindrance at C-3 (especially if C-4 is axial or substituted).

Neighboring Group Reactions

The participation of substituent groups present at carbon 2 in reactions that take place at the anomeric center is apparent. When the groups at carbon 2 and carbon 1 are *trans* to one another, reactions that take place at C-1 with net retention of configuration probably occur via participation of the C-2 acetoxy group and the double inversion mechanism discussed previously. Apparent inversion of configuration during such reactions probably occurs by a carbonium ion mechanism.

A typical example is the reaction of tetraacetyl halogeno sugars with tertiary amines. When the C-2 acetoxy group is *cis* to the C-1 halogen, quaternary amine salts are formed. However, if the acetoxy group at carbon 2 is *trans* to the halogen at carbon 1, then the quaternary amine salts are not found (Figure 7.32) [18].

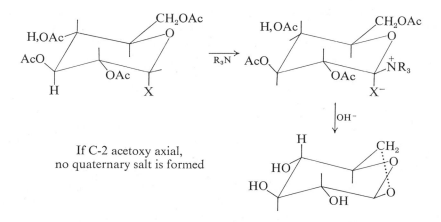

FIGURE 7.32 Reaction of α-halogeno tetra-O-acetyl D-glucopyranose with a tertiary amine.

There are clear steric considerations as well. When the incoming group is particularly bulky, then the equatorial anomer will be preferred. However, when the incoming group is highly polar, the ring oxygen (anomeric effect) may cause preferential axial attack and formation of the axial product. The shielded-ion mechanism previously mentioned for reactions of glycosyl halides receives some additional support from kinetic studies (most reactions are first order) and the necessity to add a catalyst to "promote" the dissociation of the halogen. If the dissociation of the halogen were smoothly achieved in the presence of an alcohol, then an ionic mechanism would predominate.

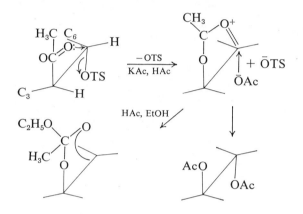

FIGURE 7.33 Reaction of a tosyloxy group with potassium acetate via the formation of a cyclic intermediate yielding the mixed acetal or *trans* diaxial products.

In cases where participation by the substituent group at carbon 2 is possible, the stereochemistry is generally better defined; this path seems to be favored. This is in agreement with the general rule stating that intramolecular reactions are favored over those involving solvent-derived nucleophiles.

A classic study of Winstein and co-workers on the acetolysis of tosyl cyclohexanols provides evidence for the participation of neighboring acetoxy groups (Figure 7.33) [19]. The relative rates of acetylation of 2-tosyl-cyclo-hexanol and *cis* and *trans* 2-acetoxy cyclohexanol are listed in Table 7.7. The displacement of the tosyloxy group by acetyl would be expected to be slower when a second acetyl group is present, but the fact that this reaction proceeds at 30 percent of the rate of the unhindered derivatives is strongly suggestive of participation. When the products are examined it is found that both the *cis* and *trans* starting materials yield *trans* products; the former presumably going by SN_2 inversion and the latter by neighboring group participation.

It is generally considered that the driving force in the participation of a neighboring group is a measure of the decrease in the energy of activation due

TABLE 7.7

Relative rates of reaction *cis* and *trans* tosyl 2-acetoxy cyclohexonals

COMPOUND	RELATIVE RATE
Tosyl cyclohexanol	1
Trans 2-acetoxy Tosyl cyclohexanol	0.3
Cis 2-acetoxy Tosyl cyclohexanol	0.0004

to the formation of the cyclic intermediate. With this in mind and with the consideration of relative electronegativity, it is possible to construct a table for relative effectiveness of group participation (Table 7.8). As indicated above,

TABLE 7.8

Driving force of selected nucleophiles compared with relative rates of displacement reactions.

GROUP	DRIVING FORCE	RELATIVE RATE
$^-SCH_2CH_2OH$	13	10
I^-	8.7	1.6×10^2
NH_2	8	10^4
O^-	6	10^{10}
OBz^-	5.2	. . .
OAc^-	4.6	. . .
Br^-	4.5	0.39
$OH^-, OCH_3{}^-$	1.34	0.1

acetoxy groups are particularly good "neighbors"; benzoyl esters are much less reactive than acetyl and there are few examples of those as participating groups. Iodo groups may even be better than acetate, but their transitory stability renders their use limited. Stable iodo derivatives at C-6 are known and provide intermediates for the synthesis of deoxy sugars (Figure 7.34). In this case, note the prior tosylation of the C-6 hydroxyl to provide a good leaving group, displacement by the iodo group, and its subsequent removal by hydrogenation. Little or no chemistry has been done on the possible use of the iodo group in a participating role in carbohydrate systems.

The feasibility of the formation of the cyclic carbonium ion intermediate depends on several factors. The ionic form gains stability due to resonance, with the positive charge distributed over both oxygen and carbon. It is necessary, however, that the intermediate be formed with a relative minimum of ring strain and distortion. Where the formation of such an intermediate and the accompanying distortion of the ring brings other substituent groups into an unfavored

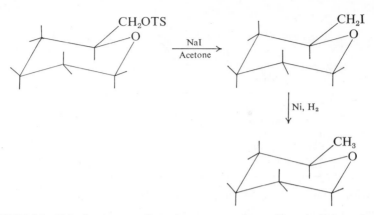

FIGURE 7.34 Displacement of tosyloxy groups by sodium iodide and acetone: a route to deoxy sugars.

axial or eclipse conformation, this pathway will not predominate. The dependence on the near planarity of the 5-membered ring structure makes it possible to predict when such intermediates are likely participants (Figure 7.35). It is possible for such ring intermediates to form in furanoside derivatives although

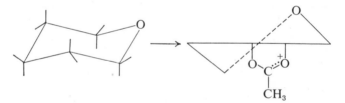

FIGURE 7.35 Distortion of the chair form to accommodate 5-membered cyclic intermediates.

they are more strained in such structures. Several examples of acetate participation are included below:

The reaction of penta-*O*-acetyl-D-glucopyranose (pentaacetyl glucose) with ethylmercaptan in HCl to form the diethyl mercaptal at carbon 1 proceeds extremely rapidly with the equatorial β anomer and slowly with the axial α anomer (Figure 7.36) [20].

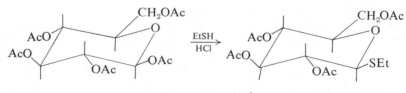

α-acetate very unreactive

FIGURE 7.36 Reaction of β-pentaacetyl D-glucopyranose with ethylmercaptan.

The reaction of pentaacetyl glucose with titanium tetrachloride to form the 1-chloro sugar proceeds very rapidly with the β and quite slowly with the α anomer (Figure 7.37). In both cases, the stereochemistry of the products and

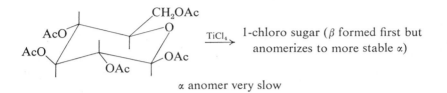

$$\xrightarrow{\text{TiCl}_4}$$ 1-chloro sugar (β formed first but anomerizes to more stable α)

α anomer very slow

FIGURE 7.37 Reaction of β-pentaacetyl D-glucopyranose with titanium tetrachloride.

the type of reaction taking place can be readily explained by participation of the group at carbon 2.

Direct evidence favoring the cyclic ionic form has been obtained by the trapping of this transitory intermediate by reaction with dialkyl cadmium to yield an alkyl-substituted cyclic ketal. This is illustrated in Figure 7.38.

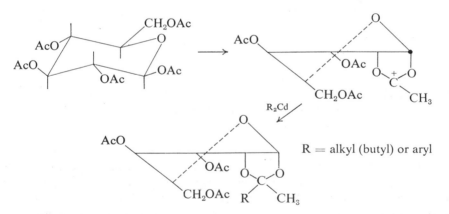

R_2Cd

R = alkyl (butyl) or aryl

FIGURE 7.38 Trapping of cyclic intermediate with dialkyl cadmium.

The treatment of β-D-glucose pentaacetate with phosphorus pentachloride yields not only displacement of the acetoxy group on C-1 to yield the α-chloro sugar, but also progressive substitution by halogen on the methyl carbon of the C-2 acetoxy group to yield the 2-trichloro acetyl 3,4,6-tri-*O*-acetyl-α-chloro-D-glucopyranoside. The mechanism proposed to explain this sequence of reactions is illustrated in Figure 7.39.

α-L-idose pentaacetate (reverse conformation with *trans* diaxial acetoxy groups C-1 and C-2) on treatment with phosphorus pentachloride under similar conditions yields the α-1-chloro sugar (Figure 7.40) [21].

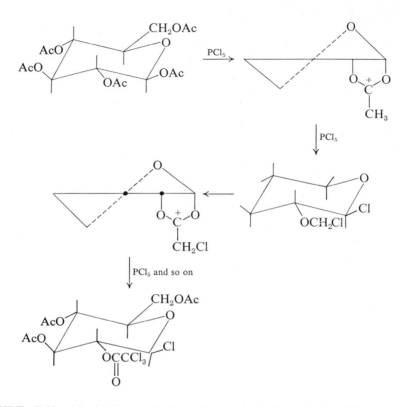

FIGURE 7.39 Mechanism of formation of 1-chloro-2, trichloro acetyl, 3,4,6-tri-*O*-acetyl D-glucopyranose by reaction of β-D-glucose pentaacetate with phosphorus pentachloride.

The reaction of piperidine with β-D-glucose pentaacetate to yield acetolysis of the group at C-2 and substitution by piperidine to form an *N*-glycoside at C-1 probably also proceeds via a neighboring group intermediate (see Figure 7.41) [22]. An additional example of group participation is the treatment of

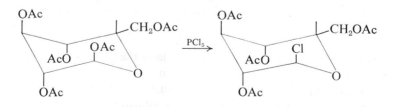

FIGURE 7.40 Reaction of α-L-idose pentaacetate with phosphorus pentachloride.

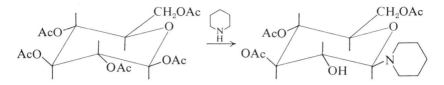

FIGURE 7.41 Reaction of β-D-glucose pentaacetate with piperidine.

1,2,3,4-tetra-O-acetyl-α-D-glucopyranose under conditions of acid catalysis. The isolated product is 2,3,4-tri-O-acetyl-1-6-anhydro-D-glucopyranose. The formation of this product is best explained by participation of the acetoxy group at C-2 to form a cyclic carbonium ion which is then opened up by internal attack of the free hydroxyl on C-6 (Figure 7.42).

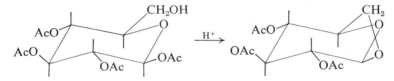

FIGURE 7.42 Acid hydrolysis of 1,2,3,4-tetra-O-acetyl β-D-glucopyranose.

When conditions are favorable, internal displacement by neighboring groups may occur at positions other than C-2 → C-1 or C-6 → C-1. The steric restrictions mentioned still apply and because *trans* diaxial chain hydroxyls are not common, relatively few examples of this type of reaction are known. The ability of *trans* diequatorial groups to react in this manner is restricted by steric forces. It is possible that a change in ring conformation is a prerequisite to neighboring group reactions of diequatorial substituents. Reactions that take place at C-1 are facilitated by the electron withdrawing effect of the ring oxygen. This serves to make the C-1 carbon more susceptible to nucleophile attack than any other carbon by effectively lowering the activation energy for the reaction.

However, when the carbohydrate is not in a ring form (sugar alcohols are the most common representatives), neighboring group reactions may take place at any position in the chain. An extended study of displacement reactions in the mannitol series has been carried out by Baker and several of the reaction sequences are illustrated below. Note particularly the control of stereochemistry by use of external versus internal displacement and the relative ease of reaction although some ring systems are present (Figure 7.43) [23].

The possible control of substitution by adjusting or fixing conformation and reaction conditions to favor SN₂ or SN₁ reactions is therefore reasonable. Whether or not *trans* diequatorial groups must go through a diaxial form in order to achieve the proper stereochemistry for anchimeric assistance is not established. The highly unfavorable interactions that would result from those carbohydrates in which several axial groups would then be present suggests that this is not an obligatory prerequisite.

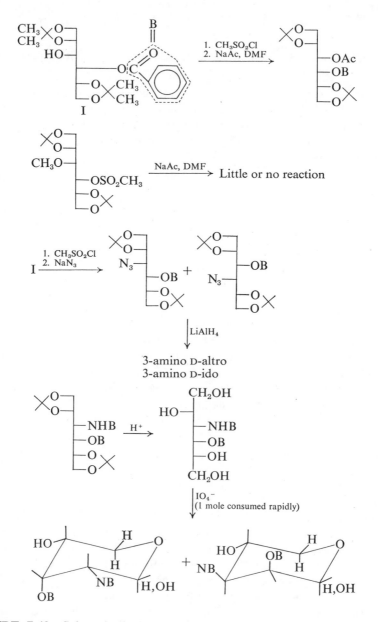

FIGURE 7.43 Selected displacement reactions in the D-mannitol series.

The mechanism of substitutions taking place at C-1 therefore depends on the nature of the groups at carbon 2, solvent and steric factors. It is possible to reduce the participation of the C-2 acetoxy group by preparation of the 2-trichloro acetyl derivative. This general approach has been utilized in the preparation of *cis* glycosides where the substitution conditions require no neighboring group participation [24]. Alternatively, having simply a hydroxyl group at carbon 2 is sufficient to reduce participation. The major exception is in tosyl displacement wherein the ionization of the hydroxyl proton contributes to the ability of the hydroxyl group to participate, and epoxide rings result.

7.5 Formation of Cyclic Acetals and Ketals of the Carbohydrates [25]

Introduction and Nomenclature

The use of cyclic acetals and ketals as specific blocking reagents for the synthesis of complex carbohydrate derivatives is widespread. As a result of this utility, there is considerable interest in forming specific derivatives and, in particular, in forming these in sufficiently high yield so that subsequent reaction sequences may be carried out without extensive loss. The mechanism of formation of these derivatives is such that steric factors largely control formation of specific acetals and ketals.

Several definitions will facilitate subsequent discussion:

1. If the cyclic acetal or ketal (cyclic derivative) is formed from hydroxyl groups which are on adjacent carbon atoms, then the ring involving the cyclic derivative will be termed an α *ring*. This will usually, although not always, be a 5-membered ring.

2. A cyclic derivative with one carbon between those bearing the hydroxyls involved in reaction is termed a β *ring*.

3. If there are two carbons between the reacting hydroxyls, the ring is termed a γ *ring*. Cases where there are more than two carbons between reacting hydroxyls are too rare to require discussion.

4. The term *residue* will refer to those portions of the parent carbohydrate chain that are not enclosed by the ring. As an example, 2, 4 methylene D-glucitol contains a β ring and CH_2OH and $CH_2OH–CHOH$ residues (Figure 7.44).

5. Fused rings will be found wherever the furanose or pyranose ring of the carbohydrate and the ring involved in the cyclic derivative have two atoms in common. The ring junction is analogous to an angular position in a steroid nucleus (Figure 7.45).

The normal projection representation of such compounds, especially the planar projection, gives a very distorted and unrealistic view of the molecule.

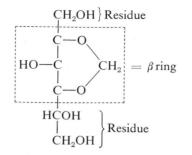

FIGURE 7.44   Nomenclature for cyclic carbohydrate derivatives.

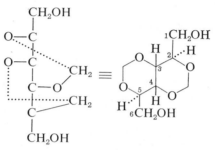

FIGURE 7.45   Representation of the acyclic derivative of a carbohydrate in Fischer projection and ring formula. Note that the hydrogen positions at carbons 3 and 4 are akin to angular positions in steroids.

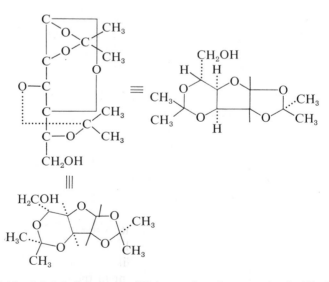

FIGURE 7.46   1,2,3,5-di-isopropylidene-D-glucofuranose in the Fischer projection and alternative structural formulations.

For example, 1,2,3,5 di-isopropylidene α-D-glucofuranose may be represented in either of the ways presented in Figure 7.46.

It can be seen from the diagram that the first formula is totally unsatisfactory as far as both stereochemistry and potential reactions are concerned and either the second or the third should be routinely used.

6. In a ring where two secondary hydroxyls are on the same side in the projection formula and are involved in formation of the cyclic derivative, the remaining residues will be *cis* (Figure 7.47). If the cyclic derivative is formed

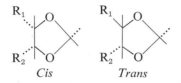

Cis   *Trans*

FIGURE 7.47 *Cis* and *trans* ring junctions in cyclic derivatives.

from secondary hydroxyls which appear on the opposite side of the projection, the residues will have *trans* stereochemistry (Figure 7.47).

7. If two adjacent carbons are involved in a ring junction, the junction will be *trans* if the hydroxls are on the same side and it will be *cis* if the hydroxyls are on opposite sides (Figure 7.48). In a way, this refers to the orientation of the groups at the angular positions.

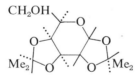

FIGURE 7.48 1,2,3,4-di-isopropylidene-D-galactopyranose. The C_2—C_3 junction is *trans*.

In a very general sense, reversible reactions in the carbohydrate field, such as acetate anomerizations, glycoside anomerizations, glycoside formation, and so on, are acid catalyzed. Irreversible reactions such as displacement reactions and the formation and cleavage of anhydro ring systems are generally not acid catalyzed although exceptions are known (Figure 7.49). Where nonreversibility is present, it is not possible to write a specific reaction path in terms of activation energy and thus more difficult to assign weight to steric and mechanistic factors which may come into play. Bimolecular elimination reactions also require a rather specific stereochemistry and are unlikely for most carbohydrates.

When a carbohydrate derivative is present in the furanose ring form it is found that adjacent *cis* hydroxyls are nearly eclipsed and thus ketalation readily leads to the formation of bridges or adjacent 5-membered rings (Figure 7.50).

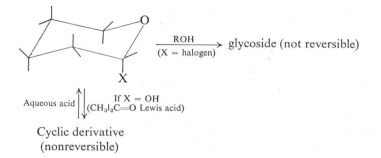

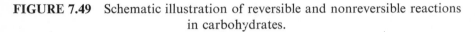

Cyclic derivative
(nonreversible)

FIGURE 7.49   Schematic illustration of reversible and nonreversible reactions in carbohydrates.

The 1,3-dioxolane ring has been relatively less studied and although it may be nearly planar, some distortion is likely (Figure 7.51). There are several general rules regarding likely ring forms and stereochemistry of ring junctions.

1. When fusion to 5- or 6-membered rings occurs, only *cis* isomers are formed. This is taken as evidence for favoring the planar configuration of the ring.

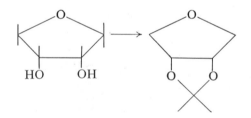

FIGURE 7.50   Formation of cyclic derivatives in 5-membered ring form when *cis* hydroxyls are present.

2. Five-membered rings can accommodate exocyclic double bonds more readily than 6-membered rings (Figure 7.52). This is due to the near planarity of the parent ring form and the lesser distortion required. When a double bond occurs in a 6-membered ring, planarity must result in the formation of skew or half-chair conformations which render these ring forms relatively unstable. This explains why aldonic acids form 5-membered ring lactones much more readily

FIGURE 7.51   1,3-dioxolane ring.

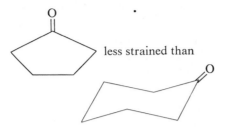

less strained than

FIGURE 7.52 Accommodation of the carbonyl group in a 5-membered rather than a 6-membered ring involves less additional ring strain.

than they form 6-membered lactones. When equilibrium conditions are present, such as in the case of glycoside synthesis, the furanoside derivative may form more rapidly than the pyranoside. However, the latter form is the thermodynamically favored one and if the reaction is allowed to proceed, the pyranoside will predominate. If the reaction conditions are such as to stabilize or provide a nonreversible pathway for derivatization, then the furanoside will be the observed product.

3. Factors that tend to increase planarity in fused 5-membered ring systems increase the stability of the *cis* derivative versus that of the *trans*. Tetrahydrofuran or 1,3 dioxolane systems only form *cis* derivatives.

4. Those derivatives containing 2 fused 6-membered rings also favor *cis* ring junctions. Contrast this with the *cis* and *trans* decalins where the *trans* form is thermodynamically favored over the *cis*.

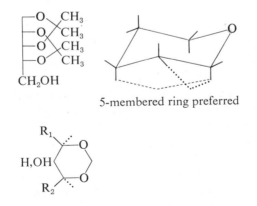

5-membered ring preferred

FIGURE 7.53 Five- and 6-membered cyclic acetals. The 6-membered cyclic acetals will be equatorially substituted at the acetal carbon.

5. The *trans* form is rigid so long as only chair forms are present. The *cis* form has at least one ring flexible so that conversion of a particular functional group from an axial to an equatorial conformation is possible by ring flexing in the *cis* derivative. A similar transformation in the *trans* form would require an intermediate, flexible (boat) ring form. This is probably pertinent to subsequent reactions but has not been extensively studied.

6. Where one 5- and one 6-membered ring are present, only a *cis* stereochemistry is observed for cyclic acetals.

7. Six-membered cyclic acetals strongly favor equatorial substitution at the acetal carbon. The residues present and the substituent at the acetal carbon are usually on the same side of the ring in the projection formula (Figure 7.53).

8. Ring systems present in 1,6 anhydro sugars are known to exist in chair forms and inspection of molecular models reveals that the normal chair can be accommodated with little or no distortion.

9. As has been previously mentioned, 3-membered rings will impose planarity requirements leading to the formation of half-chair or skew conformation. These various ring types are illustrated in Figure 7.54.

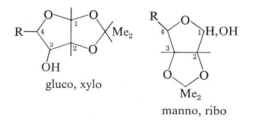

gluco, xylo

manno, ribo

FIGURE 7.54   Cyclic derivatives and configurations for some common sugars.

In practice, it is found that the reaction of a carbohydrate to form a cyclic derivative yields predominantly 5- rather than 6-membered rings. This might be considered an unexpected development because of the generally favored stability of 6-membered rings, but steric factors can satisfactorily account for the observations. Consider the following situation: Formation of an isopropylidene derivative by condensation of a sugar with acetone requires either *cis* adjacent hydroxyls or transannular diaxial hydroxyls. In the latter case, the only time that *cis* hydroxyls would not also be present would be when the hydroxyl was substituted or *trans* (axial). There would then be 3 axial hydroxyl groups, which is clearly unlikely or the position would be hindered (Figure 7.55). Major exceptions involve the primary alcoholic group at C-6 which is readily able to form 6-membered ring derivatives (Figure 7.56).

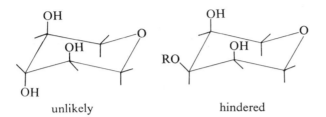

unlikely   hindered

FIGURE 7.55 Steric requirements for formation of 6-membered cyclic derivatives within the ring. In one case, three axial hydroxyls would need to be present which is rather unlikely; in the other case, the substitution would involve considerable steric hindrance.

Despite the fact that these results can be interpreted on a conformational basis, the nonreversibility of these reactions make relative stabilities of derivatives hard to assess. Entropy effects may contribute to the makeup of final reaction mixtures, and changes of the energy of activation for the formation of a given species may favor one ring form over another. The inspection of a typical carbohydrate with a view toward preparing derivatives of this type raises the following questions:

1. What is the most probable ring structure of cyclic acetal or ketal derivatives?
2. How many of these are likely to be stable forms?
3. Can specific ones be favored by choice of reaction conditions?

There is a large amount of empirical information available, particularly in the sugar alcohol field and in the area of glucose chemistry where much derivatization has been carried out. However, the utility of these data is very much dependent upon dealing with sugars of relatively stable conformation, relatively few axial groups, and where alternate structures for the parent compound are not likely to exist. Table 7.9 lists common derivatives, ring size, and where known, yield.

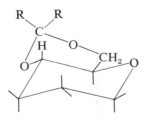

FIGURE 7.56 Six-membered cyclic derivative involving the exocyclic hydroxymethyl group.

TABLE 7.9

Derivatives and ring size for common sugars.

SUGAR DERIVATIVE[a]	RING SIZE[b]	YIELD
1,2,5,6 di IPD glucose	5,5,5	70 percent
1,2,3,4 di IPD galactose	5,5,6	70 percent
2,3,5,6 di IPD mannose	5,5,5	
1,2,3,5 di IPD glucose	5,6,5	
1,2,5,6 di IPD altrose	5,5,6	
1,2,3,4 di IPD arabinose	5,5,6	
2,3 IPD ribose	5,5	
1,2,3,5 di IPD xylose	5,6,5	
4,6 BzD glucose	6,6	
4,6 ETD glucose	6,6	
2,3,4,5 di BzD fructose	5,5,6	
1,2,3,4 di ME galactose	5,5,6	Low

[a] IPD: isopropylidene
BzD: benzylidene
ETD: ethylidene
ME: methylene
[b] Last number refers to acetal or ketal ring from reducing carbon.

The great preponderance of cyclic derivatives are formed from stable or symmetrical ketones or aldehydes such as acetone, acetaldehyde, and benzaldehyde. However, when an asymmetric ketone is employed for the formation of cyclic ketal derivatives, a type of *cis-trans* stereochemistry may exist, as illustrated in the formula in Figure 7.57 [26].

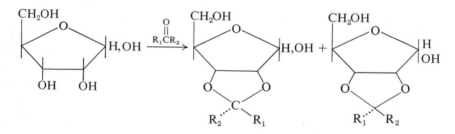

FIGURE 7.57 Possibility of structural isomers formed in the reaction of a 5-membered ring form with an asymmetric ketone.

Because these structures are not mirror images but rather diastereoisomers, they will be expected to have different physical properties, and, tedious fractional crystallization, or other separation schemes may have to be employed to obtain pure compounds. Therefore, unless one is particularly interested in the formation of such isomers for *their* direct study, symmetrical condensing agents are the choice.

Inspection of 5-membered cyclic derivatives reveals that di-fused 5-membered rings appear to be relatively stable compared to those not involved in fused ring systems. Thus, 1,2,5,6 di-isopropylidene α-D-glucofuranose on acid hydrolysis loses the 5,6 or nonfused ring system, leaving 1,2 isopropylidene α-D-glucofuranose as the product (Figure 7.58) [27]. Part of the reason for this

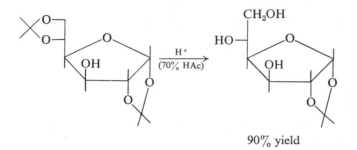

90% yield

FIGURE 7.58 Selective hydrolysis of a ketal at the primary alcohol position.

may be the greater reactivity of the primary alcohol function and also possibly the greater hindrance present in the fused ring system. Finally, because the hydrolysis of the functional group at the acetal carbon atom may involve a transition state or a steric deformation to an unfavorable configuration as compared to the hydrolysis of the exocyclic ring system, this may also lead to preferential cleavage of the 5,6 isopropylidene group. The latter case would have less nonbonded interactions that hinder hydrolysis.

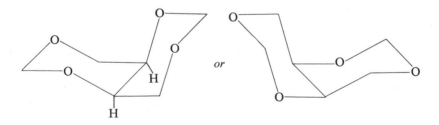

FIGURE 7.59 Ring forms possible for cyclic derivatives of an alditol with *cis* ring junctions.

A large number of cyclic derivatives of alditols have been prepared and the stereochemistry and preferential reactions extensively investigated. *Trans* bicyclic systems are unlikely to contain axial residues and *cis* ring junctions can give rise to two possible configurations (Figure 7.59).

Most of the observed reactions can be explained on steric grounds largely by taking into account the favored zigzag arrangement of the polyol chain. A list of stable and favored derivatives is given in Table 7.10 [28].

TABLE 7.10

Products formed on the condensation of aldehydes or ketones with sugar alcohols.

ALCOHOL	CONDENSING AGENT	PRODUCTS
Arabitol	⟨benzaldehyde⟩ —CHO	1,3
Ribitol	HCHO	2,4 and 1,3; 2,4
Xylitol	⟨benzaldehyde⟩ —CHO	1,2 + 3,4
Xylitol	HCHO	1,3; 2,4
Xylitol	$(CH_3)_2C{=}O$	3,5; 1,2,3,4; 1,2,3,5
Allitol	HCHO	2,4,3,5
Galactitol	⟨benzaldehyde⟩ —CHO	1,3; 4,6
Galactitol	HCHO	1,3; 4,6
Galactitol	$(CH_3)_2C{=}O$	2,3,4,5 2,3,5,6
Iditol	HCHO	2,4; 3,5
Mannitol	CH_3CHO	1,3,2,5,4,6
Mannitol	$(CH_3)_2C{=}O$	1,2 1,2,5,6 1,2,3,4,5,6
Glucitol	CH_3CHO	1,3,2,4 and 1,3,2,4,5,6
	$(CH_3)_2C{=}O$	1,2 1,2,5,6 1,2,3,4,5,6
Talitol	HCHO	2,4 and 2,3,4,5

It is difficult to visualize on an *a priori* basis why the relative freedom of rotation which obviously exists in the open chain forms does not give rise to a larger number of cyclic acetal or ketal derivatives. It would seem that almost any derivative is possible and that there would be relatively little to choose between mannitol, glucitol, or galactitol as far as reaction rates are concerned. There are features that serve to counterbalance the free rotation or equiprobability argument cited above. The relatively higher reaction rate exhibited by primary alcohols will usually lead to preferential condensation at that site with either the adjacent or once removed secondary hydroxyl participating in ring formation (Figure 7.60). Once this reaction has taken place, the rules of condensation governing ring forms now come into play. Some of the groups will be relatively restricted for ring formation because of ring junction requirements or hindrance and others will be more reactive. In the case of a sugar alcohol, both

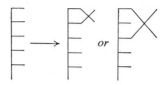

FIGURE 7.60 Possible condensation of the primary alcohol function of the sugar alcohol with the hydroxyl at either C-2 or C-3.

primary alcohol sites react; groups that are *cis* in a projection formula will react more rapidly than those that are *trans*; the distance of closest approach is between groups that are 1,3 rather than those on adjacent carbon atoms.

Monocyclic derivatives of sugar alcohols, wherein one of the primary hydroxyl groups has been left free, are intermediates for the synthesis of new aldoses via oxidation reactions (Figure 7.61). Although the over-all yield of these sequences is low, the relative accessibility of the sugar alcohols plus knowledge

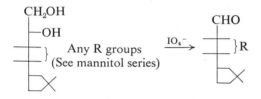

FIGURE 7.61 Treatment of a sugar alcohol cyclic derivative with periodate.

of the type of cyclic derivatives which they form has permitted synthesis of several rare sugars.

The stereochemistry of ring cleavage reactions requires a few comments.

1. The cleavage of 1,2 anhydro sugars (the 1,2 only indicates an ethylene oxide type ring) will always proceed to give products where the hydroxyl groups

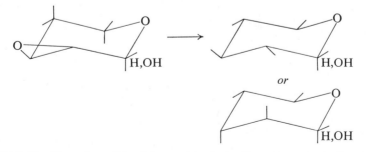

FIGURE 7.62 Reaction of the 1,2 epoxide derivative of a carbohydrate to form the *trans* products.

have a *trans* orientation. For example, the cleavage of 2,3 anhydro mannose or 2,3 anhydro allose derivatives yields the gluco (minor) or altro product (Figure 7.62) [29]. Similarly, talose and gulose open to give predominantly the ido product.

2. Such ring openings prefer to go by a route which gives two axial groups in the product. This may subsequently undergo a conformational change so that the diaxial glycol becomes diequatorial.

3. When carbon 1 is involved in the anhydro ring, cleavage takes place only by attack at the anomeric center. There are no known exceptions to this.

7.6 Cyclic Esters

Carbonates and Thiocarbonates

The use of cyclic or acyclic carbonates and thiocarbonates as blocking groups in the carbohydrate field has received increasing attention. One of the major virtues of these derivatives is that they are relatively acid stable and extremely sensitive to alkali cleavage. Thus, they are somewhat complementary

FIGURE 7.63   Ring form required for cyclic ester formation in the reaction of phosgene with sugars. As in the case of sugar lactones, the 5-membered ring is the predominant product.

to the alkylidene and similar acetals and ketals. Because the structure of cyclic carbonate derivatives will of necessity involve a carbonyl group in a ring (this can be readily recognized by its enhanced absorption in the infrared with a maximum at 1820 cm^{-1}), the preference for 5-membered ring formation is readily explained (Figure 7.63). There are, however, some 6-membered cyclic carbonates known, such as the 1,2 isopropylidene 3,5 cyclic carbonate of D-xylofuranose (Figure 7.64) [30].

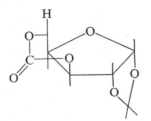

FIGURE 7.64   1,2-*O*-isopropylidene D-xylofuranose 3-5 carbonate.

Synthesis of these derivatives is generally carried out by reaction of carbohydrates with phosgene or with chloroformate esters such as ethyl or butyl-
chloro formate (Figure 7.65) [31].

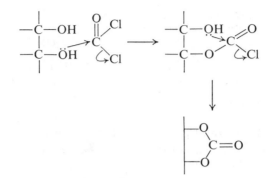

FIGURE 7.65 Mechanism of reaction of phosgene with hydroxyl groups to form cyclic derivatives.

Inert solvents have frequently been employed although it is not necessary
in the case of several simple compounds to employ solvents. For example, the
direct treatment of ethylene glycol with phosgene yields a 1,2 cyclic ethylene

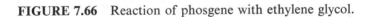

FIGURE 7.66 Reaction of phosgene with ethylene glycol.

carbonate containing a 5-membered ring with 2 oxygens (Figure 7.66). Treatment of 1,2 isopropylidene α-D-glucofuranose with phosgene in acetone yields
the 5,6 cyclic carbonate (Figure 7.67) [32], whereas direct reaction of glucose

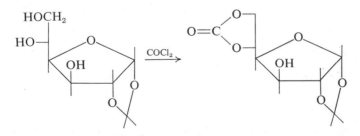

FIGURE 7.67 Reaction of phosgene with 1,2-*O*-isopropylidene D-glucofuranose.

with phosgene in pyridine (a nonparticipating solvent) yields the 1,2,5,6 di-carbonate of α-D-glucofuranose (Figure 7.68) [33].

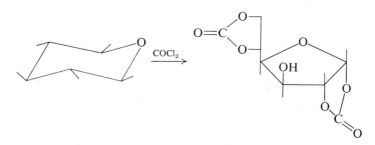

FIGURE 7.68   Reaction of phosgene with D-glucopyranose to form the 1,2,5,6-dicyclic carbonate of the furanose ring form.

It is possible to prepare noncyclic carbonate esters by reaction of a suitably blocked sugar with phosgene in an inert solvent such as toluene. The product is the chloroformate derivative (Figure 7.69). However, when the single hydroxyl

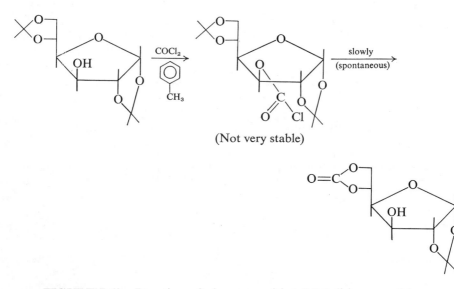

(Not very stable)

FIGURE 7.69   Reaction of phosgene with 1,2,5,6-di-isopropylidene D-glucofuranose.

group is exocyclic to the ring, as in 2,3,4-tetra-*O*-acetyl-D-glucopyranose, reaction with phosgene in pyridine yields a disaccharide derivative with the carbonate bridging the 6 position of the two sugar moieties (Figure 7.70) [34].

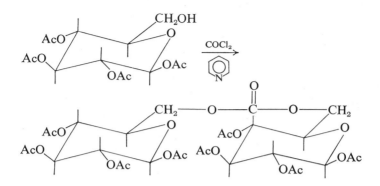

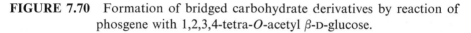

FIGURE 7.70 Formation of bridged carbohydrate derivatives by reaction of phosgene with 1,2,3,4-tetra-*O*-acetyl β-D-glucose.

In cases where acetone is employed as a solvent, isopropylidene derivatives may form faster than the cyclic carbonate at positions 1 and 2. However, the reaction at C-6 is more rapid with phosgene. These derivatives have also been employed in the pentose series as a means of preventing neighboring group participation by the C-2 function in substitution reactions carried out at the anomeric center (Figure 7.71).

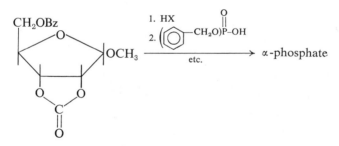

FIGURE 7.71 Synthesis of furanose α-phosphates utilizing cyclic carbonates as a deactivating group at position 2.

Summary

The following is a list of blocking groups and key properties that can be used for the protection of hydroxyl functions:

1. Etherification to form the *O*-methyl or *O*-ethyl derivative has not been frequently employed in the carbohydrate field as a blocking procedure but much more extensively as a means of structural determinations. However, the fact that such derivatives can be cleaved with boron trichloride or boron tribromide has led to their employment as protective groups in specific reaction sequences (Figure 7.72) [35].

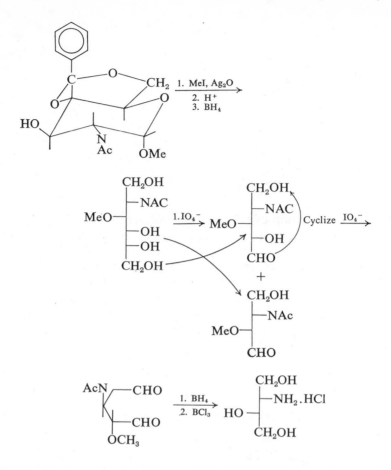

FIGURE 7.72   An example of the use of the methyl ether function as a blocking group in a synthetic sequence.

2. Benzyl and trityl ethers have been employed for the protection of the primary alcoholic function. These are particularly acid labile groups and, in addition, the benzyl group can be removed by hydrogenolysis. It is also possible that the tertiary butyl ether would be a good blocking group but this has not been investigated.

3. Trimethylsilyl ethers, although widely employed for studies in gas chromatography of carbohydrates due to their high volatility, have not received much attention as blocking groups. These are easily removed by refluxing in ethanol in the presence of a trace of acid.

4. The addition of dihydropyran to hydroxyl groups to form tetrahydro-pyranyl ethers has also been employed in the carbohydrate field. The reaction is generally carried out in chloroform with toluene sulphonic acid or acid form

cationic ion-exchange resin as catalyst. These groups are particularly acid labile and have been used where only a single hydroxyl group needs to be protected. As with other derivatives of this type, they are generally stable under basic conditions.

7.7 Esters

A wide variety of ester blocking groups have been employed at one level or another for protection of hydroxyl functions.

1. Acetates are most common and are usually removed by basic hydrolysis. Common conditions are barium methoxide in methanol, methanol-ammonia, or sodium hydroxide in ethanol. Neighboring group reactions are common when sterically feasible. The conformation of the acetoxy function may be assigned on the basis of NMR spectral data.

2. The primary advantage of the trifluoroacetate derivatives is their relative ease of removal. The trifluoroacetoxy group is hydrolyzed in boiling water and even more rapidly in the presence of a trace of alkali. In contrast to the extreme lability of the O-trifluoroacetyl derivatives, the nitrogen substituted analogs are relatively stable to these hydrolytic conditions and thus selective removal can be accomplished when dealing with amino sugars. Selective ring opening of cyclic acetals utilizing trifluoroacetic anhydride in acetic acid is possible. In this case, the attack is at the primary carbon atom if a choice exists (Figure 7.73). The cyclic acetals are more readily attacked if an α ring is present than if a β ring is present. It is presumed that the mixed solvent of trifluoroacetic anhydride and acetic acid gives rise to ionic species such as the trifluoroacetyl anion and the acetoxy cation which are the actual participating groups in the ring opening reactions.

3. Benzoate esters are somewhat more stable than the corresponding acetoxy function but due to the electronic properties of the benzoyl group are much more susceptible to acyl migration reactions.

4. Carbonates and thiocarbonates are cyclic esters with the usual steric requirements. Their relative acid stability has certain advantages.

5. Nitrates are generally prepared by reactions with nitrogen tetroxide in chloroform or nitric acid in the presence of a catalyst at 0 degrees. The removal of the nitro group is generally effected with lithium aluminum hydride, regenerating the hydroxyl function.

6. Toluenesulfonyl and frequently methanesulfonyl esters are employed in reaction sequences where subsequent displacement of the function is desired Exocyclic tosyl groups are removed by alkaline hydrolysis or by displacement with an appropriate reagent. However, endocyclic tosyloxy functions are more resistant toward displacement reactions and toward hydrolytic cleavage but susceptible to elimination by an adjacent *trans* hydroxyl. Treatment with reagents

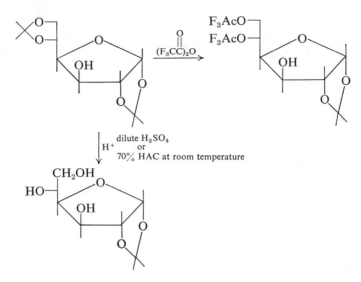

FIGURE 7.73 Reaction of carbohydrate derivatives with trifluoro acetic anhydride. In this case, although the initial substitution may have been at carbon 3, the trifluoroacetoxy group migrates to C-6 and subsequent substitution of the hydroxyl group at C-5 takes place.

such as lithium aluminum hydride in refluxing tetrahydrofuran or higher boiling solvents for several days may be required for simple cleavage. Tosyl esters on treatment with lithium aluminum hydride may also cleave by carbon–oxygen fission, forming a deoxy sugar. However, most reactions appear to go by oxygen–sulfur fission, thus regenerating the hydroxyl group.

7.8 Oxidation Reduction

It is possible to protect hydroxyl functions by oxidation to a ketone and subsequent reduction. However, for reactions in the carbohydrate field, this is generally impractical or unwise. The primary problems involve (1) the relatively low yields in oxidation reactions except for specific cases such as that of the primary hydroxyls; (2) the loss in specific stereochemistry and the fact that the subsequent reduction generates a new asymmetric center; and (3) the fact that the reactions subsequent to blocking are usually interfered with by carbonyl functions so that this classic organic method has little or no applicability.

7.9 Cyclic Acetals and Ketals

1. Isopropylidene ketals are prepared by condensation of sugars with acetone in the presence of a Lewis acid catalyst. Five-membered fused ring systems are preferred and adjacent *cis* hydroxyls are necessary. Mild acid hydrol-

ysis will cleave fairly easily. There is enough difference in stability between the ketal involving the primary alcohol function and that at C-1 so that selective acid hydrolysis is possible.

2. Ethylidene and benzylidene acetals are most commonly used to block C-4 and C-6 simultaneously. Five-membered rings will be common if secondary chain hydroxyls (*cis*!) are involved. They are readily cleaved by mild acid hydrolysis.

7.10 Adducts

Quinone adducts to hydroxyl groups have been reported, particularly for anthraquinone or phenanthraquinone. These can subsequently be removed by ozonolysis and cleavage of the resulting polycarbonyl compounds (Figure 7.74) [36].

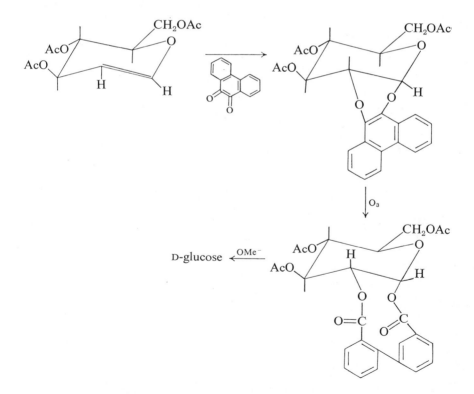

FIGURE 7.74 Effective hydroxylation of D-glucal triacetate through the use of the phenanthraquinone adduct.

7.11 Aldehyde Function

In addition to a protection of hydroxyl functions by blocking groups, it is frequently desired to protect the aldehydo function so that reactions can be carried out at other points in the molecule.

1. The most common method of protection is the formation of the glycoside or full acetal. These are classically base stable except for certain selected cases where internal displacement may occur (for example, phenylglycosides); the acetals are acid labile.
2. The aldehydo function may be blocked by formation of the semicarbazone or oxime. In both of these cases, however, regeneration of the original carbonyl is difficult. In the former, pyruvic acid interchange is most commonly employed, and in the latter, treatment with nitrous acid has been employed (Figure 7.75). In either case, these reactions proceed in low yield.

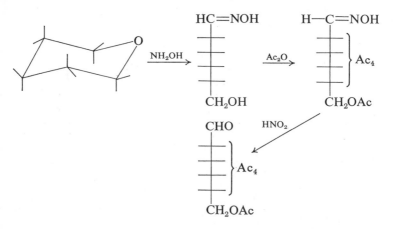

FIGURE 7.75 Reaction of free sugars with hydroxylamine to form the oxime which can then be reconverted to the carbohydrate derivative by reaction with nitrous acid. Over-all yields are quite low.

3. The aldehydo function may also be stabilized by formation of the dialkyl mercaptal. In this case, the open chain form of the sugar is obtained.

7.12 Oxidation of Chain Hydroxyls

Periodate Oxidations

There is little doubt that oxidations carried out with periodate are among the most commonly used techniques for carbon–carbon bond cleavage in all of organic chemistry. The initial discovery in 1928 by Malaprade of the utility of periodate as a glycol cleaving reagent has been followed by the application of this reagent to a large variety of both structural and preparative problems [37, 38]. The widespread application of this reagent in the carbohydrate field is due to several factors.

1. Carbohydrates are polyhydroxy compounds.

2. The nature of the reaction is such that clear steric requirements are present.

3. The stoichiometry is of a quantitative nature, and well-defined products are formed.

4. The reaction is relatively simple to carry out and quantitative analyses for reactant and product species are rapid.

5. Aqueous solutions can be employed and a great deal of information can be obtained from relatively small amounts of material.

6. The recent application of spectrophotometric techniques has permitted even greater sensitivity than has been available in the past.

The general properties of the reacting species which undergo periodate oxidation are listed in Table 7.11.

TABLE 7.11

Reaction of periodate with functional groups.

LINKAGE OR GROUP	PRODUCT	MOLES CONSUMED
$\begin{array}{c} \| \\ C\text{—}OH \\ \| \\ C\text{—}OH \\ \| \end{array}$	$\begin{array}{c} \| \\ CHO \\ \\ CHO \\ \| \end{array}$	1
$\begin{array}{c} CHO \\ \| \\ \text{—}C\text{—}OH \\ \| \end{array}$ (glycolaldehyde slow)	$\begin{array}{c} HCO_2H \\ \\ CHO \\ \| \end{array}$	1
$\begin{array}{c} R\text{—}C\text{=}O \\ \| \\ \text{—}C\text{—}OH \\ \| \end{array}$	$\begin{array}{c} RCOOH \\ \\ CHO \\ \| \end{array}$	1
$\begin{array}{c} \| \\ \text{—}C\text{—}NH_2 \\ \| \\ \text{—}C\text{—}OH \\ \| \end{array}$	$\begin{array}{c} \| \\ CHO \\ \\ CHO \\ + \\ NH_3 \end{array}$	1

TABLE 7.11—*Continued*

LINKAGE OR GROUP	PRODUCT	MOLES CONSUMED
R | C=O | CO_2H	RCO_2H + CO_2 (slow)	1
RC=O | CH_2 | R'C=O	RCOOH HCOOH R'COOH	Several; rate function of activity of methylene grouping
RC=O | C=O | H	RCO_2H HCO_2H	Slow, 1

O
||
C—H
|
  O
  ||
H—C—N—C—CH₃
|
H
—C—OH
|
	HCO_2H
	
	HCO_2H + ?
	
	CHO
	|
		Usually resistant. 2-acetamido glucose and several others with N–Ac α to reducing carbon are not

HCO_2H	Resistant	
HCHO	Resistant	
HC=O | CO_2H	Resistant (very slowly oxidized)	

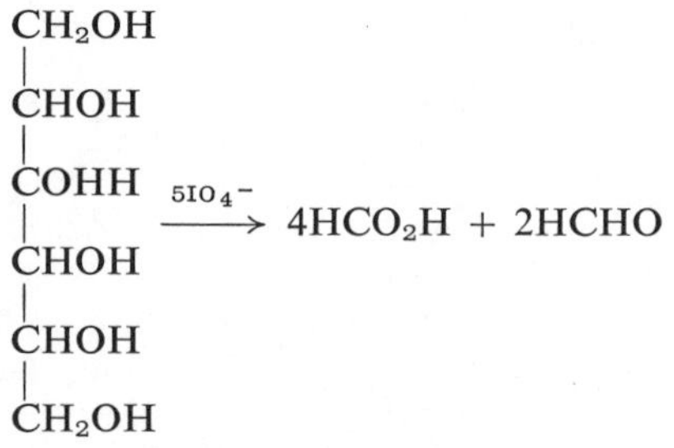

CH₂OH
\|
CHOH
\|
COHH $_{5IO_4^-}$
\| ⟶ $4HCO_2H + 2HCHO$
CHOH
\|
CHOH
\|
CH₂OH

FIGURE 7.76   Schematic reaction of periodate with a 6-carbon sugar alcohol.

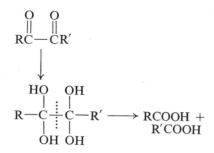

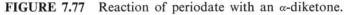

FIGURE 7.77 Reaction of periodate with an α-diketone.

Every cleavage that takes place results in the consumption of exactly 1 mole of periodate; the periodate is reduced to iodate and further reaction with iodate does not take place. The reaction for sugar alcohols may be written as shown in Figure 7.76. It can be seen that the terminal residues, which were initially primary alcohols, give rise to formaldehyde, whereas the internal or secondary hydroxyls give rise to formic acid. This simple stoichiometry is true for all of the sugar alcohols.

The reaction with α-diketones results in the formation of two carboxylic acids (Figure 7.77). Alpha hydroxyketones yield an aldehyde and a carboxylic acid (Figure 7.78). Compounds containing only a pair of adjacent hydroxyls

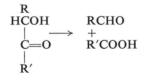

FIGURE 7.78 Reaction of periodate with an α-keto alcohol.

give dialdehydes or 2 aldehydes depending on whether the carbons are linked together in another way (Figure 7.79). If R_3 in the above formula is a hydrogen atom, the product of the reaction will be carbon dioxide; whereas if it is an alkyl function, the reaction will be slower but the product will be a carboxylic acid. In general, 1,3 diketones will be oxidized especially if they constitute part of a 5- or 6-membered ring. The consumption of periodate in these cases is generally 4 moles with the production of CO_2 and a dicarboxylic acid.

The stoichiometry of the reaction of periodate with simple aldose sugars such as glucose can be represented as occurring in the straight chain form with carbons 1 through 5 yielding formic acid and carbon 6 formaldehyde, as illustrated in the reaction scheme shown in Figure 7.80(*a*). This is an oversimplification, however, and the detailed path of the reaction of periodate with aldoses will be discussed subsequently. Reaction with ketoses may be depicted as shown in Figure 7.80(*b*).

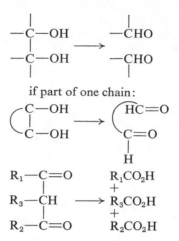

if part of one chain:

FIGURE 7.79   Schematic reaction of periodate with a vicinal glycol.

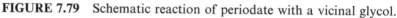

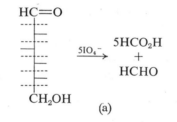

(a)

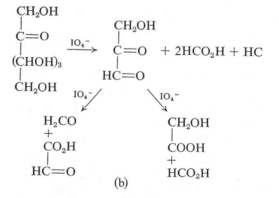

(b)

FIGURE 7.80   Representation of the reaction of periodate with the open chain
form of a hexose sugar.

    The cleavage of vicinal glycols by periodate has been studied mechanistically and also kinetically using several substrates where different steric environments are known to be present. The effect of pH on reaction extent and rate has also been examined. The cleavage has been suggested to proceed by one of two possible mechanisms [39]. The first mechanism involves the formation of a complex between the periodate and the hydroxyl species with the rate-determining step for the reaction being the disproportionation of the intermediate (Figure 7.81). If the glycol is present in excess, then pseudo first-order kinetics

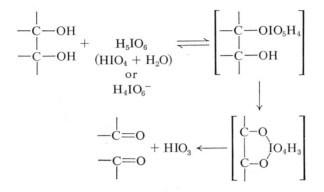

FIGURE 7.81 Proposed mechanism for a periodate cleavage involving formation of a cyclic intermediate.

are obtained. Because this condition is generally not that employed for periodate oxidation studies, interpretations from this viewpoint are rather difficult.

A second mechanism, which is kinetically second order, involves a hydrogen ion catalyzed path as well as an uncatalyzed path:

Uncatalyzed:

$$S + IO_4^- \xrightarrow{k} \text{Products}$$

$$\frac{-d[IO_4^-]^*}{dt} = k[IO_4^-][S] = k'[IO_4^-][S] \tag{7.2}$$

$$S = \text{substrate glycol}$$
$$[IO_4^-]^* = \text{all periodate species (concentration)}$$

$$k' + \frac{k}{f}, \text{ where } f = 1 + \frac{1}{K_E} + \frac{A_{H^+}\gamma_{IO_4^-}}{K_I K_E \gamma_{H_5IO_6}}$$

$$A = \text{activity} \qquad \gamma = \text{activity coefficient}$$

$$K_E = \frac{[H_2O]^2[IO_4^-]}{[H_4IO_6^-]} \qquad K_I = \frac{[H^+][H_4IO_6^-]}{[H_5IO_6]} \tag{7.3}$$

for H$^+$ catalysis

$$k' = \frac{k + k_H[H^+]}{f} \tag{7.4}$$

if catalysis is first order in H$^+$.

Spectrophotometric examination of the reaction indicates that the reactive species is a monovalent periodate ion, which may be either IO_4^- or $H_4IO_6^-$ ($IO_4^-(H_2O)_2$). In general, these two species are in sufficiently rapid equilibrium so that it is impossible to demonstrate which is actually participating in the formation of intermediate complexes. It has been suggested that the non-hydrated periodate ion prevails but it is possible that undissociated periodic acid is also reacting with oxygen attached to the iodine by a similar bipolar bond. An examination of the reaction rate as a function of pH indicates that in the pH range 4–5 and slightly above, the rate of the reaction is independent of pH and second-order rate constants are obtained. As would be expected, in the presence of large excesses of the glycol, pseudo first-order constants are found. The catalysis by hydrogen ion becomes marked as the pH is dropped below 4, and if this catalysis is assumed to be first order, then the observed second-order rate constant must be corrected for a constant for the proton catalyzed reaction. This would seem to imply that the undissociated or hydrated species may be involved in the reaction as well as the monovalent periodate ion IO_4^-.

Several observations support the postulate that a cyclic intermediate is formed during the course of the reaction.

1. The presence of an intermediate, which is rate determining in the reaction, has been demonstrated for those glycols and only those glycols that have free rotation about the hydroxyl-bearing carbon atoms.

2. The equilibrium constants for formation of this type of intermediate generally decrease with increasing methyl substitution on carbon.

3. Glycols, which from steric considerations would not be expected to form cyclic intermediates, may be completely resistant to oxidation by periodate even when the hydroxyl groups are present on the adjacent carbon atoms. An example of this is *trans* dimethyl cyclopentane (1,2) diol.

4. *Cis* glycols in 5-membered rings are oxidized extremely rapidly by periodate with rates comparable to those observed for sugar alcohols. This is due to the fact that these groups are already in an eclipsed conformation and that rotation about the carbon–carbon bond is not required.

The cyclic intermediate will be most readily formed in those cases where the hydroxyl groups are eclipsed, but its exact nature has not been definitely determined. A study of salt and acid effects on the reaction rate indicates that the intermediate has a single negative charge and that it is almost certainly a 5-membered ring (Figure 7.82).

The oxidation of alkyl substituted *cis* diols with ^{18}O labeled periodate yields ketones which contain 0 percent ^{18}O [40]. Thus, the carbonyl group of the ketone arises exclusively from the hydroxyl group of the parent diol. The oxidation of α-β diketones appears to be a more direct attack of periodate as a nucleophile upon the carbonyl group, because, in this case, the product carboxylic acid contains 50 percent ^{18}O (Figure 7.83) [41]. The oxidation of

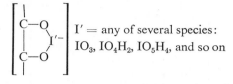

FIGURE 7.82 Cyclic intermediate form in which the group containing the iodine can be any one of several species, IO_3, IO_4H_2, IO_5H_4, and so on.

α-hydroxy ketones (Figure 7.84) shows that the hydroxyl which is on the carboxylic acid will contain ^{18}O if ^{18}O periodate is employed, whereas the ketone will contain no ^{18}O [42]. Because one of the two oxygen atoms of the product acid must have come from the carbonyl group of the hydroxy ketone and the other from either water or periodate, the results require that oxygen exchange of the carbonyl oxygen be slower than oxidation. There are two

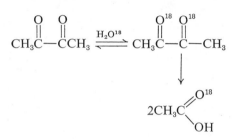

FIGURE 7.83 Reaction of 2,3-diketobutane with periodate in the presence of H_2O^{18}.

possible interpretations of these results. Direct nucleophilic attack by periodate upon the carbonyl is preferable to attack by periodate on the hydrated form because the latter scheme requires that the rate of the reaction is zero order with respect to periodate.

Several explanations have been proposed for the role of acid in the formation of the intermediate. It has been suggested that hydrogen ion catalysis requires a prior equilibration which gives rise to protonation of the reacting

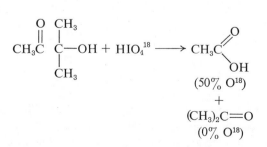

FIGURE 7.84 Oxidation of an α-hydroxy ketone with periodate ^{18}O.

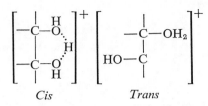

Cis   *Trans*

FIGURE 7.85   Possible formation of coordinated intermediate from *cis* and *trans* glycols.

glycol. This in turn reacts more readily with periodate than does the glycol itself. It is obvious that *cis* glycols could form a coordinate type protonated intermediate which would have a chelate 5-membered ring structure, whereas *trans* glycols could not (Figure 7.85). This is in agreement with the observation that methyl substitution increases the effectiveness of acid catalysis for *cis* glycols but has little effect on that for the *trans* isomers. The rate of intermediate formation in basic solution is decreased, possibly due to rate of periodate consumption which is very much dependent upon the stereochemistry of the hydroxyl

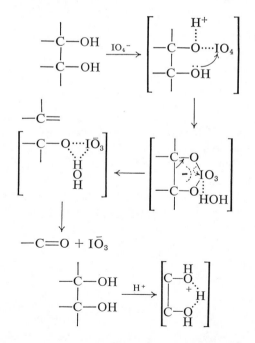

FIGURE 7.86   Reaction of *cis* glycols with periodate. The mechanism is the same as that depicted above, except that it might be considered that the chelated positively charged intermediate stabilized due to this chelation, is more readily attacked than the unchelated intermediate which would arise from the *trans* form.

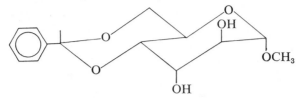

FIGURE 7.87 Methyl 4,6-benzylidene α-D-glucopyranoside with *trans* hydroxyl groups at carbon C-2 and C-3 is resistant to oxidation by periodate.

groups. It is to be expected that if the formation of half-esters and cyclic inter-mediates are requisite for periodate cleavage to occur, then those hydroxyl groups that are most readily distorted to a near planar configuration will react more rapidly than those where such distortion is hindered. *Cis* hydroxyls

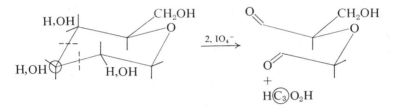

FIGURE 7.88 Initial reaction of periodate with the ring form of a carbohydrate to liberate C-3 as formic acid.

would be expected to react more rapidly than *trans*, and *trans* diaxial hydroxyls are expected to be relatively inert especially if there are fused ring systems or other steric constraints which prevent conformational shifts (Figures 7.86 and 7.87).

The most acceptable mechanism involves initial cleavage of chain second-ary hydroxyls to form dialdehydes, as in the case of mannose, glucose, and

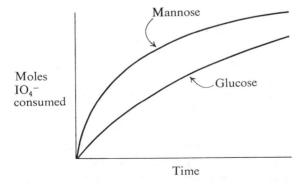

FIGURE 7.89 Rate of periodate consumption as a function of time for D-glucose and D-mannose.

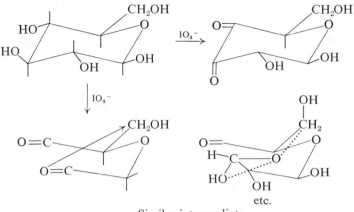

FIGURE 7.90   Oxidation of D-glucopyranose by periodate in the ring form followed by reaction of the aldehyde intermediate to yield a new hemiacetal group which is further attacked.

galactose where carbon 3 rapidly appears as formic acid (Figure 7.88). The subsequent reaction of this intermediate may follow several courses, in part explaining the complex kinetic curves obtained (Figure 7.89). One of the newly generated aldehyde functions condenses with either the anomeric hydroxyl or with the hydroxyl group at C-6 to form a new hemiacetal, thereby generating a new vicinal glycol. This intermediate then undergoes further cleavage (Figure 7.90). Where substituents are present which render oxidation relatively incomplete, such as in compounds substituted at the 6 position, the oxidation rates are far different from what would be expected on the basis of the open chain form of the sugar. Although ultimate consumption usually agrees with this kind of stoichiometry, the rate differences between sugars strongly support the above mechanism.

7.13 Reaction Conditions

Reaction conditions generally involve the use of excess sodium metaperiodate at a pH close to 4. Buffers may or may not be employed but overoxidation is clearly reduced if the reaction is carried out in the dark. The oxidation of simple compounds such as ethylene glycol is maximal between pH 2.5 and 6, and optimal oxidation of other carbohydrates proceeds in the range of pH 3 to 4. Oxidations at alkaline pH give confused results because of the further reactions of the generated aldehydes. Whenever other functional groups are present which may ionize, the pH optimum will be shifted. For example, oxidation of amino alcohols and the amino acids, serine and threonine, takes place optimally at pH 7.5, and several methylated glucose derivatives are also smoothly oxidized at this higher pH. This implies that the major cleaving species is the monovalent, nonhydrated periodate ion, IO_4^-.

Most oxidations are performed at room temperature but some evidence suggests that overconsumption of oxidant is avoided if the reactions are carried out at lower temperatures, where the reaction rates are not adversely affected.

The effect of light on the reaction is complex. Sodium metaperiodate itself will decompose in the presence of light to yield simultaneously sodium iodate and ozone. The ozone is an extremely active oxidizing agent as well as a free radical chain initiator and causes numerous side reactions. Structural studies on complex polysaccharides, where oxidations are generally slow due to the relatively rigid constraints imposed by the ring structures of the carbohydrates, demonstrate more than the theoretical periodate uptake if oxidations are carried out in the light. Thus, cellulose takes up 1.6 equivalents of oxidant per anhydro glucose residue when oxidized for 17 days in the presence of light but only the theoretical 1 equivalent when the same reaction is carried out in the dark. It is probable that the effects of light are significant only in long term reactions but when unknown structures are being investigated, reactions should be carried out in the dark.

7.14 Analyses

Periodate and iodate can be reduced to iodine by iodide ion according to the following stoichiometry:

$$IO_4^- + 7I^- + 8H^+ \longrightarrow 4H_2O + 4I_2$$
$$IO_3^- + 5I^- + 6H^+ \longrightarrow 3H_2O + 3I'_2$$
$$I_2 + S_2O_3^= \longrightarrow 2I^- + S_4O_6^=$$
$$\text{Excess } I_2 \xrightarrow{\text{amylose}} \text{Blue complex}$$

$$(7.5)$$

The free iodine liberated can then be titrated with standard thiosulfate solution to a starch end point. This is disadvantageous, however, if the iodine generated is capable of reacting with some of the intermediate oxidation products such as aldehydes. Accordingly, the most common analytical procedure is to treat the reaction mixture with an excess of arsenite to yield arsenate and iodate, respectively. The excess arsenite is then back titrated with standard iodine

$$IO_4^- + AsO_2^- \longrightarrow AsO_3^- + IO_3^-$$
$$\text{Excess } AsO_2^- + I_2 \xrightarrow{H_2O} AsO_3^- + 2I^- + 2H^+$$

$$(7.6)$$

This reaction sequence is satisfactory because the reaction between iodine and arsenite is extremely fast compared to any oxidative reaction of the iodine with aldehydes present in the solution. A recent method involves the use of ultraviolet spectrophotometry to measure iodate and periodate. Although this method has been criticized for studies of complex compounds, model studies on numerous simple carbohydrates give results that are in agreement with those obtained by titration data. In addition, the optical method has the advantage that extremely small amounts of material can be employed.

The commonly produced small molecules that are usually measured quantitatively are acetaldehyde, formaldehyde, and formic acid. The formaldehyde produced in the reaction can be measured colorimetrically by means of the chromotropic acid reagent according to the following reaction:

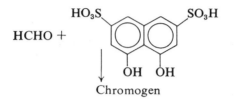

Chromogen

or by formation of the formaldehyde dimedon by condensation with dimethyl cyclohexane dione according to Figure 7.91 [43]. Because the weight of the

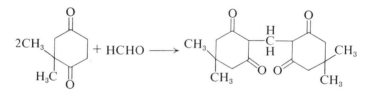

FIGURE 7.91   Condensation of formaldehyde with dimedon to form the crystalline formaldehyde dimedone.

formaldehyde dimedon is 10 times that of the starting formaldehyde and the condensation reaction is much faster with formaldehyde than with any other aldehyde, this is a very desirable reagent. Nevertheless, this reaction must be used with some caution, and determining the melting point and mixed melting points is necessary for adequate identification of the formaldehyde. Routine analyses, especially when limited by the amounts of material present, are carried out colorimetrically.

Acetaldehyde may be measured by means of bisulfite addition, enzymatic reduction with alcohol dehydrogenase, and direct colorimetry:

$$CH_3CHO + DPNH + H^+ \xrightarrow[\text{dehydrogenase}]{\text{Alcohol}} CH_3CH_2OH + DPN^+ \qquad (7.8)$$

Assay is by the change in absorbancy at 340 mμ. Molar extinction coefficient change is 6.22×10^3 for 1-cm pathlength.

The acetaldehyde is removed from the reaction mixture by a stream of carbon dioxide or by diffusion in an appropriate closed chamber and trapped in aqueous solution. Appropriate procedures may then be carried out.

Formic acid is most readily obtained by steam distillation of the reaction mixture, although procedures are available for direct titration of acidity produced during the reaction:

If a buffer is present, acidify, steam distill and titrate the distillate to phenolphthalein. Alternatively,

$$HCO_2H + HCO_3^- \xrightarrow{\text{pH 5.7}} HCOO^- + CO_2$$

Measure manometrically

(7.9)

Formic acid may also be quantitatively oxidized to carbon dioxide by mercuric salts, a technique of some importance in degradation of isotopically labeled sugars because the carbon dioxide thus generated can be swept out of the reaction mixture, precipitated as barium carbonate and assayed for radioactivity.

7.15 Use of Other Oxidizing Agents

There are numerous oxidizing agents commonly used in organic chemistry, such as permanganate and dichromate, which have relatively little application in the carbohydrate field. Nevertheless, there are certain selective situations in which these may be employed.

Potassium permanganate, although a strong oxidizing agent, can be used for the hydroxylation of suitably placed double bonds. Tetrahydroxy cyclohexene can be treated first with acetone to form the 2,3 isopropylidene 1,4 diol which, after protection of the hydroxyl groups by acetylation, can be hydroxylated with permanganate under controlled conditions to yield the fully substituted cyclohexane derivative (Figure 7.92) [44]. Permanganate can also be used for the

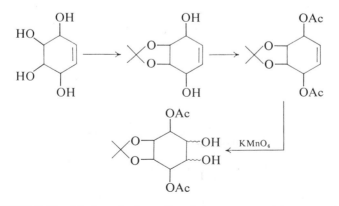

FIGURE 7.92   Hydroxylation of cyclohexene tetrol by potassium permanganate.

detection of oxidizable compounds on chromatograms, but is relatively non-specific, merely indicating susceptibility to oxidation.

A reagent that has been employed for the oxidation of carbohydrate secondary hydroxyls is the chromium trioxide-pyridine complex [45]. Although the yields of oxidized products are generally extremely small, some steric factors can be mentioned.

Oxidation of equatorial hydroxyls is generally rather nonspecific. Thus, oxidation of methyl-β-D-glucopyranoside yields a mixture of 2, 3, and 4 keto compounds, the 3 keto being obtained in the highest yield, 3.5 percent. The 2 and 4 keto products appear to be particularly labile perhaps by internal displacement reactions and were isolated in much smaller yields. In more specifically blocked compounds such as methyl 3,4 isopropylidene β-L-arabino-pyranoside, the oxidation gives a single keto product (Figure 7.93). Although

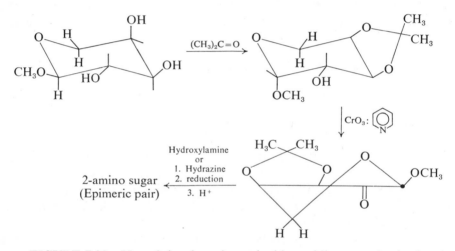

FIGURE 7.93   Use of the chromium trioxide pyridine complex in the synthesis of amino sugars.

this is obtained in low yield, it can be used as an intermediate in the preparation of amino sugars and other substituted carbohydrates. Table 7.12 illustrates the yield of keto compounds isolated after oxidation of methyl glycopyranosides with several different oxidants [46].

There seems to be relatively little specificity as far as position is concerned but axial hydroxyls are much less susceptible than equatorial hydroxyls to oxidation by this reagent. This suggests direct attack on oxygen rather than on hydrogen. There is relatively little information about the oxidation of oligo or polysaccharides with the exception of the generally recognized ability of reagents such as nitrogen tetroxide to oxidize primary alcohol functions to carboxylic acids.

TABLE 7.12

Oxidation of chain hydroxyls by oxidizing agents, such as chromium
trioxide-pyridine or platinum-oxygen.

COMPOUND	PROCEDURE	YIELD
Me β-D-xylopyranoside	CrO_3-Acetone	3-keto, 3.5 percent. Others less than 0.5 percent.
Me-α-D-ribopyranoside	$Pt—O_2$	3-keto, 6 percent.
Me-α-D-glucopyranoside	CrO_3-Acetone[a]	3-keto, up to 5 percent. Others also.
Benzyl-β-L-arabinopyranoside	$Pt—O_2$	4-keto, 15 percent.
Me, 4,6 Bzd β-D-galactopyranoside	CrO_3-Acetone	2 and 3-keto, 1 percent.
Me, 2,3 IPD L-rhamnofuranoside	CrO_3-Pyridine	Exocyclic 5-keto, 75 percent.

[a] Other oxidizing agents give other products or varying yields.

The use of finely divided platinum catalysts together with oxygen as an oxidizing system has been extensively investigated in the carbohydrate field [47]. The mechanism of this oxidation has not been thoroughly worked out but considerable stereochemical information is available; the most susceptible site of attack is the primary alcohol group. Satisfactory syntheses of substituted uronides, nucleoside diphosphouronides, uronic acid phosphates, and similar compounds have been carried out by oxidation of the corresponding aldoses with platinum and oxygen. The yields in the case of the glucose series are optimal because equatorial hydroxyls are extremely resistant to attack by this reagent. The conclusion from this result is that attack by oxygen is on the carbon bound hydrogen rather than on the hydroxyl; axial hydrogens are relatively unsusceptible due to steric factors. It is also possible that the stereochemistry of adsorption to the catalyst surface is pertinent.

The general concept of dehydrogenation as a mechanism has been confirmed by some investigations of the potential of the catalyst. The catalyst potential during oxidation is strongly on the hydrogen side rather than on the oxygen side and thus the catalyst must be saturated with hydrogen as it would be in the case of a hydrogen electrode. The catalyst may remove hydrogen directly from carbon to form an enol type intermediate and the subsequent reaction of this with water yields the final product. The oxidation of ethanol to acetic acid in the presence of ^{18}O gives rise to some ^{18}O in the product. This is mainly derived from water rather than from the oxygen used during the oxidation. This would also tend to support the dehydrogenation mechanism although isotopic exchange of the intermediate acetaldehyde could also explain this result. For reasons that are not entirely clear, platinum on carbon is a relatively inefficient catalyst. Only those compounds or substrates that are very readily attacked, such as aldehydes, are oxidized at appreciable rates, whereas other substrates are only slowly attacked. Several forms of platinum catalysts have been investigated particularly in an effort to exert control in situations where further oxidation of the product is not desired. A partially deactivated catalyst, such as 5 percent platinum on activated carbon, is frequently used. The platinum is deposited on carbon by reduction of platinum oxide with formaldehyde or hydrazine. Relatively little information is available on the effects of pH, substrate concentration, or oxygen pressure.

In general, double bonds are not attacked under the conditions of catalytic oxidation and geometric isomers retain their configurations. However, primary

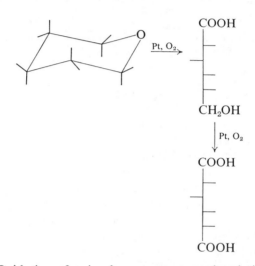

FIGURE 7.94 Oxidation of a simple pyranose sugar by platinum and oxygen.

amino groups, halogenated compounds, and tertiary amino groups are oxidized, whereas mercaptal groups serve their usual role of catalyst poison and inhibit oxidation.

Aldoses are readily oxidized to aldonic acids under rather mild conditions. The oxidation of D-glucose in the presence of the theoretical amount of alkali required to combine with the generated D-gluconic acid proceeds in nearly quantitative yield at room temperature or more rapidly at 55 degrees. More severe reaction conditions cause a sufficient increase in the rate of oxidation of the primary hydroxyl to give a 50 percent yield of glucaric acid (Figure 7.94). In the ketose series, the hydroxyl at C-1 adjacent to the carbonyl carbon is activated by that functional group so that this can be oxidized nearly as readily as the aldehydo group of an aldose (Figure 7.95). This is sufficiently rapid so that selective oxidation may be achieved without significant attack at C-6. By this process, oxidation of L-sorbose will produce 2-keto L-gulonic acid which can then be converted to ascorbic acid (Figure 7.96) [48].

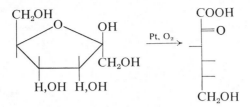

FIGURE 7.95 Oxidation of the hydroxymethyl group α to the carbonyl function by platinum and oxygen.

Axial hydroxyls are oxidized to the corresponding carbonyl compound at appreciable rates and this has been the basis for the synthesis of several di-carbonyl carbohydrates (Figure 7.97). This is also consistent with the proposed mechanism, because the proton on carbon is equatorial. Further oxidation of this functional group will generally result in chain cleavage, and a wide variety of products are subsequently obtained.

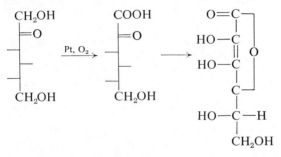

FIGURE 7.96 Synthesis of ascorbic acid.

2-amino sugars are smoothly oxidized by oxygen to the amino aldonic acids using platinum on carbon as catalyst (Figure 7.98) [49].

Because hypoiodite is not a feasible oxidizing agent for this conversion, this procedure is preferable to that employing mercuric oxide. The synthesis of amino uronic acids requires blocking of both the aldehydo function and the amino group because the oxidation of the primary hydroxyl at C-6 requires

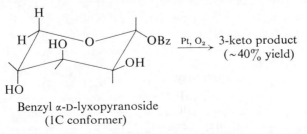

Benzyl α-D-lyxopyranoside
(1C conformer)

FIGURE 7.97 Oxidation of benzyl-α-D-lyxopyranoside by platinum and oxygen to yield a 3 keto product in 40 percent yield.

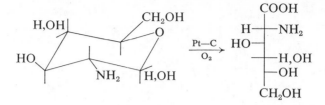

FIGURE 7.98 Oxidation of D-glucosamine to yield D-glucosaminic acid catalyzed by platinum and oxygen.

reaction conditions that are considerably more rigorous than that for oxidation of C-1. However, use of the *N*-carbobenzoxy glycoside permits relatively smooth oxidation and if the benzylglycoside is employed, the blocking groups can both be removed by hydrogenolysis (Figure 7.99).

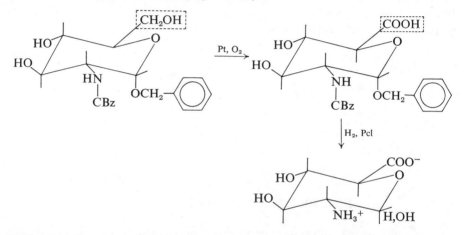

FIGURE 7.99 Oxidation of the C-6 equatorial hydroxymethyl group to carboxyl by platinum and oxygen.

Considerable application has been made of the catalytic oxidation process to studies in the cyclitol field. There are nine known isomers of the hexahydroxy-cyclohexanes that differ only in their arrangement of the hydroxyl groups (Figure 7.100). The more stable chair forms are generally energetically preferred, and in cases where all groups would be equatorial or only one group axial, only a single chair form is likely to be encountered. However, in cases where three axial and three equatorial hydroxyls are present, it is not possible to predict which ring form is present. Scyllo inositol, for example, exists in the chair form with all groups equatorial; myo inositol has a single axial hydroxyl; epi, neo, dextro, and levo have two axial hydroxyl groups; muco-, allo, and cis have three axial and three equatorial groups. Although the nomenclature is somewhat confusing, some general oxidation rules are pertinent. The axial hydroxyl in myo inositol is readily oxidized to give a good yield of the inosose

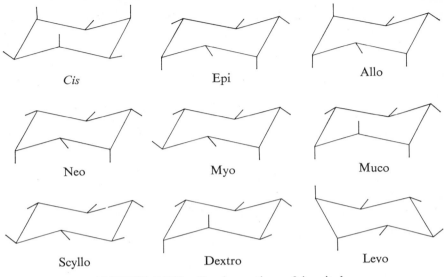

FIGURE 7.100 Conformation of inositols.

(Figure 7.101) [50]. This oxidation stops at the monoketone stage with only a trivial amount of ring fission and further oxidation. This product is identical to that formed by bacterial oxidation of myo inositol using *Acetobacter suboxydans*. The reason for this corresponding activity may relate to the mechanism of enzymatic oxidation.

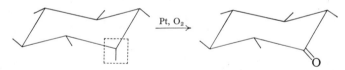

FIGURE 7.101 Stereospecific oxidation of inositols to the monoketo derivative by platinum and oxygen.

When an axial hydroxyl group is free, this will be preferentially oxidized especially when other functional groups are blocked. Other derivatives in the cyclitol field undergo similar reactions. Epi inositol, which has two axial hydroxyls, yields a mixture of stereoisomeric monoketo products, and further reaction is probably prevented by the formation of a cyclic ketal derivative (Figure 7.102). It is interesting to note that reduction of inosose with hydrogen in the presence of a platinum catalyst proceeds in a stereospecific manner, regenerating the axial hydroxl group. In this sense stereospecific reversibility exists despite the fact that this isomer is definitely not energetically favored. Reduction with sodium borohydride yields the thermodynamically preferred equatorial isomer.

When the two axial hydroxyl groups in such a molecule are sterically

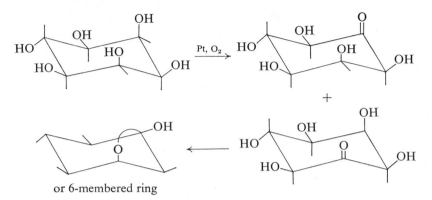

FIGURE 7.102 Oxidation of an inositol derivative by platinum and oxygen yielding the monoketone which is stabilized by formation of an internal hemiketal.

equivalent, they will be oxidized at comparable rates. However, if both hydroxyl groups, although axial, are symmetrically not equivalent, a high specificity may be exhibited by the catalysts. The best illustration of this is the oxidation of (+) pinitol wherein only the hydroxyl group at C-1 is attacked and not the other axial hydroxyl (Figure 7.103) [51]. There are several such examples in the cyclitol field.

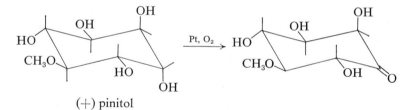

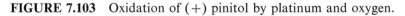

FIGURE 7.103 Oxidation of (+) pinitol by platinum and oxygen.

The steric requirements for cyclitol oxidation by platinum–oxygen may be summarized as follows:

1. Only axial hydroxyl groups are attacked.
2. The oxidation is also applicable to suitably blocked derivatives.
3. The reaction generally proceeds only to the stage of the monoketone even if there is more than one axial hydroxyl group present in the molecule.
4. If there are two equivalent axial hydroxyls present, they will be oxidized at the same rate to give similar products. However, if the axial hydroxyls are nonequivalent, it is expected that only one of these will be preferentially oxidized.

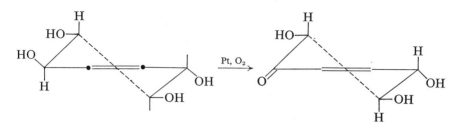

FIGURE 7.104 Oxidation of conduritol.

5. In the case of a cyclohexene tetrol such as conduritol, which is in a half-chair conformation, oxidation proceeds with axial and pseudoequatorial groups attacked in preference to other hydroxyl groups (Figure 7.104) [52]. The oxidation stops at the monoketone stage as it does in the inositol series. The susceptibility of the hydroxyl groups adjacent to the double bond has no known exceptions but this is not explicable by steric factors alone. It is probable that electronic interactions are also involved.

7.16 Bacterial Oxidations

The bacterial oxidation of sugar alcohols to give keto compounds has been known for some time and is the basis of several commercial processes. L-sorbose is prepared via prior reduction of D-glucose to sorbitol followed by bacterial oxidation (Figure 7.105) [53].

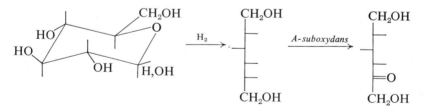

FIGURE 7.105 Production of L-sorbose by bacterial oxidation of D-glucitol.

The steric requirements for oxidation are fairly straightforward—a *cis* pair of secondary hydroxyls adjacent to the primary alcoholic function. The secondary hydroxyl adjacent to the primary hydroxyl is oxidized to a keto group (Figure 7.106). If the terminal group is methyl, it can be considered as though it were hydrogen and oxidation will occur at the third carbon from the terminus rather than at the second.

The organism most commonly employed is *Acetobacter suboxydans*. Several examples are given in Figure 7.107. The bacterial oxidation is not limited

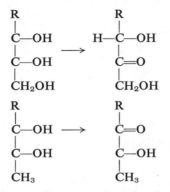

FIGURE 7.106 Steric requirements for the bacterial oxidation of sugar alcohols.

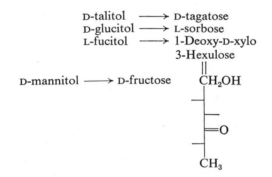

FIGURE 7.107 Oxidations carried out by *Acetobacter suboxydans*.

to open chain carbohydrates because inositols such as myo inositol are also susceptible.

There are a wide variety of enzymes known that catalyze oxidative reactions involving carbohydrates. Several of these are worthy of specific mention because they form the basis for highly selective enzymatic assays for specific sugars.

The most widely utilized enzyme in this group is probably the glucose oxidase produced by several species of penicillium. The stoichiometry of the reaction catalyzed by glucose oxidase is illustrated in Figure 7.108. The enzyme

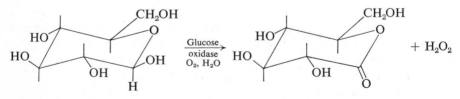

FIGURE 7.108 Oxidation of D-glucose by glucose oxidase. Reaction is highly specific for the β form.

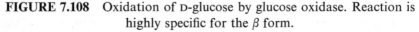

is highly specific for β-D-glucose, and the only other substrate that reacts to a significant extent is 2-deoxy-D-glucose [54]. Typical reaction rates are summarized in Table 7.13. Because the other product of the reaction is hydrogen

TABLE 7.13

Oxidation of various sugars by glucose oxidase. Relative rates to β-D-glucose as 100.

SUGAR	RELATIVE RATE
β-D-glucose	100
2-deoxy-D-glucose	25
6-methyl-D-glucose	1.85
D-mannose	1
D-xylose	1
α-D-glucose	0.64
D-altrose	0.16
D-galactose	0.14
D-glucuronate	∼0.04
D-glucosamine	∼0.03

Inactive: D-idose, D-talose, D-allose, D-gulose, D-fructose, 2 or 3 *O*-methyl D-glucose, all di or tri *O*-methyl glucoses and other simple sugars.

peroxide, this enzymatic glucose analysis generally couples the peroxide production to a peroxidase system and a leuco dye, the oxidation of which produces a suitable chromogen which can be measured spectrophotometrically (Figure 7.109) [55].

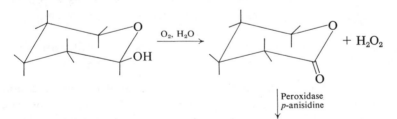

Oxidized dye (yellow) λ_{max} at 401 mμ

FIGURE 7.109 Analytical procedure for the assay of glucose by glucose oxidase depends on the further reaction of the generated hydrogen peroxide as illustrated.

An enzyme has recently been described that is relatively specific for D-galactose although 2-amino-2-deoxy-D-galactose and its *N*-acetyl derivative also react. This enzyme, which is a copper containing protein, is particularly interesting because it catalyzes an oxidation reaction according to the scheme illustrated in Figure 7.110 [56].

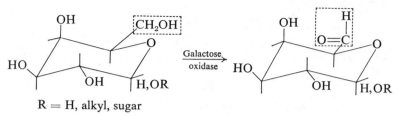

R = H, alkyl, sugar

FIGURE 7.110   Reaction catalyzed by galactose oxidase.

In this case, the oxidation of the terminal hydroxyl methyl to yield an alde-hydo function can also be carried out on galactosides. Oxidation of nonreducing galactose derivatives to the dialdose stage can be followed by oxidation of the newly formed aldehyde to a carboxylic acid with reagents such as bromine water (Figure 7.111). In this manner, galactose can be converted to galacturonic acid

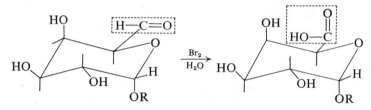

FIGURE 7.111   Further oxidation of the product of galactose oxidase action results in the formation of a uronic acid derivative.

within an oligosaccharide. This is a useful technique for obtaining selective disaccharides by partial acid hydrolysis due to the increased stability of the uronidic bond. Because this system also produces peroxide as a product, a coupled assay similar to the glucose one described above can be employed for quantitative colorimetry.

The oxidation of glucose in mammalian systems is generally carried out in one of two ways.

1. Dissimilation of the carbohydrate to the level of pyruvate can be achieved without any oxidative steps (Figure 7.112). The energy present in pyruvate is then released by combustion to CO_2 and water via the tricarboxylic acid cycle (Figure 7.113).

2. The alternative scheme of oxidation employed diverges from the above after the initial phosphorylation of glucose to yield D-glucose-6-phosphate. Oxidation takes place at the 1 position according to the reaction illustrated in Figure 7.114.[3] The next step in this pathway is also an oxidative one. The intermediate 3-keto compound is thought to spontaneously decarboxylate on

[3] This reaction can also be utilized to assay for glucose by employing a hexokinase in the first step and the dehydrogenase in the second. The reaction is followed by the specific spectrophotometric absorption of reduced pyridine nucleotide at 340 mμ. This is a highly sensitive procedure because the molar extinction coefficient for the reduced pyridine nucleo-tide is 6.2×10^3 (Figure 7.115).

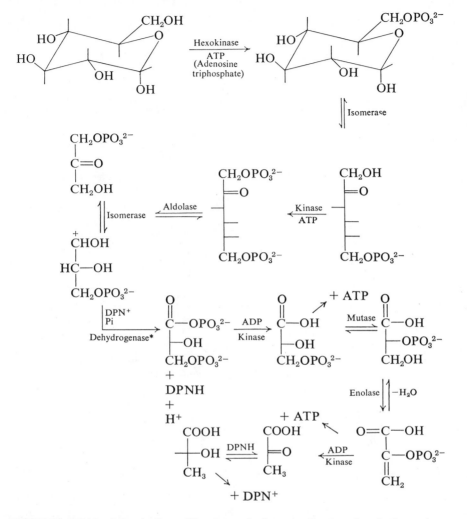

FIGURE 7.112 Metabolic utilization of glucose via the glycolytic pathway. The reaction of D-glyceraldehyde 3-phosphate with DPN^+ and phosphate is an oxidative step but the pyridine nucleotide is present in catalytic quantities and is regenerated by reaction with pyruvate or oxidation by mitochondrial systems using oxygen as the ultimate electron acceptor.

Dehydrogenase (*)—Apparently an oxidative step, but DPN^+ can be regenerated and thus, no net oxidation takes place, nor is there an oxygen requirement.

the enzyme surface but whether this is facilitated by specific groups on the protein is not known. The ribulose 5-phosphate is reconverted to glucose 6-phosphate by the sequence of reactions illustrated in Figure 7.116. Note that

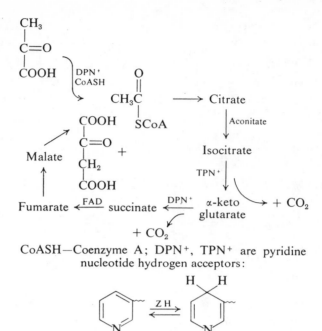

CoASH—Coenzyme A; DPN+, TPN+ are pyridine nucleotide hydrogen acceptors:

FIGURE 7.113 Further oxidation of pyruvate by the tricarboxylic acid cycle. The pyridine nucleotides are hydrogen acceptors which react as shown.

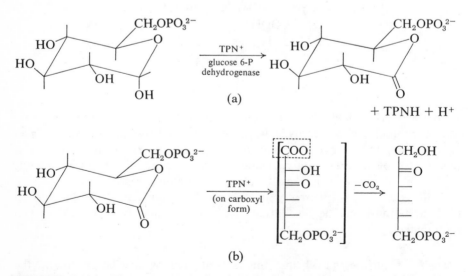

FIGURE 7.114 First two steps in the catabolism of glucose by the direct oxidative pathway.

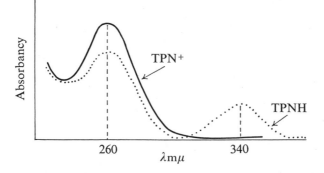

FIGURE 7.115 Absorption spectrum of oxidized and reduced pyridine nucleotide; the spectra are substantially the same for DPN$^+$ and TPN$^+$. Assay techniques depend on the unique absorbance of the reduced form at 340 mμ.

none of these steps are oxidative but merely provide a return route to the C-6 level. The production of CO_2 from the carbonyl of the glucose has been utilized in isotopic tracer experiments to assess the extent to which this pathway is operative.

The enzymatic oxidation of other carbohydrates, such as galactose, mannose, fructose, amino sugars, and so on, for carbon and energy sources generally proceeds via intermediates similar to those obtained from the oxidation of glucose. For example, amino sugars are converted to the corresponding ketoses by an isomerase type reaction (Figure 7.117). Mannose and fructose are converted to glucose derivatives in the same fashion. The reactions described above are currently the most pertinent for oxidative enzymatic analysis of carbohydrates. There are numerous other specific enzymes that are employed for the estimation of carbohydrates; these are discussed in Chapter 14.

7.17 Polysaccharides

The oxidation of oligo and polysaccharides, although of some commercial importance, has not been extensively studied from a theoretical viewpoint. In most cases, oxidations are carried out to generate carboxyl functions which are then substituted or, when anionic products are desired, left unchanged. The most common oxidizing agents are halogen, nitrogen tetroxide, and hydrogen peroxide. The oxidations take place mainly at the primary alcohol function to yield the uronic acid derivatives, although the oxidation of secondary hydroxyls can also occur. Keto derivatives are invariably further substituted, with

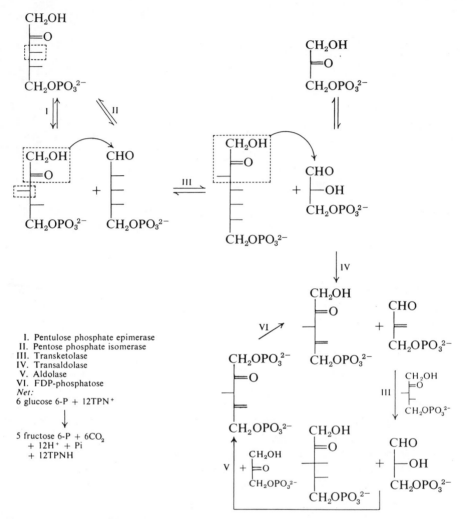

I. Pentulose phosphate epimerase
II. Pentose phosphate isomerase
III. Transketolase
IV. Transaldolase
V. Aldolase
VI. FDP-phosphatose
Net:
6 glucose 6-P + 12TPN⁺

5 fructose 6-P + 6CO₂
  + 12H⁺ + Pi
  + 12TPNH

FIGURE 7.116 Reactions associated with the direct oxidative pathway of glucose catabolism leading to the regeneration of hexose.

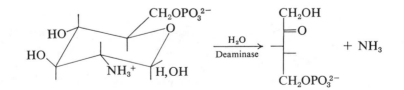

FIGURE 7.117 Enzymatic deamination of D-glucosamine 6-phosphate. This is a type of isomerase reaction.

hydrazine for example, and provide a class of sizing agents (Figure 7.118). Relatively little stereochemical information is available.

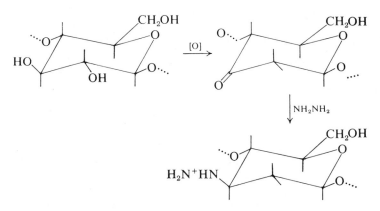

FIGURE 7.118 Reaction of oxidized cellulose with hydrazine to form a cationically substituted derivative.

7.18 Photooxidation of Carbohydrates

Photooxidation of sugars by exposure to ultraviolet light generally occurs from the "underside" of the molecule, where the axial CH bonds are somewhat more accessible (Figure 7.119). β-D-galactose is oxidized faster than β-D-glucose

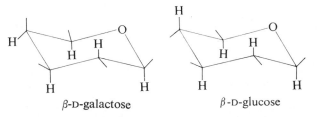

β-D-galactose   β-D-glucose

Axial hydrogens at C1,3,5
and Eq. at C4 accessible

FIGURE 7.119 Hydrogen positions of D-glucose and D-galactose. The axial hydrogens at positions 1, 3, and 5 are susceptible to photo-oxidation.

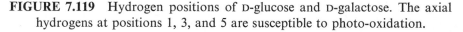

with the α analogs being in the same order and slower [57]. This relates to the relative accessibility of the underside CH bonds. The mechanism of photo-oxidative reactions has not been extensively studied but presumably proceeds via free radical intermediates (Table 7.14).

TABLE 7.14

Relative rates of photooxidation of carbohydrates
at 2500 Å.

CARBOHYDRATE	RELATIVE RATES OF OXIDATION (2500 Å uv)
β-D-galactose	100
α-D-galactose	43
β-D-glucose	72
α-D-glucose	31
β-D-mannose	93
α-D-xylose	37
Me α-D-glucopyranoside	27
Me β-D-glucopyranoside	45
Me α-D-mannopyranoside	36
Sucrose	44

CHAPTER 8

Structure Analysis by Periodate and Lead Tetraacetate

8.1 Polysaccharide Structure Analysis by Periodate

The application of periodate to the study of polysaccharide and oligosaccharide structure is almost limitless. In the ideal situation, a simple linear polysaccharide can be examined both for periodate consumption and for either acid production or for the products of periodate cleavage that may still be attached to carbon chains (Figure 8.1). Such dialdehydes will result from

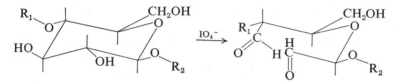

FIGURE 8.1 Reaction of a segment of the cellulose molecule with periodate. R_1 and R_2 represent additional glucose residues and the cleavage takes place between hydroxyls at C-2 and C-3.

cleavage between carbons 2 and 3 or 3 and 4 without concomitant production of formic acid or formaldehyde. A polymer containing aldohexopyranoside units linked 1,3 will be completely resistant to oxidation by periodate (Figure 8.2). However, the failure to consume periodate cannot be taken as definitive

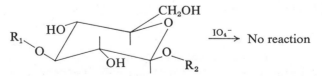

FIGURE 8.2 Reaction of periodate with laminarin. R_1 and R_2 represent glucose and as can be seen because there are no adjacent hydroxyl groups there is no reaction with the oxidizing agent.

277

evidence for the exclusive presence of this kind of linkage. Polymers that contain 1,4 linkages may undergo oxidation at C-2, C-3 very slowly, particularly if the hydroxyls are *trans* and if there are bulky or anionic substituent groups present. However, consumption of 1 mole of carbohydrate per mole of sugar does not permit us to distinguish between 1,2 and 1,4 linkages (Figure 8.3).

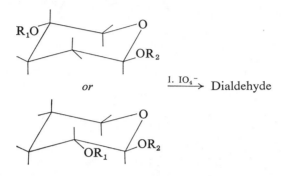

FIGURE 8.3 Typical segment of a polysaccharide chain substituted at C-4 or C-2 where reaction with periodate will give rise to a dialdehyde.

It should be apparent that the type of information obtained from these studies is limited in several ways.

1. When dealing with a linear homopolymer (see Chapter 12) with uniform linkages, straightforward consumption and product formation are expected.
2. When a polymer has mixed linkages, integral molar consumption of periodate may not occur. For example, 1→3 linkages will be resistant, 1→6 linkages will consume 2 moles of periodate and produce 1 mole of formic acid, and so on.
3. Branched polymers will consume at least 2 moles per nonreducing end, making assignments within the chain more difficult.
4. Differentiation between very slow rates of consumption due to steric hindrance and slow overoxidation is frequently difficult.
5. The information obtained is a composite average of all linkages and structures; details of fine structure are not revealed.

Aspects of the above problems have been examined in several laboratories. One of the most useful approaches is that developed by Smith and co-workers [1]. This procedure involves periodate oxidation of the polymer, reduction of the newly formed aldehyde groups to alcohols with sodium borohydride, mild acid hydrolysis of the resulting polyalcohol, and identification of products (Figure 8.4). In this case, the glycol, glycerol, or tetritol groups that are formed as a result

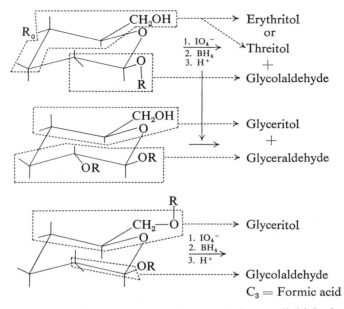

FIGURE 8.4 Application of the Smith degradation to dialdehydes formed by periodate oxidation in polysaccharides. The indicated products are formed after reduction by hydrolysis.

of the borohydride reduction are extremely acid labile and may be readily cleaved from the bulk of the polysaccharide molecule without extensive hydrolysis of the pyranoside linkages (Figure 8.5). Failure to reduce to the polyalcohol yields extremely complicated results after acid hydrolysis due to the tendency of the polyaldehydes to undergo numerous side reactions. Isolated branching and isolated furanoside linkages can be detected by careful analysis of the alcohol products. The sensitivity of the procedure is greatly enhanced by the use of gas-liquid chromatography for the identification of the polyol fragments (Figure 8.6).

A typical example of the utility of the Smith degradation is discussed below (Figure 8.7).

The fine structure of a natural dextran obtained from a strain of Leuconostoc mesenteroides was examined, as shown in Figure 8.8 [2]. The usual procedures of partial hydrolysis and acetolysis were performed on the dextran and fragments identified as glucose, isomaltose, nigerose (3-α-D-glucopyranosyl-D-glucose), and a trisaccharide (characterized as α-D-glucopyranosyl 1,6-α-D-glucopyranosyl 1,3-D-glucose) were obtained and all were satisfactorily identified. The combined presence of these products established at least 1,3 and 1,6 linkages but neither the fine structure nor the type and extent of branching could be readily determined from these data. One question that remained was the possible existence of sequential 1,3 linkages in the parent polysaccharide. Because a nigerotriose

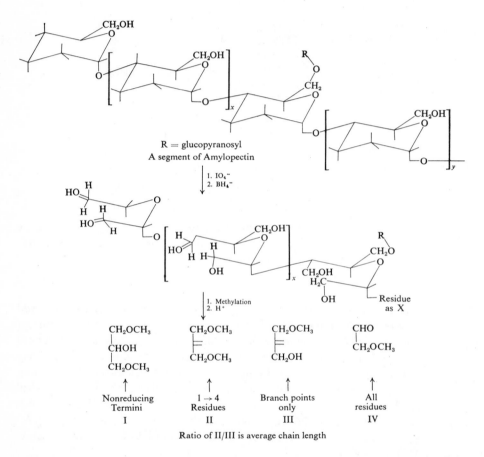

R = glucopyranosyl
A segment of Amylopectin

Ratio of II/III is average chain length

FIGURE 8.5 Application of the Smith degradation to the structural study of amylopectin. The indicated products arise after methylation and hydrolysis and their ratio gives average chain length.

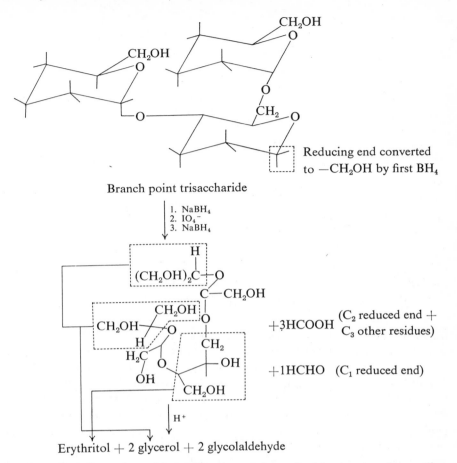

FIGURE 8.6   Detection of branching in a polysaccharide structure by application of the Smith degradation.

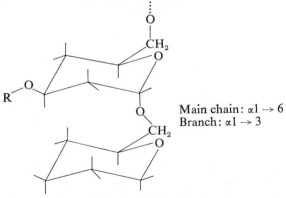

FIGURE 8.7   Application of the Smith degradation to examination of the fine structure of a Leuconostoc dextran.

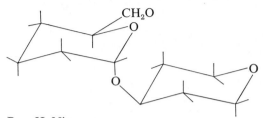

R = H, Nigerose
R = α-D-glucopyranosyl, trisaccharide fragment

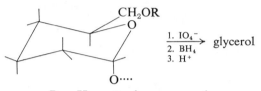

R = H or α-D-glucopyranosyl

FIGURE 8.8   Segment of a structure of the dextran with main chain containing α1 → 6 linkages and branch points containing α1 → 3 linkages.

fragment could not be detected in any of the partial hydrolysates, this would seem to preclude sequential 1,3 linkages. However, this negative evidence was not sufficient and a further study was made by use of the Smith degradation. The parent dextran was oxidized with periodate, reduced with borohydride, and hydrolyzed with dilute mineral acid according to the method previously described. Both glycerol from nonreducing end groups and 1,6 linked glucose units could be identified. The major additional product was nonreducing and was subjected to periodate oxidation. The pattern obtained was consistent with assignment of its structure as 1-*O*-glucopyranosyl glycerol which might be expected to arise from a 3-substituted glucose joined in a 1,6 linkage to the next glucose residue, according to Figure 8.9. Two other nonreducing substances

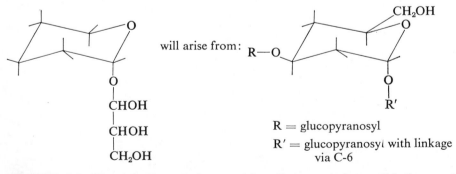

will arise from:

R = glucopyranosyl
R′ = glucopyranosyl with linkage via C-6

FIGURE 8.9   Degradation products arising from periodate oxidation and borohydride reduction of dextran.

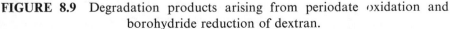

appeared in trace amounts: one of these yielded glucose and glycerol on hydrolysis and chromatographically did not behave as a disaccharide derivative.

A consideration of structural features requires that oligosaccharide segments containing sequential 1,3 linkages would be resistant to attack by periodate, and thus, would give rise to disaccharide or larger derivatives containing sugar alcohol substituents after application of the periodate-borohydride sequence. Because no such fragments could be identified, the conclusion was reached that the majority of the 1,3 glycosidic bonds in this polymer were isolated from one another, and that branching was either very extensive or a considerable amount of 1,6 linkage was present.

Equally useful information might have been obtained from a study of methylation patterns. However, these will give only an average picture of linkage groups without any indication as to their frequency, frequency of branching, or the possible presence of isolated branches in such a structure. The primary advantage of the above procedure is its utility in determining isolated branches and its applicability to problems of unusual linkages in polysaccharides.

A second degradation procedure that has been applied to oxidation products formed by the action of periodate on complex polysaccharides was developed by Barry [3]. The reaction sequences with oxidized polysaccharides are illustrated in Figure 8.10. Aqueous solutions of periodate oxidized starch were treated with phenylhydrazine to yield a yellow amorphous precipitate. Upon heating this material, very rapid cleavage of the glycosidic linkage at the altered residues takes place without the necessity for using acid catalysis, thus avoiding hydrolysis of unreacted units. The starch product readily yields glyoxal bis-phenylhydrazone as a crystalline derivative.

This general scheme has been applied to examine isolated nonreducing ends in polysaccharides such as the glucan (containing predominantly 1,3 linkages) of yeast cell walls. Because 1,3 linked polysaccharides are only oxidized at terminal sugar units, the oxidation of such residues eliminates carbon 3 as formic acid; carbons 2 and 4 are oxidized to the aldehyde stage. Treatment with phenylhydrazine yields a rapid separation of glyoxal bis-phenylhydrazone and simultaneously, the carbohydrate chain is shortened by one glucose unit (Figure 8.11). The polymer may be readily recovered from solution by alcohol precipitation and the process may then be repeated. In this way, for example, the presence of isolated 1,4 or 1,6 linkages in the chain could be ascertained and also branch points and chain length can be estimated. The results obtained by Barry for the yeast glucan indicated one terminal nonaldehyde unit per 16 hexoses or a chain length of about 16 units. Other condensing agents besides phenylhydrazine have been employed in this degradative scheme. Cyclohexylamine rapidly yields the crystalline Schiff base of glyoxal; phenylene diamine and substituted anilines have also been used.

It is interesting to note that analysis of condensation products at the polymer stage shows that the potential dialdehyde groups, which are capable of reacting with the carbonyl reagent, react with 1 rather than with 2 moles of the

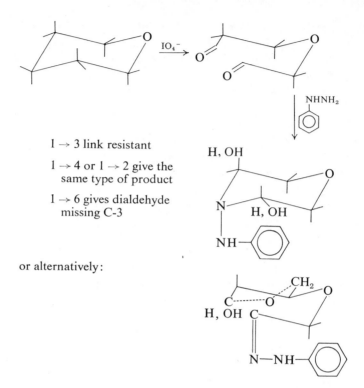

1 → 3 link resistant

1 → 4 or 1 → 2 give the
same type of product

1 → 6 gives dialdehyde
missing C-3

or alternatively:

FIGURE 8.10 The schematic representation of the Barry degradation as applied to carbohydrate residues and a polysaccharide chain.

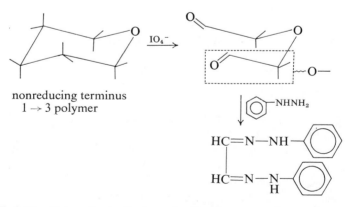

nonreducing terminus
1 → 3 polymer

FIGURE 8.11 Formation of glyoxal phenylosazone from the nonreducing termini in the 1,3 linked polysaccharide.

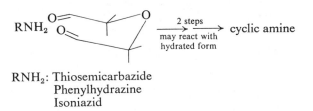

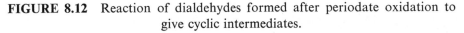

RNH₂: Thiosemicarbazide
Phenylhydrazine
Isoniazid

FIGURE 8.12 Reaction of dialdehydes formed after periodate oxidation to give cyclic intermediates.

reagent. It was thus postulated that the amino group acts as a bridging agent between the dialdehyde, as illustrated in Figure 8.12. Because such a condensation would now result in the regeneration of a center of asymmetry, it is possible that during the course of the reaction involving these aldehyde groups, a large change in optical rotation could be observed. This phenomenon can be demonstrated and roughly correlated with the number of reactive groups. A direct estimation of the proportion of α-1,2 glycol groups in various polysaccharides may be made.

TABLE 8.1

Results of Barry degradation on several polysaccharides. Periodate oxidation followed by condensation with thiosemicarbazide. Calculated values based on results of methylation experiment.

POLYMER	EXPECTED N	INCORPORATION S	FOUND N	FOUND S
Amylose	16.7	12.7	16.1	12.1
Amylopectin	16.7	12.7	15.9	11.8
Corn starch	16.7	12.7	15.2	11.8
Alginic acid	15.8	12.1	17.5	13

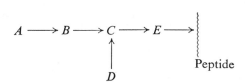

FIGURE 8.13 Schematic glycopeptide structure. *A*, *B*, and so on represent sugars. During the action of periodate *A* and *D* are rapidly destroyed, *B* and *E* will be destroyed at a much lower rate or they will be completely resistant. *C* will be cleaved by periodate only if hydroxyls at positions 2 and 3 are free. The removal of residues by borohydride reduction and mild hydrolysis and a repeat of the oxidation will establish the order in which the residues occur.

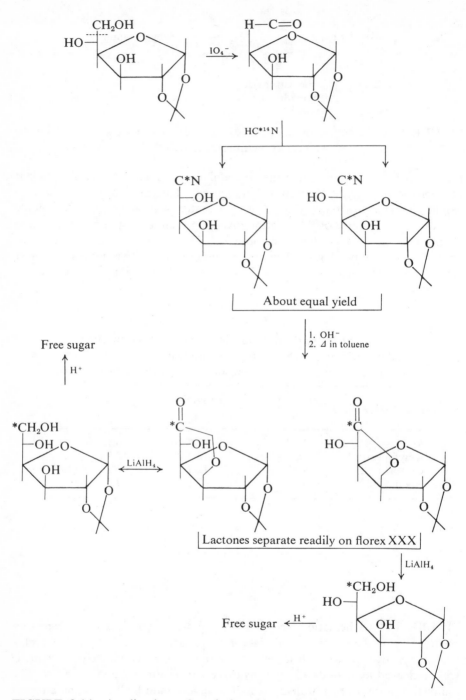

FIGURE 8.14 Application of periodate in synthetic sequences to prepared isotopically labeled sugars.

Amylose contains glucose units almost exclusively linked α-1,4, whereas in alginic acid, the mannuronic acid units are β-1,4 linked. After periodate oxidation of these polymers, each hexose or hexuronic acid unit initially present provides a potential reactive site for the condensation of 1 mole of carbonyl reagent. The proportion of glycol groups in such polysaccharides can then be obtained by analysis of the condensation products. The results obtained are illustrated in Table 8.1 and show remarkably good agreement with the expected values.

Periodate oxidation techniques have also been applied to the study of oligosaccharides and glycopeptides in an effort to get preliminary structural information prior to carrying out methylation studies. The establishment of linkage may not be possible from periodate oxidation results, but the rates of consumption and the rates of disappearance of individual monosaccharide residues are indicative of the types of linkages present and the order of the sugar units (Figure 8.13). In a study on glycopeptides derived from a serum globulin, it was found that rapid periodate consumption coincided with initial loss first of the glucosamine units and sequentially of the mannose and then the galactose. It was inferred from these results that the structure of the oligosaccharide moiety was such that the glucosamine was peripheral and the mannose and galactose portions closer to the peptide unit. Similarly, advantage has been taken of specific reaction with periodate to selectively destroy terminal nonreducing ends in both oligo and polysaccharides.

Numerous uses of periodate in synthetic sequences have been reported. These include the preparation of isotopically labeled sugars such as D-glucose 6-C^{14} (Figure 8.14), and sugars of the ido configuration [4]. Periodate has also been particularly useful in the degradation of isotopically labeled sugars to yield formaldehyde and formic acid from specific carbon atoms depending upon the structure under consideration. (See Chapter 14.)

8.2 Lead Tetraacetate

The use of lead tetraacetate or red lead in carbohydrate analysis stems from the initial observations by Dimroth and subsequently by Criegee of the ability of this oxidative reagent to cleave vicinal glycols [5, 6]. One of the most valuable properties of lead tetraacetate as an oxidizing reagent is the difference in reaction rates exemplified by sterically different glycols, frequently permitting the assignment of structure and stereochemistry on the consideration of rates of consumption of oxidant. In most cases that have been examined, the reaction follows second-order kinetics; this has been useful in mechanistic interpretations. Susceptible linkages are summarized in Table 8.2. There are several aspects of lead tetraacetate oxidations that are similar to those carried out with periodate.

1. *Cis* glycols are more rapidly attacked than are *trans* glycols. As would be expected on the basis of angular translation of the hydroxyl groups,

TABLE 8.2

Reactions of lead tetraacetate.

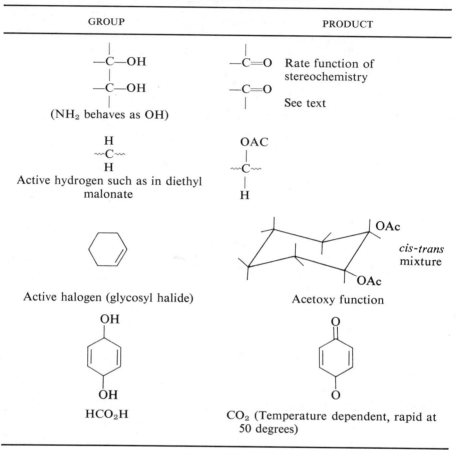

GROUP	PRODUCT

—C—OH → —C=O Rate function of stereochemistry

—C—OH → —C=O See text

(NH₂ behaves as OH)

Active hydrogen such as in diethyl malonate → Acetoxy function

Active halogen (glycosyl halide) → *cis-trans* mixture

HCO₂H → CO₂ (Temperature dependent, rapid at 50 degrees)

this difference is much more marked in 5-membered rings than in 6-membered rings.

   2. *Trans* diaxial glycols that are fixed in space by means of fused or bicyclic ring systems are relatively resistant to oxidation.

   Table 8.3 illustrates relative rates of oxidation of some typical glycols. Aliphatic alcohols are cleaved at rates somewhat intermediate between that of 5-membered *cis* and 6-membered *cis* or *trans* glycols—this is not an unexpected result. The aliphatic glycol has relatively unrestricted rotation about its respective carbon–carbon bonds and these rotational barriers lead to preferred conformations that have the hydroxyls on adjacent carbons in the eclipsed position as infrequently as possible. Despite the free rotation, the preferred conformation for cleavage is the least favored one. This is very temperature dependent and

TABLE 8.3

Relative Pb(OAc)$_4$ oxidation rates of glycols.

GLYCOL	RING SIZE	CONFIGURATION	k
1,2 acenaphthendiol	5	*Cis*	1200
1,2 diphenyl acenaphthendiol	5	*Cis*	331
1,2 dithenyl acenaphthendiol	5	*Trans*	2.8
1,2 cyclopentanediol	5	*Cis*	400
1,2 cyclopentanediol	5	*Trans*	0.13
Methyl-α-D-mannofuranoside	5	*Cis*	9
1,2 IPD α-D-glucofuranose	5	Exocyclic	0.006
1,2 cyclohexanediol	6	*Cis*	0.05
1,2 cyclohexanediol	6	*Trans*	0.002
Ethylene glycol	. . .	Aliphatic	0.0003

the rates of oxidation of glycols are much more influenced by temperature than are the rates of oxidation of cyclic structures. The steric requirements for lead tetraacetate oxidation are similar to those for borate complexing, except that *trans* diequatorial vicinal hydroxyls are slowly oxidized.

The proposed mechanism of the oxidation suggests the formation of an intermediate not dissimilar from the one postulated for periodate oxidation, a cyclic 5-membered ring structure (Figure 8.15). This is cleaved by the transfer

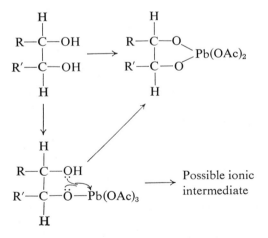

FIGURE 8.15   Reaction of lead tetraacetate with *cis* 1,2 glycols via the formation of a cyclic intermediate.

of an electron pair from oxygen to the tetravalent lead. The initial reaction may involve the formation of an ester with one of the hydroxyl groups. This intermediate ester may then undergo oxidation and cyclization to form the ring structure shown above.

Electron releasing groups tend to accelerate the rate of oxidation, whereas electron attracting groups tend to reduce the rate. This is consistent with the postulate that electrons are transferred from oxygen to the tetravalent lead.

These are several examples of marked solvent effects during the course of lead tetraacetate oxidation. 1,2 *trans* cyclohexane diol is far more rapidly oxidized in the relatively nonpolar tetrachloroethane than in glacial acetic acid. Water, although very infrequently used as a solvent because of the rapid hydrolysis of the lead tetraacetate, nevertheless can be employed when suitably diluted (usually with glacial acetic acid), when a sufficient excess of lead tetra-acetate can be employed or when the rate of cleavage of the susceptible glycol is sufficiently fast so that hydrolysis is not a serious problem. Water generally accelerates the rate of oxidation but several other reactions including the formation of lead dioxide take place, which tend to complicate the picture. Quantitative measurement of oxidant consumption is particularly difficult under these conditions.

An examination of the oxidation potentials of lead tetraacetate and periodate reveals that they are quite similar. In theory, other oxidizing agents with similar redox potentials should be capable of carrying out substantially the same type of oxidative cleavages. This has been confirmed by examination of trivalent silver and sodium perbismuthate as oxidizing agents. Although these are suitable glycol cleaving agents, in view of their relative unavailability, they are not likely to come into widespread use.

One cleavage product of glycols by lead tetraacetate is similar to that observed when periodate is employed. Sugar alcohols and glycerol give rise to formaldehyde from the primary alcoholic function. However, this is the only major end product resemblance during the early stages of reaction and several important points of difference need to be noted. Formic acid is produced from secondary hydroxyls during the course of the reaction but is oxidized to carbon dioxide at a very appreciable rate. As a result of this, water is frequently added to the reaction system and the temperature increased to 35–45 degrees, thus accelerating the oxidation of formate and making the yield of CO_2 quantitative. This can be done during the course of the oxidation so that the carbon dioxide is generated continually, or it can be done subsequently. In any case, the CO_2 must be measured separately.

Rate studies on cleavage of secondary and primary alcohols indicate that cleavage between secondary alcohols is faster than cleavage between a primary and a secondary alcohol. The exact reason for this is not at all clear. Studies of cleavage in cyclic systems show that *cis* hydroxyl functions are cleaved more rapidly than are *trans*. When the *trans* hydroxyls are diaxial, as in sugars of the mannose series, then cleavage is extremely slow and a change of ring conformation must apparently take place before reaction is possible. Because the consumption of an oxidant can be measured rapidly by either potentiometric or titrimetric means, careful analysis of rate curves gives some clue as to the nature of the reacting groups.

The oxidation of simple sugars such as glucose and galactose takes place in the ring form. D-glucose rapidly consumes 2 moles of lead tetraacetate with production of neither formic acid nor formaldehyde. Analysis of the reaction mixture indicates that the product at this stage is 2,3 diformyl D-erythrose (Figure 8.16) [7]. Similar reactions take place for other aldoses. This rapid

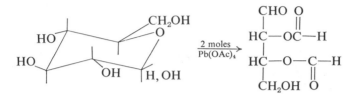

FIGURE 8.16   Reaction of β-D-glucose with 2 moles of lead tetraacetate yield to the diformyl erythrose product shown. It is possible that this intermediate may also be formed by oxidation of the furanose form of the sugar.

reaction to yield the erythrose ester has been made the basis of preparative syntheses of erythrose from D-glucose and of erythrose 4-phosphate from D-glucose-6-phosphate.

The oxidation of methyl α-D-glucopyranoside results in consumption of 2 moles of oxidant without production of formaldehyde, As a general rule, all methyl glycosides of aldohexoses will consume 2 moles of lead tetraacetate upon oxidation. Those compounds bearing *cis* hydroxyls consume 1 mole extremely rapidly, whereas those having all *trans* arrangements consume the ultimate 2 moles rather slowly. Where the three hydroxyls contain one *cis* and one *trans* pair, the first mole is consumed very rapidly by the *cis* hydroxyls. These sugars may be further subdivided into two groups. Those that are able to reform a new hemiacetal and thus regenerate a *cis* vicinal glycol grouping will consume the second mole rapidly (Figure 8.17). Sugars that are unable to reform the hemiacetal and yield this glycol grouping will consume the second mole rather slowly. This is illustrated in the diagram of Figure 8.17.

As indicated above, even for sugars that react rather slowly for steric reasons, the ultimate cleavage products are similar for most of them. Figure 8.17 illustrates the consumption of lead tetraacetate by simple sugars and can be explained largely on conformational grounds. Because the oxidations are generally carried out at elevated temperatures in acetic acid, the interconversion of conformers is extremely rapid. Because the reactions themselves are irreversible, it is expected that they would proceed through susceptible intermediates to completion.

The oxidation of ketoses is generally similar to that of aldoses with a consumption of 2 moles of oxidant without the production of either formic acid or formaldehyde. Analysis of the oxidation of fructose shows that an intermediate

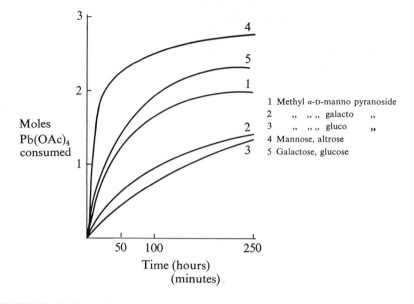

FIGURE 8.17   Relative oxidation rates of sugars and glycosides by lead
tetraacetate.

diester of D-glyceraldehyde has been formed which is a formate glycolate
diester (Figure 8.18) [8]. This is what would be expected on the basis of analogous reactions with the aldoses.

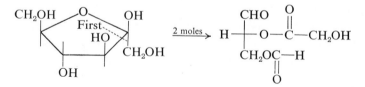

FIGURE 8.18   Reaction of a keto sugar with 2 moles of lead tetraacetate to
yield the indicated derivative.

Lead tetraacetate has also been used to examine the structure of several
disaccharides and, in particular, to carry out specific oxidations of susceptible
linkages [9]. Almost no work has been done with this reagent on polysaccharides, partly because of solubility problems and partly because of attendant
hydrolytic problems.

In contrast to periodate, acetylation of amino nitrogens generally renders
these resistant to cleavage by lead tetraacetate. However, similarly to periodate,
amino groups behave as primary alcohols yielding ammonia and the appropriate
aldehydo or formic acid product.

Lead tetraacetate is prepared by the reaction of lead dioxide with glacial acetic acid. The experimental conditions generally employed use glacial acetic acid as solvent at slightly elevated temperatures. For those sugars where solubility problems are serious, the sugar may be dissolved in a minimal amount of water and the resulting solution diluted with glacial acetic acid. Organic solvents are satisfactory for the reaction, and polarity does not seem to be requisite for satisfactory oxidation; solvents such as benzene and tetrachloro ethane have been successfully employed. Pyridine is a very good solvent for oxidative cleavage but other reactions take place that sometimes render it unsuitable. Excess oxidant is generally destroyed by the addition of hydrazine or can be removed by ion-exchange resin. Lead tetraacetate consumption can be followed by potentiometric methods or by the addition of iodide ion to an aliquot and titration of the resulting iodine with thiosulfate. In this case, the problems that may be encountered with periodate are not found.

CHAPTER 9
Methylation Techniques

9.1 Introduction

The use of methylation as a technique in oligo and polysaccharide structure analysis, as well as a method of assignment of ring size, requires very little in the way of background or historical development. In some sense, the earlier development of the ring structure of the sugars left historical gaps because the argument in favor of 6-membered rings can be developed on structural grounds alone. However, the chemists of 30 years ago were not conversant with modern structural interpretations and so the decision between 5- and 6-membered rings had to be based on chemical evidence alone. As previously mentioned, Fischer favored the 5-membered ring because he knew that γ lactones formed readily and were stable, whereas δ lactones (6-membered) were uncommon and not very stable. A desirable technique for resolving this problem would involve substitution of the hydroxyl groups by a suitable reagent that would be stable and thus prevent changes in ring size during hydrolytic or other degradative

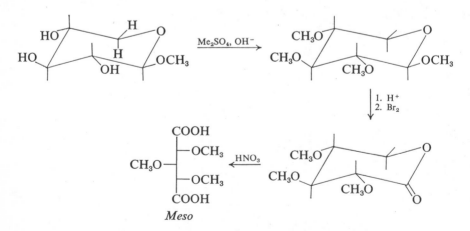

FIGURE 9.1 Proof of the 6-membered ring structure for methyl β-D-xylopyranoside by methylation and oxidation.

294

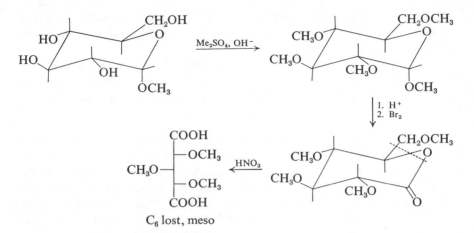

FIGURE 9.2 As previous but glucopyranoside.

procedures. This problem was initially attacked by Purdie and Irvine and more thoroughly and successfully by Haworth and his colleagues [1–3].

The type of methylation evidence accumulated in favor of the 6-membered ring may be briefly summarized as follows:

1. Methylation of methyl β-xyloside yielded a crystalline tri-O-methyl derivative.

2. Oxidation of this with bromine water yielded an unstable lactone, presumably 6-membered.

3. Further oxidation of this product with nitric acid gave meso trimethoxy glutaric acid.

This sequence is only consistent with the structural formulas illustrated in Figure 9.1.

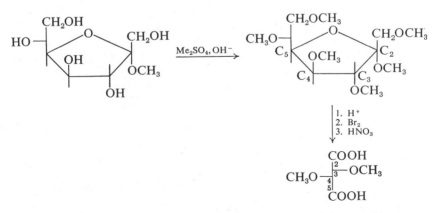

FIGURE 9.3 Methylation-oxidation of a fructofuranoside.

4. Methylation of α-methyl glucoside yielded a tetra-*O*-methyl derivative, which, on acid hydrolysis, gave a tetra-*O*-methyl free sugar similar in properties (optical rotation) to α-D-glucose.

5. Oxidation of this with bromine water produced an unstable lactone.

6. Oxidation of the lactone with nitric acid yielded the same meso-tri-methoxy glutaric acid obtained from D-xylose. These reactions are shown in Figure 9.2.

Similar data were obtained for galactose and arabinose. A methyl fructo-side, however, yielded dimethoxy succinic acid after a similar sequence. This was shown to arise via 5-membered ring intermediates, illustrated in Figure 9.3.

These data established the predominant ring structures for the simple carbohydrates and paved the way for extension to oligo and polysaccharide structural analysis. It is apparent that methylated reference sugars, synthesized by unequivocal routes, are necessary prerequisites for such studies.

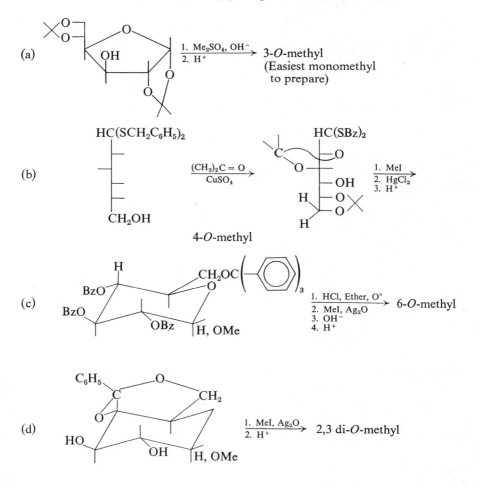

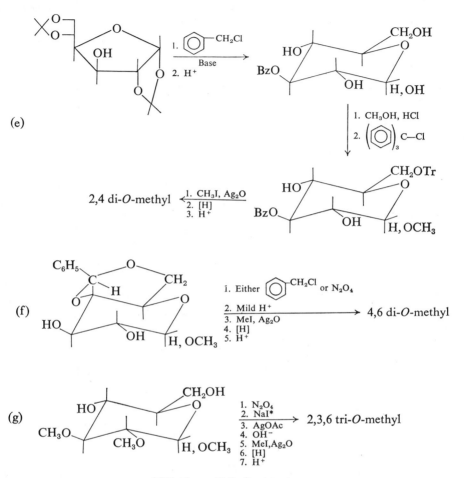

* Displaces C-6 nitrate ester.

FIGURE 9.4   Outline of reaction sequences for the preparation of methylated glucose derivatives. Note that the preparation of the 4,6-dimethyl and 2,4,6-trimethyl derivatives requires the use of a nonmigrating blocking group. The 2,3,6-trimethyl derivative is much more readily obtained by methylation of cellulose, but this is after the fact.

9.2 *General Synthetic Approach*

The general methods for synthesis of such methylated reference compounds can be summarized in the following way.

1. The methyl ethers themselves are both acid and alkali stable, and thus, once their introduction into a molecule is complete, appropriate hydrolytic

procedures may be employed without fear of either loss or migration of these substituents.

2. The relatively high volatility of these derivatives permits rapid separation and identification by the use of gas-liquid chromatography. They also can be separated by thin-layer chromatography. The ability to utilize these techniques is more marked in the case of fully methylated carbohydrates than it is in the case of monomethyl derivatives, but even the latter groups can be fairly readily separated in short periods of time.

3. Because of the above-mentioned properties of the desired final products, either acid or base sensitive blocking groups can be employed in order to produce the desired reference compounds. Those most commonly used are isopropylidene ketals, acetyl groups, benzoyl groups, exocyclic tosyl groups, and nitrate esters. In specialized syntheses, primary alcohols may be protected with trityl ethers, or dihydropyran may be added to single hydroxyls. Typical synthetic sequences are illustrated in Figure 9.4, which schematically describes the synthesis of the methylated glucoses. This represents more an exercise in problem solving than it does in highly selective chemosynthetic techniques. Nevertheless, considerations of over-all yield are real, especially because some of the required blocked derivatives or intermediates, which may be relatively easy to produce by means of a "paper sequence," may be more difficult to obtain in actual laboratory practice.

9.3 Methods for the Introduction of the Methoxyl Group

The procedures for methyl ether formation are limited in scope. The methylating agents used are either dimethyl sulfate or methyl iodide; the former usually in conjunction with a strong alkali, which serves to promote ionization of the pertinent hydroxyl function, and the latter with an agent such as silver oxide, which serves a catalytic role as well. More drastic techniques have been employed such as the use of sodium and liquid ammonia to form alkali metal salts of a carbohydrate followed by treatment of the intermediate with methyl iodide. Other bases, particularly thallous hydroxide, have also been employed with some success. Reaction conditions are summarized in Table 9.1.

TABLE 9.1

Summary of procedures for introducing methyl substituents.

METHYLATING AGENT	COMMENTS
$(CH_3)_2SO_4$, NaOH	Mono to polysaccharides: Glycoside desirable
$(CH_3)_2SO_4$, TlOH	Mono to polysaccharides: Glycoside desirable
CH_3I, Ag_2O in CH_3OH	Glycoside essential
CH_3I, BaO $(CH_3)_2SO \rightarrow O$	Steric problems minor: Nonsolvating polar solvent
Na-NH_3 then CH_3I	Specialized suitably blocked cases only

The problems involved in the treatment of natural products with a view toward obtaining methylated derivatives can be divided into two general categories.

The first involves the lability of the compounds, especially those with free reducing groups, to methylating conditions. This problem has been approached in several ways. One of the most powerful techniques is the use of solvents such as dimethyl sulfoxide wherein methylation reactions proceed with favorable kinetic rates under relatively mild conditions. Highly polar solvents of this type which do not solvate hydroxyl groups frequently permit reaction rates several thousand times higher than those encountered in solvents such as methanol. When a free reducing group is present, it is usual to treat the carbohydrate under conditions so that methyl glycosides are formed first, thus protecting the sensitive carbonyl function from destruction during treatment with alkali or with silver oxide (a good oxidizing agent). Methylation with dimethyl sulfate may be carried out using neutral conditions until the carbonyl is protected, when more vigorous methylating techniques may be utilized.

The second category is one of solubility of higher molecular weight compounds and the relatively low efficiency of the heterogeneous methylation reactions which may be required. The problem of solubility is most commonly encountered when dealing with plant products or more generally with oligo and polysaccharides. Considerable technical difficulties then arise when looking for structural details in insoluble glucans, mannans, xylans, and hemi-celluloses, because it will be difficult to distinguish incomplete methylation from substitution in the parent molecule. Methods applied to overcome this obstacle have had varying success and in practice are usually employed on an empirical basis; several are indicated below.

If the molecules contain uronic acid groups, their anionic character markedly reduces solubility in solvents such as methanol. Esterification of the free acid form of the polymer may be accomplished by reaction with diazomethane or methanol-hydrogen chloride. For best results, the material should be finely dispersed in ether and the diazomethane added at low temperature. Even though this is a two-phase system, esterification is efficient. Such derivatives are frequently methanol soluble thus permitting direct methylation with methyl iodide-silver oxide. A small amount of *O*-methyl may be introduced into the molecule when diazomethane is employed as an esterifying agent, but this does not interfere with the over-all process (Figure 9.5).

Several oligosaccharides may be converted to acetylated derivatives which are then simultaneously deacetylated and methylated using alkaline methoxide and dimethyl sulfate. This technique has been successfully employed with compounds such as cellobiose, although it has relatively limited use in the polysaccharide field (Figure 9.6). Many polysaccharides are soluble in strong alkali and can then be methylated with dimethyl sulfate. Some chain cleavage may take place but is usually considered minimal.

The methylation of a given compound will involve both steric and kinetic

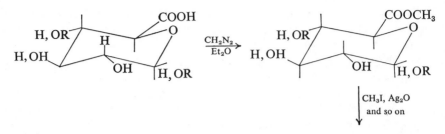

FIGURE 9.5 Methylation of uronide derivatives by prior esterification with diazomethane followed by conventional procedures. The diazomethane may also introduce a significant amount of *O*-methyl.

factors. Highly hindered axial hydroxyl groups are relatively resistant to methylation, and equatorial groups in polysaccharides adjacent to linkage positions are frequently difficult to methylate. When polar groups such as sulfate, phosphate, or carboxyl are present in the molecule, the efficiency of methylation is significantly decreased; this might be expected on electronic grounds alone. As a result of these factors, it is frequently necessary to carry out methylation procedures numerous times until either the hydroxyl content is constant or else no free hydroxyl remains. The easiest way to monitor the product is to examine for the hydroxyl function by infrared spectroscopy, which provides a satisfactory and sensitive method for determining complete methylation.

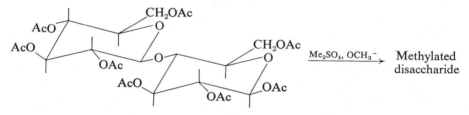

FIGURE 9.6 Reaction involved in methylation of fully acetylated cellobiose.

When quantitative methoxyl determination is desired, derivatives are hydrolyzed by treatment with refluxing hydriodic acid and the resulting methyl iodide is distilled in a stream of carbon dioxide and trapped in bromine. The iodine bromide formed is titrated according to the following stoichiometry:

$$R - OCH_3 + HI \longrightarrow CH_3I + ROH$$
$$CH_3I + Br_2 \longrightarrow CH_3Br + IBr$$
$$IBr + Br_2 \text{ (excess)} + 3H_2O \longrightarrow HIO_3 + 5HBr$$
$$\text{Excess } Br_2 \text{ destroyed by } HCO_2H$$
$$5H^+ + HIO_3 + 5I^- \longrightarrow 3H_2O + 3I_2$$
$$2S_2O_3^= + I_2 \longrightarrow S_4O_6^= + 2I^-$$

(9.1)

Each OCH_3 liberates 6 atoms of iodine. Thus, 1.0 ml of $0.01N$ $S_2O_3^=$ represents 0.0517 mg of methoxyl.

This technique is relatively infrequently employed unless known derivatives are being examined for criteria of purity.

The general use of methylation techniques may be illustrated with some specific examples taken from the oligo and polysaccharide field. The equations in Figure 9.7 and Figure 9.8 demonstrate the types of product distribution

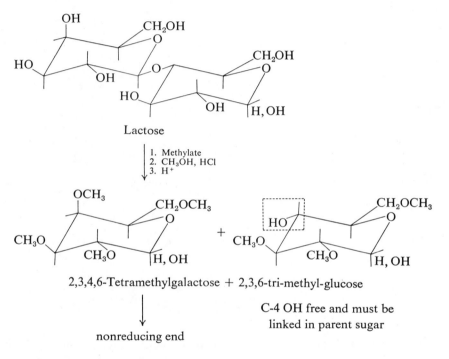

Lactose

1. Methylate
2. CH_3OH, HCl
3. H^+

2,3,4,6-Tetramethylgalactose + 2,3,6-tri-methyl-glucose

nonreducing end

C-4 OH free and must be linked in parent sugar

FIGURE 9.7 Methylation of lactose and expected products after acid hydrolysis.

that may be expected after methylation of representative oligo and polysaccharides. The hydroxyl groups that initially were free on the parent molecule now bear methyl ether functions, whereas those that were tied up in glycosidic linkage or by substitution with another functional group not removed during the methylation procedure now become free hydroxyls. Accordingly, by comparison of the products with standard reference compounds, a reasonable estimate as to the structure of the parent may be formulated. It should be emphasized that from the consideration of such data it is only possible to offer a probability statement regarding the structure of the precursor molecule. This is particularly true in the case of branched chain polymers or those with complex structures. Thus, if methylation data indicates one branch point for every eight

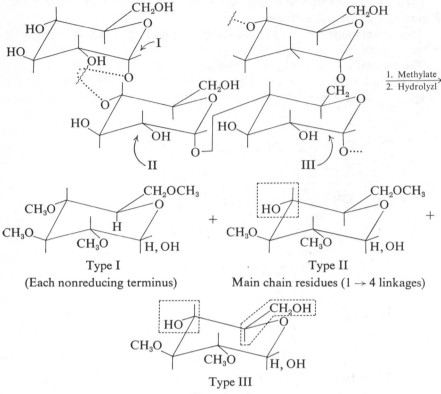

Type I
(Each nonreducing terminus)

Type II
Main chain residues (1 → 4 linkages)

Type III
Branch points

Relative proportions give number of branches
and average chain length (except "main chain," if one
exists).

FIGURE 9.8 Results of methylation analysis of amylopectin. Different products are expected for nonreducing termini (Type I), main chain residues (Type II), and branch points (Type III). The relative proportions of these products give the number of branches and the average chain length.

sugar units, this is no more than an indication of the frequency of branching and offers very little information about fine structure. It is also obviously true that where branching is infrequent, the location of such branch points along an oligosaccharide or polysaccharide backbone chain cannot be determined by this method with any degree of accuracy. For such structures, a combination of enzymatic, partial degradative, and methylation techniques is required for a complete structural analysis. Although there is not sufficient evidence to support this contention, it seems likely that branching frequency in natural polymers is a function of relative enzyme affinities and that precise localization for physiological or structural reasons is not necessary.

CHAPTER 10

Chemistry of Amino Sugars

10.1 Introduction

The amino sugars glucosamine (2-amino 2-deoxy D-glucose) and galactosamine (2-amino 2-deoxy D-galactose) have been known as carbohydrate derivatives for nearly 100 years. In particular, glucosamine was known to be a constituent of lobster shells, and galactosamine as a component of cartilage was identified prior to 1900 (Figure 10.1) [1]. However, it was not until very exten-

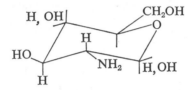

FIGURE 10.1 Structure of 2-amino 2-deoxy D-gluco(galacto)pyranose. These are the most widely distributed of the naturally occurring amino sugars.

sive work was carried out in the antibiotic field, and when N-methyl L-glucosamine was identified as a constituent of the antibiotic streptomycin, that the field of amino sugar chemistry began to mushroom. Currently it is probably the most active single area in carbohydrate research, since many new antibiotic substances contain unusual amino sugars. In addition, several variations of these basic compounds are present in bacterial cell walls.

The *de novo* chemical synthesis of amino sugars can be carried out by a variety of means. Some of these are rather specific for the synthesis of 2-amino sugars, some will work at other positions in the chain, and all of them have rather special stereochemical and stability problems.

10.2 Cyanide Addition

The combination of the addition of an aliphatic amine and cyanide to an aldose is a variation of a similar synthesis for amino acids [2]. This reaction proceeds to give a mixture of anomeric 2-amino aldonic acid nitriles in which the product with a *trans* stereochemistry at carbons 2 and 3 predominates. Hydrolysis and lactonization is followed by reduction of the lactone to the aldehydo function using palladium on barium sulfate as a catalyst in the presence of HCl (Figure 10.2). It should be noted that it is not possible to synthesize other

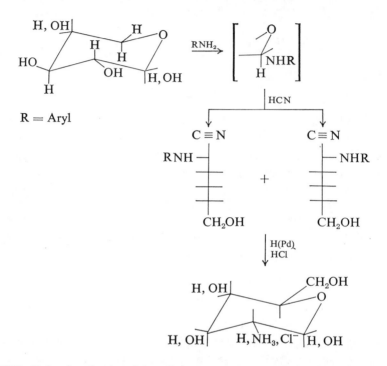

FIGURE 10.2   Synthesis of 2-amino sugars by reaction with an amine and cyanide with an aldose sugar.

than 2-amino sugars this way; an epimeric mixture results but can usually be readily resolved by ion-exchange chromatography.

10.3 *Amadori Rearrangements* [3]

The synthesis of *N*-substituted 2-amino sugars by Amadori type rearrangements of a keto sugar has been known for some time. A typical transformation occurs in the reaction of fructose with benzylamine to give a fructosylamine intermediate which rearranges readily in the presence of acetic acid to give a mixture of 2-deoxy 2-benzylamino D-glucose and the corresponding D-mannose derivative. In this reaction sequence, the gluco isomer is very significantly preferred probably due to the desire for the large benzyl group to be equatorial (Figure 10.3).

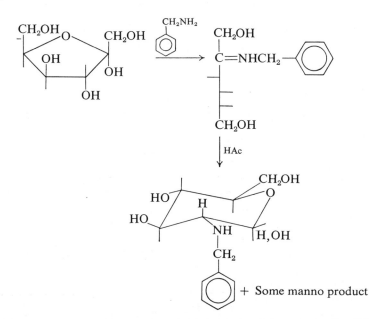

FIGURE 10.3 Reaction of fructose with benzylamine to form the Schiff base followed by rearrangement of this product to yield the *N*-benzyl aldose.

10.4 Anhydro Sugars

The syntheses of glucosamine and galactosamine, which served to establish their configuration and structure, proceed via the ammonolysis of ethylene

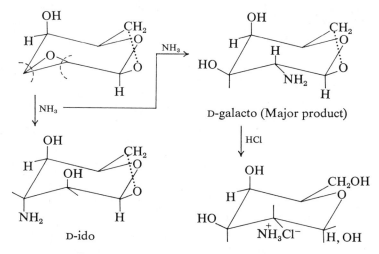

FIGURE 10.4 Synthesis of amino sugars by treatment of epoxides with NH_3. Illustrated is the synthesis of D-galactosamine.

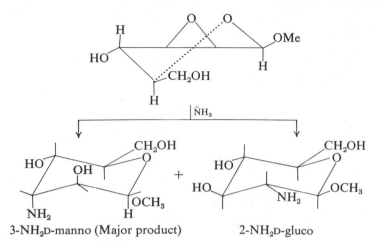

FIGURE 10.5   Synthesis of D-glucosamine by the epoxide method.

oxide type rings. 1,6,2,3-dianhydro-D-talose was reacted with ammonia, to
yield a mixture of 2-deoxy 2-amino-1,6-anhydro-D-galactose and 3-deoxy
3-amino-1,6-anhydro-D-idose (Figure 10.4) [4]. The galacto isomer predominates
in this ring opening. A similar sequence was employed for the synthesis of
glucosamine (Figure 10.5) [5]. This reaction can be generally applied to amino
sugar syntheses. The pair of amino sugars that are obtained will have the amino
group at two different (adjacent) carbons with the stereochemistry being opposite at both of those centers. Thus, in the opening of a 2,3-anhydro-D-sugar, a
2-amino D-sugar, and another 3-amino D-sugar are obtained. The pair are
epimeric at both carbons 2 and 3. This type of displacement is not restricted to
epoxides at carbons 2 and 3, but will also take place at other positions (for
example, on C_3 and C_4). Thus, 3,4,1,6-dianhydro-D-talose on ammonolysis

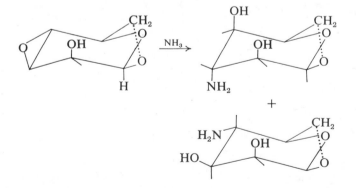

FIGURE 10.6   Formation of 3-amino D-idose and 4-amino D-mannose by the
epoxide method.

yields 3-deoxy 3-amino-D-idose and 4-deoxy 4-amino-D-mannose, respectively (Figure 10.6) [6].

10.5 Displacement Reactions

The employment of displacement reactions, particularly as developed by Baker and co-workers has provided several rather elegant methods for the

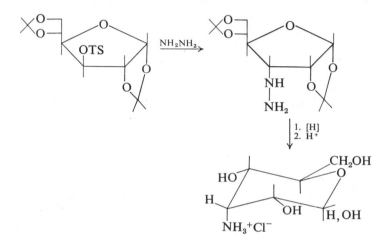

FIGURE 10.7 Introduction of an amino group by displacement with hydrazine and reduction. Product is 3-amino D-allose.

introduction of an amino group. 1,2,5,6-di-isopropylidene 3-tosyl α-D-gluco-furanose can be treated with hydrazine and the product reduced to yield the 3-deoxy 3-amino-D-allo derivative (Figure 10.7) [7]. Removal of the blocking

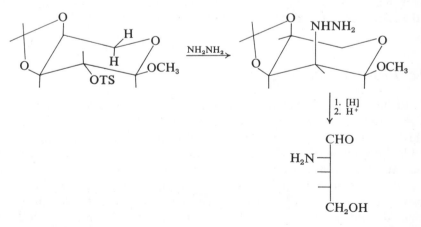

FIGURE 10.8 Synthesis of 2-amino L-ribose by the hydrazine displacement procedure.

groups yields 3-deoxy 3-amino D-allose. Selective removal of carbon 1 or 6 by methods to be discussed subsequently will give rise to the ribose derivatives. Similarly, 3,4-isopropylidene 2-tosyl α-methyl-L-arabinoside will, on displacement with hydrazine, reduction with LiAlH$_4$ and graded acid hydrolysis of the blocking groups, yield 2-deoxy 2-amino-L-ribose [8] (Figure 10.8). Other displacing agents that have been employed besides hydrazine include azide and ammonia itself. In the latter case, the reaction goes more smoothly with exocyclic tosyloxy groups and has been used to synthesize 5-amino pentoses (Figure 10.9).

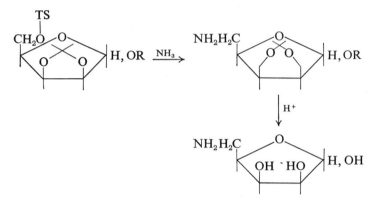

FIGURE 10.9   Direct replacement of an exocyclic tosyloxy group by reaction with ammonia yielding a 5-amino pentose.

Displacement of endocyclic leaving groups is sometimes difficult and usually requires several days refluxing under anhydrous conditions. The stability of the sugar derivative to these conditions may affect the yield.

10.6   Reductive Methods

Reduction of phenylhydrazones, phenylosazones, or oximes has also been widely employed. Maltose, when treated with phenylhydrazine in excess, yields maltose phenylosazone. This can subsequently be catalytically reduced with hydrogen in acetic acid to yield the so-called maltosamine with the amino group on the carbon 2 of the reducing glucose moiety (Figure 10.10) [9]. Similarly, if a carbonyl group is present in the chain of the carbohydrate ring (possibly as a result of an oxidative sequence), this can be treated with hydroxylamine to yield an oxime which may then be reduced. This reductive step generates a new asymmetric center and a pair of epimeric amino sugars are produced (Figure 10.11). In some situations, the stereochemistry can be con-

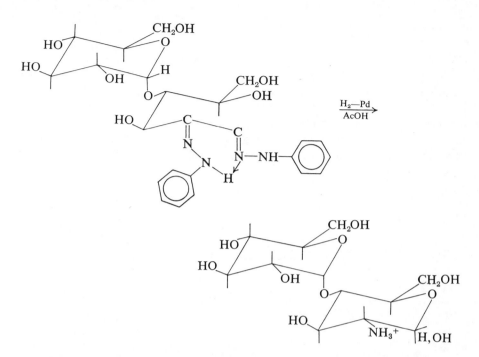

FIGURE 10.10 Introduction of the amino function by catalytic reduction of a phenylosazone. Product is 2-amino maltose (trivial name, see Appendix 1 for nomenclature rules).

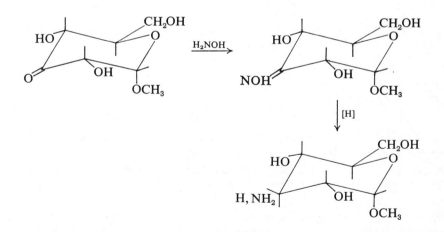

FIGURE 10.11 Reaction of 3-keto α-methyl-D-glucopyranoside with hydroxylamine. Reduction with sodium borohydride gives the equatorial product whereas reduction with platinum–hydrogen gives predominantly the axial product.

trolled by a choice of suitable reducing agents. The oxime of 3-keto methyl-α-D-glucopyranoside upon reduction with sodium borohydride yields predominantly the D-gluco isomer (stability control), whereas reduction with hydrogen and platinum yields predominantly the D-allo product (stereochemistry determined by mode of adsorption to the catalyst surface). In a similar manner, the reduction of phenylhydrazones to amino sugars has been reported. 1,2-isopropylidene α-D-xylofuranodialdehyde formed by the periodate oxidation of 1,2-isopropylidene-α-D-glucofuranose, can be condensed with phenylhydrazine and the phenylhydrazine group cleaved by hydrogenolysis with Raney nickel [10] (Figure 10.12).

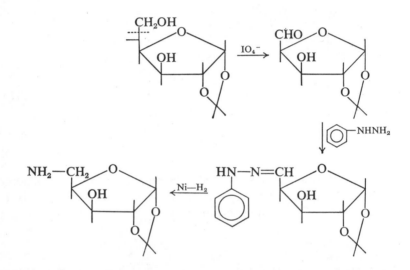

FIGURE 10.12   Synthesis of 5-amino xylose by reduction of the phenylhydrazone derivative.

10.7 Addition Reactions

The addition of ammonia to a double bond can also be used to synthesize amino sugars. Treatment of D-arabinose with nitromethane yields the C-nitro compound isolated as an acetate after treatment with acetic anhydride. Addition of ammonia to the double bond between carbons 1 and 2 gives a mixture of the D-manno and D-gluco products [11]. As might be anticipated from the stereochemistry of such addition reactions, the major product has the D-manno configuration. Hydrolysis yields the respective 2-amino sugars (Figure 10.13). This method is likely to have a rather limited application because it is essentially restricted to the synthesis of 2-amino sugars which are usually accessible by a more convenient route.

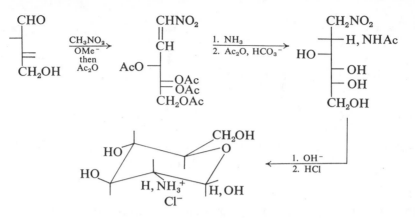

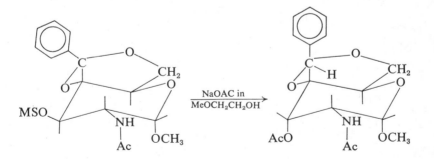

FIGURE 10.13   Introduction of the amino function by addition of ammonia to the unsaturated intermediate formed during a nitromethane synthesis. The axial amino group predominates.

10.8 *Neighboring Group Effects*

In those cases where neighboring group assistance is possible, then inversion of hydroxyl configuration may be anticipated. This will occur when an acetamido function is transdiaxial to the expected leaving group. Treatment of 2-deoxy 2-acetamido 3-mesyl[1] 4,6-benzylidene-α-methyl-D-glucopyranoside with sodium acetate in methoxyethanol proceeds with inversion at carbon 3 to yield the D-allo derivative [12] (Figure 10.14). The mechanism of this reaction undoubtedly involves participation of the acetamido function at carbon 2. Internal displacement of the mesyl group by the carbonyl oxygen yields a cyclic

FIGURE 10.14   Reaction of substituted 2-acetamide sugar resulting in inversion at the three position.

---

[1] Methanesulfonyl.

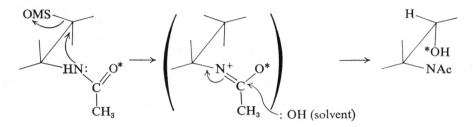

FIGURE 10.15 Mechanism of neighboring acetamido group participation in the reaction illustrated in Figure 10.14.

intermediate with a positive charge, presumably on the nitrogen. This renders the carbon of the acetoxy function susceptible to attack by the incoming nucleophile. The oxygen originally present in the carbonyl carbon now appears on the adjacent carbon (Figure 10.15). Although this mechanism is very attractive, and the stereochemistry of the products consistent, it has yet to be confirmed by ^{18}O studies.

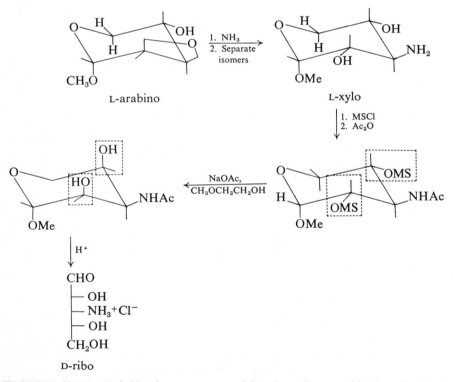

FIGURE 10.16 Neighboring group participation of acetamido function leading to inversion at both adjacent centers.

It is possible to carry out hydroxyl inversion at other points of a synthetic sequence. In the synthesis of 3-amino 3-deoxy D-ribose, 2-tosyl methyl α-L-arabinofuranoside on treatment with methoxide yielded 2,3 anhydro-α-methyl L-ribofuranoside (Figure 10.16). The epoxide ring was opened with ammonia to give as one of the products the 3-deoxy 3-amino α-methyl-L-xylofuranoside derivative. Acylation of the nitrogen followed by mesylation of the free hydroxyl and displacement similar to that just discussed converted the sugar to the D-ribo configuration, from which the blocking groups could be removed by hydrolysis [13]. This type of reaction has not been extensively investigated although it probably has fairly widespread application.

10.9 Nitromethane

The application of the nitromethane synthesis described above for the preparation of 2-amino sugars is not the only method by which this reagent can be employed for the preparation of amino sugars. The dialdehydes formed by periodate oxidation of glycosides can be condensed with nitromethane to yield C-3 nitro alcohols which, upon reduction, will yield 3-amino sugars [14].

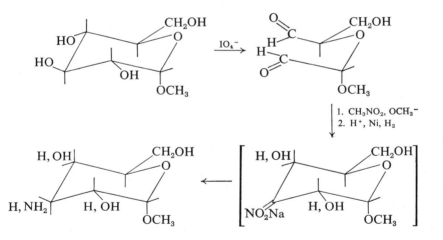

FIGURE 10.17 Introduction of the amino group by reaction of nitromethane with the dialdehyde formed after periodate oxidation of a methyl hexopyranoside. The D-manno isomer is the predominant product.

This very unusual condensation reaction is probably one of the few cases where three asymmetric centers are generated during the course of a single reaction sequence (Figure 10.17). Without some clues as to how such a sequence might proceed, we would be tempted not to undertake it at all because the resulting

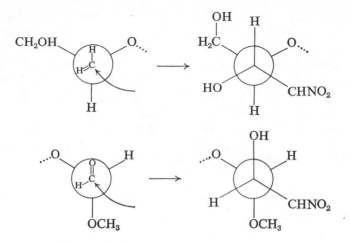

FIGURE 10.18   Stereochemistry of addition reactions to the carbonyl group. The preferred carbonyl orientation in the transition state is between the less bulky groups as visualized in the Newman projection.

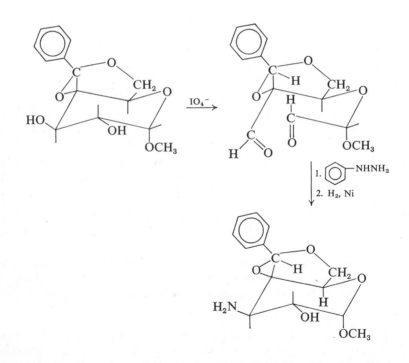

FIGURE 10.19   Reaction of "periodate" dialdehyde with phenylhydrazine followed by reduction. The stereochemistry is not well worked out.

mixture of products would be almost hopeless to separate. Nevertheless, additions to carbonyl functions generally follow fairly specialized stereochemistry. This reaction seems to follow the Cram rule, which states that attack at a carbonyl will take place via the least hindered side [15] (Figure 10.18).

As illustrated in Figure 10.18, the D-manno compound is by far the predominant product with the D-gluco and D-allo products being obtained in much lesser amounts. The other possible isomers are obtained in extremely small yield.

This same general reaction can be carried out by condensation with phenylhydrazine. 4,6-benzylidene-α-methyl-D-glucopyranoside on treatment with periodate yields a dialdehyde which can be condensed with phenylhydrazine [16] (Figure 10.19). Removal of the blocking groups yields 3-deoxy 3-amino glucose. The stereochemistry of this condensation is not quite as clear as the previous one.

10.10 Degradative Sequences

By application of suitable degradative schemes for removal of either the glycosyl carbon or the terminal carbon, it is possible to synthesize new classes

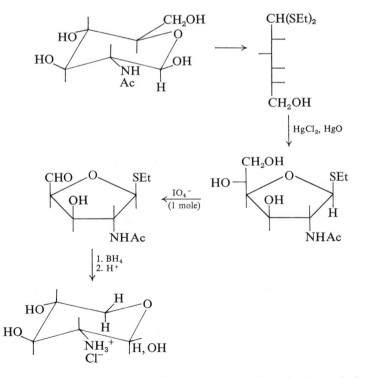

FIGURE 10.20 Synthesis of 2-amino 2-deoxy D-xylose by degradation of the D-gluco derivative.

of amino sugars. Condensation of 2-deoxy 2-acetamido D-glucose with ethyl mercaptan yields the diethyl mercaptal. Treatment of this with mercuric chloride yields the ethyl furanoside derivative in which the bond between carbon 5 and carbon 6 may be cleaved by periodate (Figure 10.20). Reduction of the aldehyde at C-5 with borohydride followed by hydrolysis yields 2-deoxy 2-amino D-xylose [17]. In a similar way, treatment of 2-acetamido 2-deoxy D-galactose by the same sequence of reactions will give 2-deoxy 2-amino D-arabinose. In sequences such as this, it is not necessary to start with an aldehydo sugar. Condensation of benzylaldehyde with sorbitol forms 2,4-benzylidene sorbitol which on oxidation (C5–C6) with lead tetraacetate and acid hydrolysis gives an L-pentose. This can then be converted to the 3,4-isopropylidene 2-tosyl derivative, the tosyl function displaced by hydrazine and the product reduced to yield 2-deoxy 2-amino L-lyxose.

10.11 Reaction of Unsaturated Sugars

Addition of nitrosyl chloride to D-glucal triacetate yields the 1-chloro-2-nitroso adduct which can be readily reduced to the corresponding 2-amino sugar halide. Both β-gluco and α-manno products are formed as a result of *trans* addition.

10.12 Epimerization

One additional method for synthesis of 2-amino sugars deserves mention because it involves a reaction similar to the Lobry de Bruyn transformation and also because comparable reactions are known to take place in biochemical systems. The epimerization of 2-acetamido sugars, particularly that between 2-acetamido D-glucose and 2-acetamido D-mannose readily occurs in mild alkali

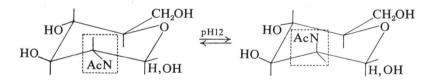

FIGURE 10.21   C-2 epimerization of *N*-acetyl amino sugars.

[18] (Figure 10.21). The mechanism of this reaction is probably similar to the reaction for a typical Lobry de Bruyn transformation except in this case the formation of a keto intermediate is not possible. The abstraction of a proton from carbon 2 with the formation of a double bond between carbons 1 and 2 and a negative charge on the carbon 1 oxygen is the expected first intermediate. This planar form can then add back a proton from the protonated base to yield the C-2 epimer (Figure 10.22). The readiness by which this reaction takes place

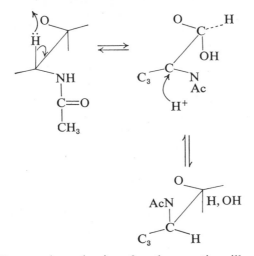

FIGURE 10.22 Proposed mechanism for the reaction illustrated in Figure 10.21.

suggests that the *N*-acetyl group accelerates the reaction, presumably through an inductive effect. This reaction is not dissimilar to that involved in the biosynthesis of amino sugars.

Similar enzymatic transformations are known to take place. The conversion of 2-deoxy 2-acetamido D-glucose 6-phosphate to 2-deoxy 2-acetamido D-mannose 6-phosphate is enzymatically catalyzed by extracts of liver. The presumption is that a group on the protein acts as a proton acceptor with the proton being returned in such a way as to cause epimerization at carbon 2. These enzymatic reactions (epimerizations) generally do not occur with proton-solvent exchange.

10.13 Enzymatic

In several cases, the rather marked advances in biochemical methodology provide more suitable and indeed, more stereoselective syntheses for certain amino sugar intermediates. 2-deoxy 2-amino D-glucose 6-phosphate is far more

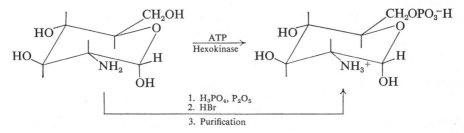

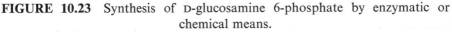

FIGURE 10.23 Synthesis of D-glucosamine 6-phosphate by enzymatic or chemical means.

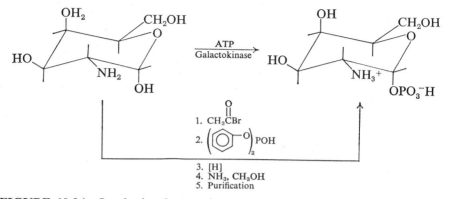

FIGURE 10.24   Synthesis of α-D-galactosamine 1-phosphate by enzymatic or chemical means.

readily obtained by phosphorylation of D-glucosamine with adenosine triphosphate and hexokinase than it is by direct chemical synthesis (Figure 10.23), although in this case, the polyphosphoric acid technique permits processing of large amounts of sugar [19]. However, in the case of D-galactosamine the availability of a specific kinase which phosphorylates at the 1 position makes the glycosyl phosphate available [20]. This has obvious advantages over chemical procedures which are necessarily much more involved (Figure 10.24). These are the two best examples of enzymatic techniques for the synthesis of amino sugar phosphates. There is so little information regarding the biochemistry of unusual amino sugars, particularly 3 and 4 amino, branch chain and dideoxy amino sugars that the applicability of enzymatic methods to their synthesis or the synthesis of suitable intermediates is still unknown. A summary of methods for amino sugar synthesis is given in Table 10.1.

TABLE 10.1
Summary of methods for amino sugar synthesis.

METHOD	COMMENTS
Aminonitrile	2-amino sugars only; epimeric mixtures.
Ammonolysis of epoxides	2, 3, or 4 positions. Mixed adjacent products. Stereochemistry is predictable.
Tosyl displacement	Exocyclic easier. Stereochemistry predictable.
Hydroxyl inversion of pre-existing amino sugar	Neighboring group needed. Numerous examples.
Carbonyl additions	Via oxime-epimeric mixture, keto intermediate usually low yield. Osazone reduction — 2 NH_2 only. Ketose addition — Rearr. 2-NH_2 only.
Nitrosyl chloride	2-amino sugars. Convenient for glycoside synthesis.
Nitromethane	Several products. Asymmetric induction reduces total number.

CHAPTER 11

Synthesis of Sugar Phosphates

11.1 Introduction

The tremendous expansion in biochemical research during the past 25 years is in part due to the ability to examine synthetic substrates as potential intermediates in metabolic reactions. Almost all of carbohydrate metabolism is intimately concerned with esters of phosphoric acid; and the chemical synthesis of sugar phosphates is of considerable importance. Besides functioning as intermediates in energy producing pathways, sugars are essential constituents of nucleic acids, structural polysaccharides, numerous enzymes, and complex lipids, and are ubiquitous in nature.

Many of the synthetic reactions are carried out in heterogeneous systems because of solubility problems, but the conversion of the carbohydrates to fully substituted derivatives soluble in organic solvents and the use of organic salts of the phosphates soluble in nonpolar solvents has provided much improved yields.

Some general aspects of the chemistry of phosphate esters may be worthwhile reviewing at this point. Phosphoric acid with its three ionizable protons will have properties in part based on those of a relatively strong acid and in part based on those of a weak acid (Figure 11.1). There is a marked tendency for

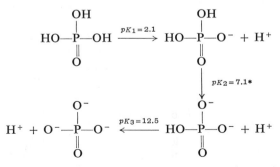

FIGURE 11.1 Ionization of phosphoric acid. Activity is markedly influenced by ionic strength; at $\mu = 0.15$, pK'_2 is 6.8.

319

displacement reactions to proceed on carbon but nucleophilic displacement on phosphorus is also frequently encountered. Simple triesters of phosphoric acid such as trimethyl phosphate are relatively stable and undergo hydrolysis in alkali via a bimolecular mechanism [1] (Figure 11.2). Hydrogenolysis can be effected

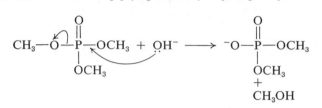

FIGURE 11.2 Hydrolysis of trimethyl phosphate by alkali. The dimethyl product is very resistant to further hydrolysis.

with benzyl and phenyl esters using platinum and palladium catalysts; if an appropriate inhibitor is added, only one of the substituent groups will be removed [2] (Figure 11.3). Debenzylation can also be carried out with sodium and

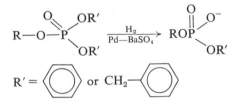

FIGURE 11.3 Removal of phenyl or benzyl groups from substituted phosphate esters by hydrogenolysis.

liquid ammonia; this is particularly valuable when sulfur containing compounds are present. In general, monoalkyl phosphates or monoesters (the type of derivative most often present in natural carbohydrates) are relatively stable substances.

There are several problems that must be considered in the synthesis of phosphate esters.

1. The acid catalyzed hydrolysis of the glycosidic bond must be taken into account in the preparation of glycosyl phosphates.

2. The presence of hydroxyls adjacent to the phosphate group will permit cyclic ester formation and phosphate migration (Figure 11.4). For example, it is quite easy to equilibrate α and β glycosyl phosphates without any significant amount of hydrolysis occurring.

3. The general ease of hydrolysis of sugar phosphates as compared to a simple aliphatic alcohol phosphate is quite possibly due to the successive migration of the phosphate group to position 1, whereby it is cleaved in the usual manner.

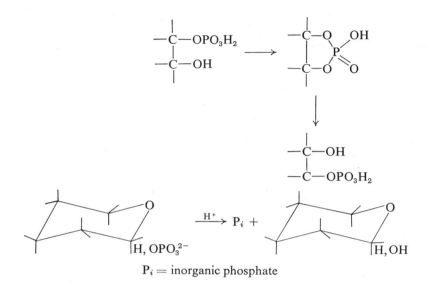

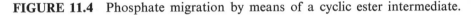

P$_i$ = inorganic phosphate

FIGURE 11.4   Phosphate migration by means of a cyclic ester intermediate.

4. Whenever there is a carbonyl group or potential carbonyl group β to the phosphate ester, then extreme lability may be expected due to a β-elimination reaction (Figure 11.5). This is particularly pronounced in alkali and has been observed for glyceraldehyde-3-phosphate and for glucose-3-phosphate.

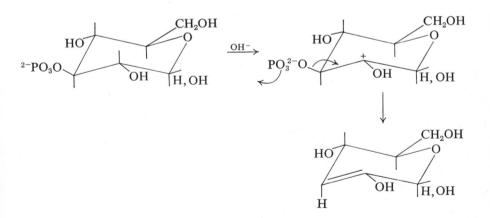

FIGURE 11.5   Elimination of 3-phosphate by treatment of D-glucose derivative with alkali. This reaction may occur in the open chain form. The hydrogen at position 2 is considered somewhat acidic due to its position α to the carbonyl function.

5. In the presence of neighboring hydroxyl groups, the removal of secondary phosphate esters is quite readily achieved. Thus, uridine-3'-dibenzyl phosphate decomposes quite rapidly to the monobenzylphosphate; this in turn is rapidly hydrolyzed at *p*H 10 or above.

6. The base catalyzed migration of phosphate groups does not occur possibly because of the inability of the neighboring function (usually hydroxyl) to attack the already negatively charged residue and also perhaps because there is no displacing group on the rear side with respect to the attacking hydroxyl function.

The methods of introducing phosphate esters are quite numerous. Relatively simple procedures will apply for primary phosphates and the usual problems of suitable protection groups arise. This is analogous to the synthesis of appropriately methylated model compounds and in choosing functional groups we must keep in mind the problems of phosphate migration, acid lability of the glycosyl phosphates, and so on. A phosphate anion may be phosphorylated much more readily than is an alcohol but the pyrophosphate linkage formed is somewhat less stable than the ester linkage (Figure 11.6). As might

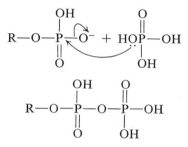

FIGURE 11.6 Formation of pyrophosphates; the yield in such a reaction is more a function of the stability of the product and its reactivity toward further substitution. The depicted reaction is schematic; see text.

be expected from general problems of the synthesis of carboxylic esters and anhydrides, the synthesis of phosphate esters and pyrophosphates requires activation either of the phosphorylating agent or of the reacting substrate. The majority of phosphorylations depends on activation of the phosphate function according to the general equation shown in Figure 11.7. The group X is normally

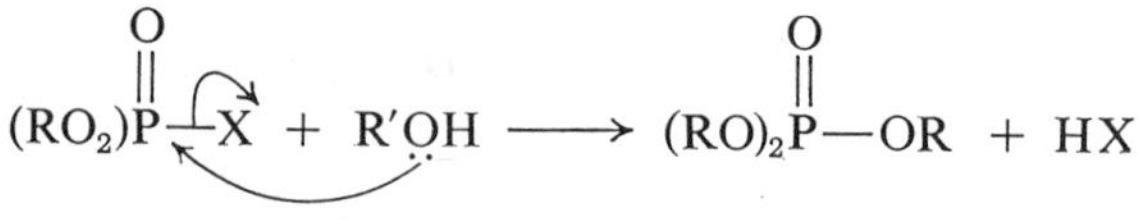

$$(RO_2)P{\longleftarrow}X + R'OH \longrightarrow (RO)_2P{-}OR + HX$$

FIGURE 11.7 Substitution of activated phosphate derivative. If HX is a stronger acid than phosphoric acid (HCl or HBr for example), this reaction will generally proceed satisfactorily.

one which undergoes ready nucleophilic displacement to yield the stable anion. The acid that is generated in the reaction should be stronger than the substituted phosphate. This would be true if X were halide and also possibly when X is phosphate as well. It is possible to activate the phosphate group by activating the X function at the actual time of reaction. Thus, substituted derivatives such as phosphoramidates are relatively stable anions but when protonated will act as mild phosphorylating agents (Figure 11.8). The phosphorylating agent may also be activated with an oxidizing agent such as iodine.

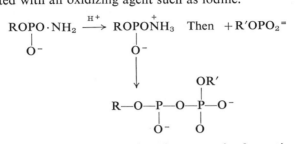

FIGURE 11.8   Activation of phosphate ester by formation of the phosphoramidate.

Another type of reagent that has been used to effect the synthesis of phosphates is dicyclohexylcarbodiimide [3]. With this reagent, phosphate esters may be converted to the pyrophosphates or may be esterified, the reaction usually proceeding by way of the urea phosphate intermediate depicted in Figure 11.9. Under the conditions normally employed for such phosphorylation reactions, activation of the intermediate by protonation is necessary and the driving force for the reaction might be considered to be a separation of the urea from the phosphorus–oxygen bond.

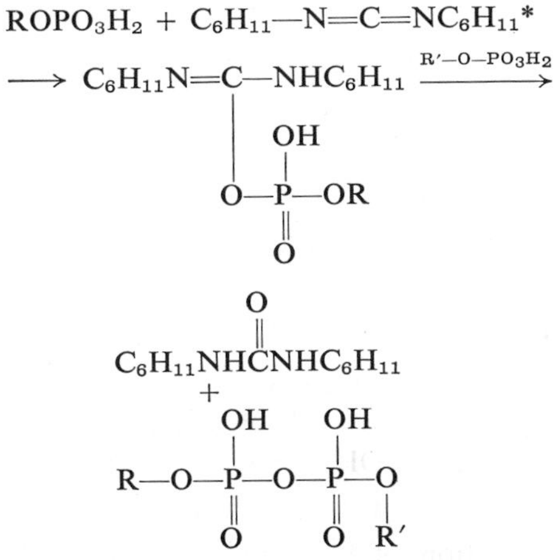

$$ROPO_3H_2 + C_6H_{11}—N{=}C{=}NC_6H_{11}{*}$$

$$\longrightarrow \; C_6H_{11}N{=}C—NHC_6H_{11} \xrightarrow{\;R'—O—PO_3H_2\;}$$

with the intermediate:

$$C_6H_{11}N{=}C—NHC_6H_{11}$$
$$|$$
$$OH$$
$$|$$
$$O—P—OR$$
$$\|$$
$$O$$

$$\overset{O}{\overset{\|}{C_6H_{11}NHCNHC_6H_{11}}}$$
$$+$$

$$\underset{O \quad\; O\; R'}{\overset{OH \quad\; OH}{R—O—P—O—P—O}}$$

FIGURE 11.9   Use of dicyclohexylcarbodiimide in the synthesis of pyrophosphates.

Appropriate activation of the alcohol will also lead to the formation of phosphate esters according to the general equation shown in Figure 11.10. This is frequently carried out with halides and epoxides.

$$(RO)_2\overset{\overset{\displaystyle O}{\|}}{P}\!\!-\!\!O^- + Al\!-\!X \longrightarrow (RO)_2\overset{\overset{\displaystyle O}{\|}}{P}\!\!-\!\!O\!-\!Al + X^-$$

Al = alkyl group or aliphatic residue
X = halide, epoxy function or diazo group

FIGURE 11.10   Schematic representation of the reaction of a phosphate ester with an "activated" alcohol (glycosyl halide).

11.2 Specific Reagents

POCl$_3$

Phosphorus oxychloride in the presence of a base, such as pyridine, or in an inert solvent, such as benzene, with a calculated amount of tertiary amine is one of the oldest phosphorylating agents known. The presence of a base is required because low yields will result from further attack by halide on the alkyl group or on the protonated alkyl phosphate (Figure 11.11). Due to the high

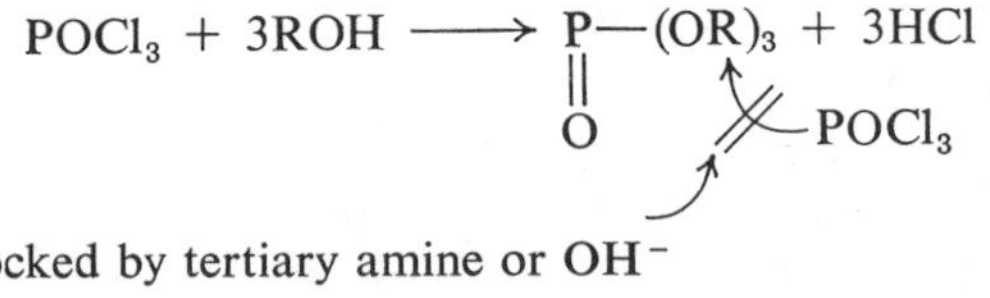

$$POCl_3 + 3ROH \longrightarrow \underset{\underset{\displaystyle O}{\|}}{P}\!\!-\!\!(OR)_3 + 3HCl \qquad POCl_3$$

Blocked by tertiary amine or OH$^-$

FIGURE 11.11   Reaction of phosphorus oxychloride with an alcohol.

activity of this phosphorylating agent, it is somewhat less satisfactory for the synthesis of primary and secondary phosphates than several other reagents. The reaction with 1 or 2 moles of an alcohol will lead to products as indicated in Figure 11.12. However, using stoichiometric amounts of base, such as sodium

$$POCl_3 + ROH \longrightarrow ROPOCl_2 + (RO)_2POCl$$

FIGURE 11.12   Reaction as in Figure 11.11 with limiting amounts of ROH.

or barium hydroxide, phosphorylation of primary alcohols can be readily carried out in appropriately blocked compounds. If two hydroxyl groups are present in the molecule and are so situated that cyclic ester formation is possible, then phosphorus oxychloride and pyridine will initially give a good yield of the cyclic product. The intermediate cyclic phosphoryl chloride decomposes to give a mixture of two monophosphates (Figure 11.13). However, with 1,3 diols, the 6-membered cyclic phosphate is the primary product [4].

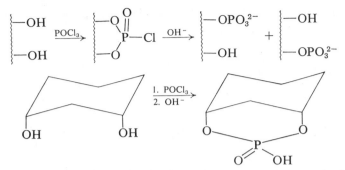

FIGURE 11.13 Formation of mixed products on reaction of phosphorus oxychloride with a compound containing vicinal hydroxyl groups.

Diphenylphosphoryl Chloride (Diphenylphosphorochloridate)

The desire to synthesize specifically monophosphate esters led to the employment of agents such as diphenylphosphoryl chloride. This may be prepared from phenol and phosphoryl chloride followed by fractional distillation (Figure 11.14). Reaction with an alcohol in the presence of pyridine proceeds quite

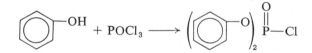

FIGURE 11.14 Synthesis of diphenylphosphoryl chloride.

smoothly and the blocking phenyl groups are easily removed by catalytic hydrogenation. This reagent has been used in the synthesis of a large number of carbohydrate phosphates as indicated in Table 11.1 [5]. Regardless of the carbo-

TABLE 11.1

Carbohydrate phosphates synthesized by reaction of the indicated derivative with diphenylphosphoryl chloride.

SUGAR	FINAL PRODUCT
2,3,4,6-tetra-*O*-acetyl D-glucopyranose	α-D-glucosylphosphate
1,2,3,4-tetra-*O*-acetyl D-glucopyranose	D-glucose-6-phosphate
2-acetamido-3,4,6-tri-*O*-acetyl D-glucopyranose	*N*-acetyl α-D-glucosamine 1-phosphate
Appropriate blocked glucose	2,3, or 4 phosphate derivative
Isopropylidene erythrose diethyl acetal	Erythrose 4-phosphate
1,3 benzylidene glycerol	Glycerol 2-phosphate
Monobenzyl dihydroxy acetone diethyl acetal	Dihydroxy acetone monophosphate diethyl acetal

hydrate being synthesized, it is necessary to protect all of the other hydroxyl groups, much as in the case of methylation reactions.

Dibenzylphosphorochloridate

An improved derivative of a similar type is dibenzylphosphorochloridate which is also suited to the preparation of monophosphate derivatives. This has the advantage over the diphenyl analog in that the benzyl groups are somewhat more easily removed. This reagent is prepared by reaction of *N*-chlorosuccinimide with dibenzyl phosphite; the insoluble succinimide formed in the reaction precipitates out and the freshly prepared material is used directly (Figure 11.15).

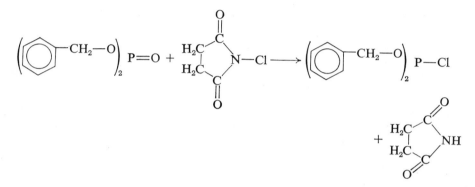

FIGURE 11.15   Synthesis of dibenzylphosphorochloridate.

This agent has been used to phosphorylate the hydroxymethyl group of ribose and of isopropylidene nucleotides [6] (Figure 11.16). The benzyl group is readily removed by catalytic hydrogenation and the isopropylidene group by mild acid hydrolysis.

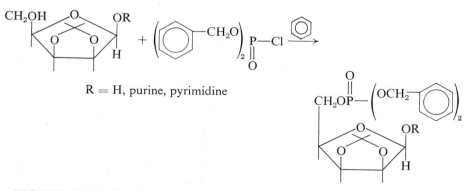

FIGURE 11.16   Synthesis of 5′ nucleotides employing dibenzylphosphoro-chloridate as the phosphorylating agent.

Polyphosphoric Acid

It is possible to take advantage of the differing stability of primary and secondary phosphates in the synthesis of carbohydrate phosphate esters of the primary alcohol function. Polyphosphoric acid is a mixture of phosphorus pentoxide and 85 percent phosphoric acid, and has a degree of polymerization that ranges from 2–10. This has been employed in the direct phosphorylation of several free sugars. The initial product is a mixture of both mono and di-phosphates with the carbohydrate containing as many as three or four phosphate groups. In general, no effort is made to isolate the intermediates in this reaction and the mixed phosphorylated product is then treated with hydrobromic acid under reflux conditions to effect the hydrolysis of the secondary phosphates. This method is advantageous because starting materials are generally accessible in large quantities and the laborious and involved procedures to produce suitably blocked intermediates are not necessary. This has been particularly useful in the synthesis of D-glucose and D-galactose 6-phosphates and their respective 2-deoxy 2-amino analogs [7, 8] (Figure 11.17).

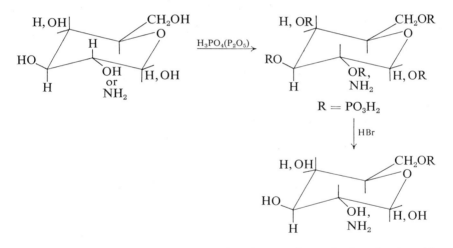

FIGURE 11.17 Synthesis of sugar phosphates using polyphosphoric acid.

Dicyclohexylcarbodiimide

Dicyclohexylcarbodiimide (DCC) is most frequently used for the formation of nucleotide pyrophosphate linkages, as illustrated in Figure 11.18. However, the synthesis of several, not readily accessible, carbohydrate phosphates may also be achieved with the reagent. Thus, treatment of an aldose 1-phosphate, which is *cis* to the hydroxyl at carbon 2 (usually axial–equatorial), with the carbodiimide in the presence of triethylamine leads to ready formation of the 1,2 cyclic phosphate (Figure 11.19). Graded acid hydrolysis of this

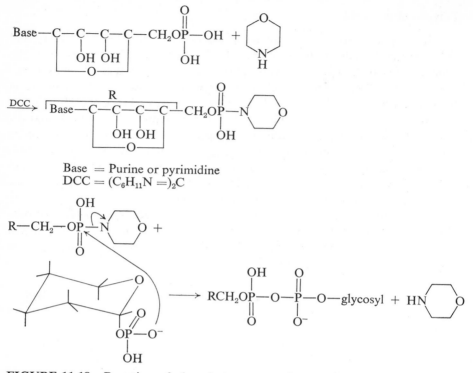

FIGURE 11.18 Reaction of phosphate esters to form anhydrides catalyzed by dicyclohexylcarbodiimide. In this case, the formation of a nucleoside diphosphate sugar is depicted.

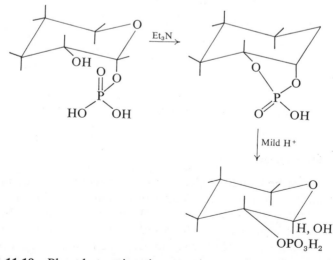

FIGURE 11.19 Phosphate migration reaction catalyzed by triethylamine and proceeding through a cyclic ester intermediate.

compound causes ring opening of the cyclic phosphate to give primarily the 2-phosphate product plus some free sugar. Similarly, treatment of ketose-1-phosphates such as fructose-1-phosphate with DCC and triethylamine yields the 1,2 cyclic phosphate which on alkaline hydrolysis yields fructose 2-phosphate [9] (Figure 11.20).

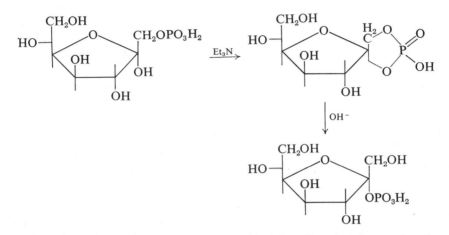

FIGURE 11.20 Synthesis of fructose 2-phosphate by phosphate migration.

Activated Carbohydrate Intermediates

The condensation of activated carbohydrate derivatives with salts of phosphoric acid has been widely used in the synthesis of glycosyl phosphates. Reactions may be carried out with the bromo or chloro sugar in tertiary base solvents

TABLE 11.2

Reactions of silver phosphate and derivatives in the preparation of glycosyl phosphates.

REAGENT	DERIVATIVE	PRODUCT
Trisilver phosphate	Ac$_4$ α-Br glucopyranose	α-1-phosphate
Trisilver phosphate	Ac$_4$ α-Br mannopyranose	α-1-phosphate
Trisilver phosphate	Ac$_4$ α-Br galactopyranose	α-1-phosphate
Trisilver phosphate	Ac$_3$ β-L-arabinopyranose	β-L-1-phosphate
Silver diphenyl phosphate	Ac$_4$ α-Br glucopyranose	α-1-phosphate
Silver diphenyl phosphate	Ac$_4$ α-Br mannopyranose	α-1-phosphate
Silver diphenyl phosphate	Ac$_4$ α-Br galactopyranose	α-1-phosphate
Silver dibenzyl phosphate	Ac$_4$ α-Br glucopyranose	β-1-phosphate
Silver dibenzyl phosphate	Ac$_4$ α-Br galactopyranose	β-1-phosphate
Silver dibenzyl phosphate	Ac$_4$ α-Br mannopyranose	α-1-phosphate

using silver monophosphate, trisilver phosphate, silver dibenzyl phosphate, and similar derivatives. The configuration of the reaction products is such as to suggest primarily thermodynamic control although some shielded ion mechanisms may also be operative. The reaction of fully acetylated glycosyl halides with monosilver or silver dibenzyl phosphate apparently proceeds primarily with inversion, whereas silver diphenyl phosphate appears to react with retention of the anomeric configuration. Up to the present time no satisfactory explanation of the difference between these two has been advanced but it is probably true that the acetoxy function at C-2 participates in the reaction of the dibenzyl phosphate, whereas with silver diphenyl phosphate, this participation does not take place. Typical results are summarized in Table 11.2 [10].

Anhydrous Phosphoric Acid

The recent introduction by MacDonald of anhydrous phosphoric acid as a phosphorylating agent has produced several phosphate derivatives which were previously difficult to obtain. In this interesting reaction, the fully acetylated carbohydrate is treated with anhydrous phosphoric acid in the absence of solvent. The reaction is generally carried out as a melt at 50–60 degrees, under constant evacuation to remove the generated acetic acid. Although the initial studies on this reaction indicated that the β anomers of glucose, galactose, and their 2-deoxy 2-acetamido analogs underwent this reaction with inversion of configuration at the anomeric center, more recent studies have shown that

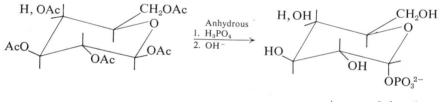

$+$ some β phosphate

FIGURE 11.21 Synthesis of glycosyl phosphates by direct reaction of fully acetylated aldose with anhydrous phosphoric acid. The gluco and galacto compounds react predominantly with inversion at position 1.

mixtures of products are obtained (Figure 11.21) [11–14]. Two types of mechanisms may be proposed for this reaction. The first involves a bimolecular displacement of acetoxy by the incoming phosphate nucleophile. The second involves prior dissociation of the C-1 acetoxy function to yield an ionic intermediate which then reacts with phosphate to give the more stable product (Figure 11.22). The use of derivatives with a C-1 axial acetoxy group[1] (leaving aside cases where neighboring group participation is possible) requires much

[1] Pentaacetyl α-D-glucopyranose, for example.

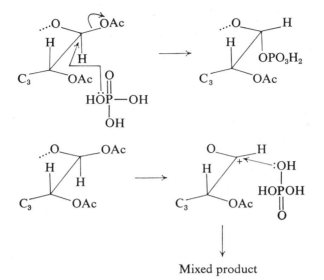

FIGURE 11.22 Mechanism of reaction with anhydrous H_3PO_4.

more forcing conditions. This suggests that prior dissociation of the acetate must take place before the incoming phosphate can attack. The increased stability of the axial acetoxy function necessitates higher reaction temperatures which promotes decomposition of the carbohydrate due to the strong dehydrating conditions that are present in the reaction.

In the case of derivatives of the ido and manno configuration, neighboring group participation yields almost exclusive retention of configuration by the mechanism illustrated in Figure 11.23. This is the predicted result because internal displacement would be favored over attack by external reagents. In both of these cases, a small amount of the equatorial phosphate may have been formed but its extreme lability, not only due to anomeric effects but also to the $\Delta 2$ effect, would suggest that it does not survive the course of the reaction.

Oxidation

An interesting report has appeared on the synthesis of monoalkyl phosphates using a rather unusual phosphorylating agent. Treatment of an aliphatic alcohol with *phosphorous* acid and iodine in an inert solvent or employing the alcohol itself as a solvent was reported to give a quantitative yield of the monoalkyl phosphate derivative. The yield was based on the amount of phosphorous acid employed. This reaction was presumed to go through the unstable iodo phosphate intermediate illustrated in Figure 11.24 [15].

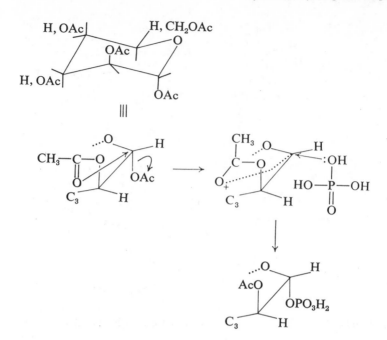

FIGURE 11.23 Reaction of acetylated aldoses with *trans* diaxial acetoxy groups at C1, C2 with anhydrous phosphoric acid. As shown, the reaction proceeds with retention of configuration due to participation of the C_2 acetoxy function.

This highly interesting reaction might be employed with a suitably substituted carbohydrate derivative but up to the present time there have been no reports of its use in the carbohydrate field. Under these conditions, the potential reducing function would have to be protected by a suitable blocking group, or oxidation at this site would take place as well.

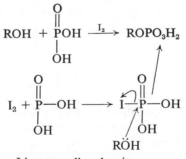

I is an excellent leaving group

FIGURE 11.24 Phosphorylation of an alcohol with phosphorous acid and iodine.

Epoxides

Epoxide rings may be opened with inorganic phosphate to yield mono-phosphate esters in a reaction substantially the same as that of an epoxide with any nucleophile. The ring opening may result from attack on the neutral epoxide or its conjugate acid. As with bimolecular displacements on carbon, it follows that the displacement will be preferentially on primary carbons and not as fast on the secondary carbons. The stereochemistry is that which is expected from typical epoxide openings and the *trans* diaxial configuration of the product is the rule. When both hydroxyls are secondary, it is possible that there is some asymmetric induction although this is not likely since the axial phosphate in either case would not be favorable. Some ring conformational changes may ensue but this has not been studied to any extent.

Summary

For the synthesis of biologically significant phosphate esters, the following general points may be noted.

1. When suitable blocking groups are available, the synthesis of phosphates, where the phosphate ester group is not at the glycosyl carbon atom, takes place readily with reagents such as diphenylphosphorochloridate or even in certain cases, phosphorus oxychloride. When these are not so readily available, other routes must be employed.

2. Phosphates at the primary alcohol position are almost always accessible due to the ease with which the C-6 position can be blocked with a trityl group, the other functional groups blocked by acetoxy or some similar ester and then detritylation accomplished without accompanying change in the functional group distribution.

3. Phosphates in the middle of the chain require an appropriate acetal, ketal, carbonates, and so on, as blocking agents.

4. A special case is the synthesis of secondary phosphates adjacent to the glycosidic carbon atom. This may be achieved through a cyclization reaction with dicyclohexylcarbodiimide followed by graded acid hydrolysis to cleave the glycosyl phosphate bond. This is possible only when suitable stereochemistry prevails. Ketose phosphates such as fructose-1-phosphate can be made to undergo the same cyclization, and then hydrolyzed with alkali to yield the ketal phosphate.

5. The synthesis of glycosyl phosphates can be achieved in several different ways. It is most common to employ the glycosyl halide as the activated agent and a phosphate salt such as silver diphenyl phosphate, silver dibenzyl phosphate, or monosilver phosphate as the attacking nucleophile. As would be expected from most reactions taking place at the glycosidic carbon atom, the stereochemistry of such reactions is both asymmetry controlled and partly thermodynamically controlled as well. The reaction mechanisms are generally

first order with the slow step being dissociation or facilitated dissociation of the halide to provide the carbonium ion. A base catalyst that will assist in removing the halide is frequently employed, usually silver ion or a tertiary amine. Empirical control of stereochemistry has been achieved, with reagents such as dibenzyl phosphate proceeding to give primarily inversion at C-1. Suitable choice of work up conditions can also be employed to favor the isolation of a single product. Thus, the equatorial β phosphates of the sugars are appreciably more acid labile than are the α phosphates and the use of acid gradients during chromatography will favor the isolation of almost pure α product. The separation of α and β glycosyl phosphate anomers by chromatography on ion-exchange resin has been reported. The use of anhydrous phosphoric acid with fully acetylated sugars has the obvious advantage of avoiding the preparation of a glycosyl halide, but the stereochemistry is rather less clear. If participation by the group at carbon 2 is possible, the reaction will generally go with retention of configuration. Thus, α-L-ido and α-D-manno pentaacetates yield the respective α-1-phosphates. When such participation is unlikely or not possible, then mixtures may result with the yield being a function of the ease with which the C-1 acetoxy bond is cleaved, and the relative stability of the α and β phosphates. The equatorial acetates are appreciably more reactive, generally give higher yields and go predominantly with inversion of configuration. However, the axial phosphates may go by both mechanisms with mixed products resulting.

   6. The use of specialized phosphorylating reagents such as cyanoethylphosphate, phosphorous acid-iodine, and so on, has not been extensively investigated in the carbohydrate field.

   7. The formation of pyrophosphate linkages is usually achieved by reacting morpholidate derivatives of a nucleotide with the carbohydrate phosphate in a solvent such as pyridine. Solubility problems are generally avoided by converting the sugar to the salt of a long chain aliphatic amine. Similar condensations with more complex derivatives or those containing several functional groups have not been studied.

CHAPTER $\boxed{12}$
Polysaccharides

12.1 Introduction

The concepts of polysaccharide structure may be reasonably felt to represent a logical extension of those structures that have been worked out for the simple carbohydrates. The conformation of the individual monosaccharide units that comprise a polysaccharide chain can be readily assessed, some information can be obtained about the likelihood of groups interacting with one another, and additional data is usually available regarding the mode and position of linkage, the possibility of branching, and so on. However, it becomes clear that many of the properties that make polysaccharides something more than a summation of monosaccharides reside not in the arrangements of the individual structural units but rather in the conformation of the polymer chain as a whole.

The general methods previously outlined for determining polysaccharide structure such as methylation, periodate, periodate–borohydride, periodate–phenylhydrazine, end group analysis, and so on, provide what may be considered a probability statement regarding both the fine structure and the general distribution of residues in the molecule. Even when considerable information is available regarding the number of branch points, the linkages present, and their anomeric configuration, it is still not possible to do any more than write probable structures. For example, if we know that a branch point occurs every seventh residue based on methylation analysis, it is not possible to state that a branch point occurs exactly at every seventh residue, but rather that one occurs at every such residue on the average. Branch points may occur in one chain at the sixth residue, the next chain at the eighth residue, and so on. The same thing is true of isolated branches that may be present in very high molecular weight polysaccharides. If a polymer has a molecular weight[1] of 100,000, it is probably beyond the limits of detection and available chemical methodology to locate 1 or 2 branch points in such a macromolecular structure. This limitation, which would appear damaging in many areas of structural and biochemical investigation, is not quite as serious as it seems on the surface. It appears likely from biological, chemical, and physical observations that are available that most

---

[1] We will not define this term for the moment.

335

polysaccharides can "get by" in a functional sense with this kind of flexibility as regards structure. It probably makes very little difference to the metabolic utility of a glycogen molecule if branches occur at the fourth, fifth, or sixth residue from a given branch point, or to structural polysaccharides if one residue in 50 bore a branch or if one residue in 30 were not charged. The very high specificity that is built into protein molecules as regards the arrangement of their amino acid sequence and the tightly coupled relationship between structure and function or, structure, function, and information content probably does not pertain to polysaccharides in general. There are obvious exceptions to this rule. Carbohydrates that serve as antigenic determinants or prosthetic groups in enzyme systems have a rigidly defined chemical structure. Those engaged in structural or energy storage roles apparently have less well-defined fine structure.

12.2 Classification[2]

Polysaccharides may be conveniently subdivided into four general categories, two in each of two main headings.

Homopolysaccharides

The first main group is termed *homopolysaccharides*. Members of this group are defined as containing only a single type of carbohydrate residue although linkages and configurations may vary. Probably satisfactory examples are chitin, cellulose, glycogen, starch, xylan (certain types, not most), and several plant polysaccharides whose gross chemical structure is still not well defined (Table 12.1). This group can be subdivided into two sets[3]: the straight chain and the branched chain structures.

TABLE 12.1

Representative linear homopolysaccharides.

POLYSACCHARIDE	SUGAR COMPONENT AND LINKAGE
Cellulose	Glucose, $\beta\ 1 \to 4$
Amylose	Glucose, $\alpha\ 1 \to 4$
Chitin	N-acetylglucosamine, $\beta\ 1 \to 4$
Xylan (not all)	Xylopyranose, $\beta\ 1 \to 4$
Yeast glucan	Glucose, $\beta\ 1 \to 4$, and $\beta\ 1 \to 6$
Nigeran	Glucose, $\alpha\ 1 \to 3$, and $\alpha\ 1 \to 4$
Inulin	Fructose, $\beta\ 2 \to 1$
Levan	Fructose, $\beta\ 2 \to 6$
Galactan (Pectin)	Galactose, $\beta\ 1 \to 4$

[2] Classification is a form of taxonomy and frequently reflects the prejudice of the cataloger. This one is not an exception but the scheme is broad enough to cover most objections.
[3] Borrowing from "contemporary mathematics" now presumably familiar to all grade school children.

The straight chain structures include polymers such as cellulose and chitin; several are listed in Table 12.1. In general, these tend to serve as structural or cell wall materials in plants and lower animals. The cell wall content of molds, fungi, crustaceans, and insects contains a large proportion of chitin, whereas many plant structures contain cellulose or similar glucans, as structural components.

The branched chain set could be further subdivided on the basis of branching frequency but because this is variable, the limits are hard to define. Typical representatives are listed in Table 12.2. Many of these, particularly the glycogens, function primarily as energy reserves and not in a structural capacity,

TABLE 12.2

Representative branched homopolysaccharides.

POLYSACCHARIDE	SUGAR COMPONENTS AND LINKAGES
Amylopectin[a]	Glucose, $\alpha\,1 \rightarrow 4,\ 6 \leftarrow 1\ \alpha$
Glycogen	Glucose, $\alpha\,1 \rightarrow 4,\ 6 \leftarrow 1\ \alpha$
Dextrans	Glucose, $\alpha\,1 \rightarrow 6,\ 4 \leftarrow 1\ \alpha,\ \alpha\,1 \rightarrow 6,\ 3 \leftarrow 1\ \alpha$
Triticin	Fructose, $\beta\,2 \rightarrow 1,\ 6 \leftarrow 2\ \beta$
Galactan (snail)	Galactose, $\beta\,1 \rightarrow 6,\ 3 \leftarrow 1\ \beta$
Mannan	Mannose, $\alpha\,1 \rightarrow 2$ and $\alpha\,1 \rightarrow 3,\ 6 \leftarrow 1\ \alpha$

[a] There are numerous representatives of each of these types throughout animal and plant systems. Differences will lie mainly in branching frequency but occasionally unusual linkages or other minor sugar components are present.

whereas some of the mannans function in a structural role. The highly branched energy reserve polysaccharides such as glycogen are located *within* cells; in this locus, they are subject to rapid enzymatic degradation and release of the constituent sugars. One type of glycogen storage disease is characterized by an enzymatic defect that results in an inability to form branches. As a consequence of this, the cells become grossly distorted (a packing problem) and extreme liver pathology results. There are several known examples of this very direct structure-function relationship.

The homopolysaccharides generally have well-defined chemical structure. The linear homopolymers contain a single unbranched chain connected in a uniform manner both with regard to linkage position and configuration at the anomeric center. The branched polymers most commonly have a linear main chain with linkages that are uniform both as to position and configuration and, at the branch points, new chains of this same general type are initiated with all branch points alike. This is the expected finding and is in agreement with concepts regarding the enzymatic synthesis of such polymers. It is possible to chemically synthesize randomly linked homopolymers by pyrolysis procedures, but other than studies on antigenicity and molecular weight there has been relatively little interest in these materials.

Heteropolysaccharides

The second major group of polysaccharides is termed the *heteropoly-saccharides*. These are defined as containing two or more different carbohydrate units. There is the additional possibility that covalently bound lipid or protein may also be present. A cursory inspection of the above definition makes it clear that it is intended to cover a multitude of sins. The number and type of sugar units, covalent linkages to protein or lipid, and structure function relationships are only some of the desired information. Structural studies are correspondingly more difficult and probability structures may contain gross errors. Despite this complexity and attendant experimental obstacles, several subsets can be recognized.

The linear set is best represented by connective tissue polysaccharides such as hyaluronic acid and chondroitin sulfate, wherein there are repeating disaccharide units of two different sugars, as illustrated in Figure 12.1 [1, 2].

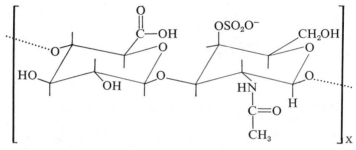

Chondroitin 4-sulfate

FIGURE 12.1 Structural formula for chondroitin 4-sulfate. The size of x varies with the source of the material and may range from 25–50.

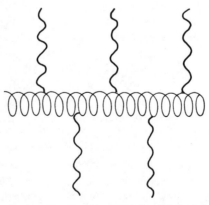

FIGURE 12.2 Schematic structure for protein polysaccharide complex. Helical segment represents the peptide core.

Table 12.3 is a classification of connective tissue polysaccharides that serves to illustrate the types of structural entities present. Most if not all of these polysaccharides are covalently linked to polypeptide chains to form very large aggregate molecules with molecular weights as high as 500,000 [3]. Schematic

TABLE 12.3

Classification of connective tissue polysaccharides primarily linear, heteropoly-saccharides.

POLYSACCHARIDE	PROTEIN BOUND	MOLECULAR WEIGHT	CHARGE DISTRIBUTION
Hyaluronic acid	Uncertain Not more than 2% protein	10^6 or higher	1 equatorial (COO^-) per disaccharide
Chondroitin sulfate C (C-6S)	Yes 10% protein in complex. Covalent to serine hydroxyl	Complex not done	2 equatorial (COO^-, $-SO_3^-$) per disaccharide
Chondroitin sulfate A (C-4S)	Yes 10% protein in complex. Covalent to serine hydroxyl	440,000 for complex (M_w). 13,000 for chain (monodisperse)	1 equatorial (COO^-) and 1 axial ($-SO_3^-$) per disaccharide
Chondroitin sulfate B (Dermatan-SO_4)	Probably to fibrous protein (collagen?) Not readily soluble	Complex unknown. Chains: $23,000 = M_n$ $27,000 = M_w$ $41,000 = M_z$	2 axial (COO^-, $-SO_3^-$) per disaccharide
Keratosulfate	Yes Linkage not established but probably threonine or glutamic	Not known for either complex or chains.	1 equatorial ($-SO_3^-$) per disaccharide
Heparitin sulfate	Unknown	Unknown	1 equatorial (COO^-) variable $-SO_3^-$ per disaccharide

structures for such complexes are illustrated in Figure 12.2. This type of structure may have a biological "information" content appreciably higher than that present in homopolysaccharides. Such complexes are generally present in the extracellular space of connective tissues and their local concentration is such that they exist largely as gels. Ascribed functional roles include cation binding (especially calcium), water binding, diffusion barrier, fibrous protein orientation, lubricant, shock absorber, and so on.

Other examples of the linear set include several capsular polysaccharides of bacterial origin (Table 12.4). It is of interest that the majority of heteropolysaccharides contain charged residues such as carboxyl, sulfate, or phosphate, whereas the majority of homopolysaccharides are composed of neutral sugars.

TABLE 12.4

Representative heteropolysaccharides.

POLYSACCHARIDE	SUGAR COMPONENTS AND LINKAGES
Type III pneumococcus	Glucose, glucuronic acid $\beta\ 1 \to 4$
Slippery elm mucilage	Galacturonic acid, L-rhamnose, $\beta\ 1 \to 2$
Pectin	Galacturonic acid, galacturonic acid methyl ester $\alpha\ 1 \to 4$
Alginic acid	D-mannuronic acid, L-guluronic acid[a] $\beta\ 1 \to 4$
Type VIII pneumococcus	Glucuronic acid, glucose, galactose $\beta\ 1 \to 4$ and $\alpha\ 1 \to 4$
Hyaluronic acid	Glucuronic acid, N-acetyl glucosamine $\alpha\ 1 \to 3$, $\beta\ 1 \to 4$
Chondroitin sulfate C (C6S)	Glucuronic acid, N-acetyl galactosamine 6-O-sulfate, $\beta\ 1 \to 3$, $\beta\ 1 \to 4$
Chondroitin sulfate C (C4S)	Glucuronic acid, N-acetyl galactosamine 4-O-sulfate, $\beta\ 1 \to 3$, $\beta\ 1 \to 4$
Chondroitin sulfate B (Dermatan-SO$_4$)	L-iduronic acid, N-acetyl galactosamine 4-O-sulfate, $\alpha\ 1 \to 3$, $\beta\ 1 \to 4$
Keratosulfate	D-galactose, N-acetylglucosamine, 6-O-sulfate, $\beta\ 1 \to 3$
Heparitin sulfate	D-glucuronic acid, N-acetyl glucosamine 6-O-sulfate, α
Heparin	D-glucuronic acid, N-sulfoglucosamine ester sulfate, $\alpha\ 1 \to 4$

[a] C-5 epimer of D-mannuronic. Contrast with L-iduronic in dermatan sulfate.

The remaining set, branched chain heteropolysaccharides, may contain as many as 6 different carbohydrate residues, and is frequently found in combination with protein or lipid; few structures have been elucidated. Many of these are "type specific" for microorganisms or animals (blood group substances), others serve recognition functions for cell surfaces.

Nucleic acids may be regarded as a specialized type of substituted polysaccharide, wherein the main chain contains ribose or deoxyribose units linked together by phosphate ester bridges. Each sugar is further substituted at the glycosidic carbon by a purine or pyrimidine base (Figure 12.3).

The glycosides present in the nucleic acids are N rather than O glycosides and typical structures are indicated in Figure 12.4.

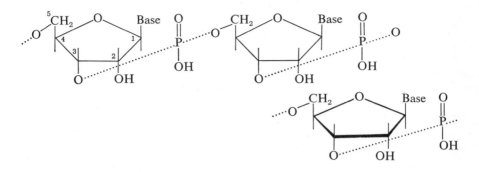

FIGURE 12.3 Schematic structure of segment of ribonucleic acid (RNA). Base may be purine (adenine or guanine) or pyrimidine (uracil or cytosine). In deoxyribonucleic acid, C2 of the carbohydrate is methylene; uracil is not present but thymine is one of the constituent bases. The three-dimensional structure of RNA and DNA, the presence of other bases, and so on is adequately discussed in any contemporary biochemistry text.

The pyrimidine *N*-glycosides are resistant to mild acid hydrolysis; this is one method of distinguishing them from the purine *N*-glycosides.

The reactions of the carbohydrate moiety of the nucleosides are relatively straightforward. The vicinal hydroxyl groups are readily oxidized by periodate or converted to a cyclic ketal (isopropylidene). The exocyclic hydroxymethyl group may be selectively phosphorylated although prior ketalation is usually employed. The synthesis of purine or pyrimidine glycosides is rather specialized with the properties of the aglycone commanding the most attention. The considerable biological interest in these compounds has resulted in very extensive synthetic studies which are summarized in several review articles.

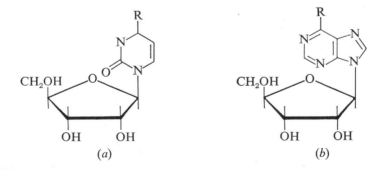

FIGURE 12.4 Purine or pyrimidine nucleosides. (a) R = − OH, β-D-ribofuranosyl uracil. R = − NH₂, β-D-ribofuranosyl cytosine, (b) R = NH₂, β-D-ribofuranosyl adenine. R = OH, β-D-ribofuranosyl guanine.

12.3 Synthesis

Consider the steps involved in the chemical synthesis of a typical di-saccharide:

1. Activation of the C-1 carbon of the intended nonreducing mono-saccharide unit.
2. Suitable protection for all hydroxyls on both monomers except for the desired linkage position on the reducing unit.
3. Condensation under conditions that favor the desired anomeric configuration.
4. Removal of blocking groups.
5. Separation of anomeric isomers.

A characteristic sequence is illustrated in Figure 12.5.

An extension of this to higher oligosaccharides or polysaccharides is well beyond the limits of current chemical techniques. In a very real sense, the above circuitous route is the work necessary to overcome the entropy associated with

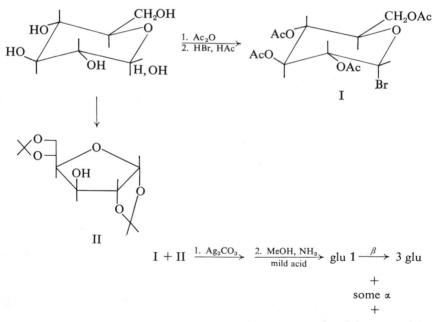

$$I + II \xrightarrow[]{1.\ Ag_2CO_3} \xrightarrow[\text{mild acid}]{2.\ MeOH,\ NH_3} glu\ 1 \xrightarrow{\beta} 3\ glu$$

$$+$$

$$\text{some } \alpha$$

$$+$$

$$\text{breakdown products}$$

FIGURE 12.5 Chemical synthesis of laminaribiose. This is one of the more readily synthesized disaccharides.

our current level of knowledge.[4] Examination of natural polysaccharides reveals that they are constructed with considerable uniformity within a given molecule. The required knowledge resides in the specificity of the enzymes responsible for their synthesis. Nevertheless, there are certain features of the enzymatic pathways that resemble the chemical sequence.

The over-all equation for the synthesis of a disaccharide may be written as follows:

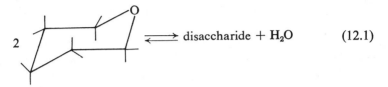

$$2 \quad \rightleftharpoons \text{disaccharide} + H_2O \qquad (12.1)$$

However, the free-energy change of the reaction as written is approximately +3000 kcal per mole. Recalling that

$$\Delta F^\circ = -RT \ln K_{eq}$$

the equilibrium constant at 25 degrees

$$\ln K_{eq} = -\frac{3000}{(1.98)(298)} \qquad (12.2)$$

will be

$$K_{eq} = \text{Antilog}_{10} \sim -2.3 \qquad (12.3)$$
$$\sim 0.005$$

Activation of glucose:

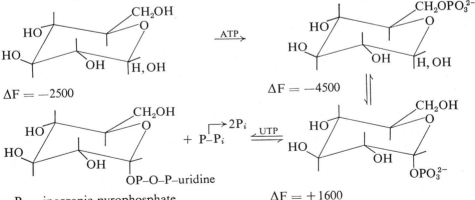

P_i = inorganic pyrophosphate

FIGURE 12.6 Mode of biological activation of glucose units prior to glycosyl transfer reactions. The base is represented as uridine but other purine or pyrimidine bases are found in such structures depending on the source.

---

[4] More properly, ignorance. Entropy is inversely proportional to knowledge and the only mechanism for reducing entropy is by the investment of work.

and therefore the reaction will not proceed spontaneously. Accordingly, the biochemical path involves activation of the nonreducing monosaccharide unit according to the general scheme shown in Figure 12.6. The energy change for hydrolysis of the nucleotidyl glycoside is sufficiently negative (about -7000 kcal/mole) to insure that subsequent synthetic reactions are substantially irreversible (Figure 12.7). The specificity for linkage position and configuration is built into the protein catalyst.

$$\text{UDP—glucose} + \text{ROH} \xrightarrow{\text{Enzyme}} \text{glucosyl—R} + \text{UDP}$$
$$\Delta F = -4500$$

FIGURE 12.7 Glycosyl transfer reaction utilizing a nucleotidyl sugar as carbohydrate donor. The ROH may be a carbohydrate; the configuration and position of linkage are determined by the specificity of the enzyme system.

The one exception to the above involves the synthesis of sucrose and trehalose (Figure 12.8) [3].

Because both glycosidic carbons are involved in the linkage for these disaccharides, the free energy of hydrolysis of sucrose and trehalose is appreciably higher than that for a disaccharide such as maltose. Accordingly sucrose

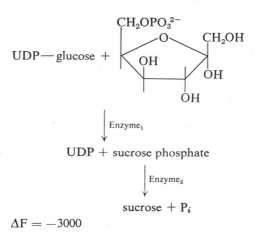

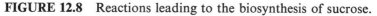

$$\Delta F = -3000$$

FIGURE 12.8 Reactions leading to the biosynthesis of sucrose.

may function directly as a donor in polysaccharide synthesis [4] (Figures 12.9 and 12.10). By the same reasoning, the biosynthesis of these disaccharides involves an additional step to insure the nonreversibility of the reaction in the natural system.

A consideration of the pathways by which polysaccharides are synthesized reveals certain features that also can be deduced from a consideration of the molecular size and molecular weight distribution of such polymers. It is most attractive to consider that polysaccharide synthesis, unlike protein synthesis,

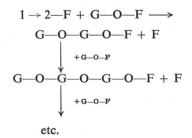

$$1 \rightarrow 2\text{—F} + \text{G—O—F} \longrightarrow$$

$$\text{G—O—G—O—F} + \text{F}$$

$$\downarrow + \text{G—O—F}$$

$$\text{G—O—G—O—G—O—F} + \text{F}$$

$$\downarrow + \text{G—O—F}$$

etc.

Action of dextran sucrase

G—O—F = sucrose

FIGURE 12.9 Role of sucrose (G—O—F) as a donor in dextran synthesis.

$$\text{F—O—G} + \text{FO—G} \longrightarrow \text{F—O—F—O—G} + \text{G}$$

$$\downarrow \text{F—O—G}$$

$$\overset{\text{F—O—G}}{\longleftarrow} \text{F—O—F—O—F—O—G} + \text{G}$$

etc.

Action of levansucrase

F—O—G = sucrose

FIGURE 12.10 Role of sucrose (F—O—G) as a donor in levan synthesis.

occurs by means of a polymerization process where the recognition by the re-sponsible enzyme is that of the immediately adjacent nonterminal, nonreducing carbohydrate (Figure 12.11). Thus, transfer may continue indefinitely to form

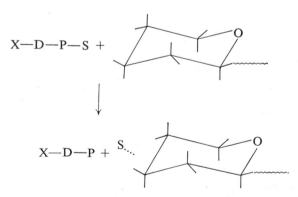

X—D—P—S +

↓

X—D—P + S....

FIGURE 12.11 Schematic illustration of 'end-addition' mechanism of poly-saccharides synthesis. The minimum site required for binding of the acceptor to the enzyme probably varies from one to 4 or more residues. XDPS is a general term for a nucleoside diphospho sugar.

chains whose size will mainly be dictated by the accessibility of the enzyme to both small molecular weight substrate and high molecular weight acceptor.[5]

12.4 Polymerization

Processes of the type described above can indeed yield products of enormous molecular weight. This is well illustrated by studies that have been carried out on dextrans and glycogen, where molecular weights as high as 50 million have been found. It is also apparent that any such polymerization occurring in a natural system will lead to the production of a family of molecules that do not have a single molecular size. Therefore, the assignment of molecular weight to a polysaccharide molecule is conditioned by whether we are talking about mole fraction, number average, weight average, Z average, or viscosity average molecular weights.

12.5 Chemical Structure

General

The complete structure of a molecule may be taken to represent a combination of chemical and physical data. The polysaccharides, because of their synthetic origin, impose certain limitations on the description of their physical structure. However, the methods for determining chemical structure are usually sufficient to allow a working formula to be proposed. The most common ones are summarized below.[6]

1. Periodate oxidation. Oxidant consumption, formic acid production. (a) Smith degradation; (b) Barry degradation.
2. Methylation.
3. Acetolysis.
4. Partial acid hydrolysis and further degradation or identification of isolated oligosaccharide fragments.
5. Specific enzymatic hydrolysis.
6. Infrared spectra.

A combination of the above methods is usually required for complete chemical structure determination. This is best illustrated by several specific examples.

---

[5] These are not the only control mechanisms that may be operative. See subsequent discussion.

[6] Most of the individual methods have already been described. It is inherent in any structural analysis that the starting material be as nearly homogeneous as possible. In these cases, some size heterogeneity is to be expected but will not affect the chemical structure. Prior information needed will be the empirical formula, number of sugars present, and their identification.

Cellulose

Complete acid hydrolysis of cellulose produces glucose as the only reducing sugar. The yield of crystalline glucose is better than 90 percent and the cellulose structure can be schematically represented as Figure 12.12, which is in agreement with the empirical formula $C_6H_{10}O_5$.

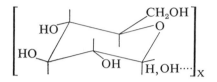

FIGURE 12.12 Structural formula for cellulose based on the information that glucose is the only constituent sugar.

Direct derivatization of the polysaccharide leads to the introduction of 3 acetoxy or 3 methyl groups per monosaccharide residue and therefore, there are 3 free hydroxyl groups present.

The fully methylated cellulose derivative yields on acid hydrolysis 2,3,6-tri-*O*-methyl glucose in almost 90 percent yield. This fact taken together with the relatively slow rate of acid catalyzed hydrolysis of the parent polysaccharide permits the structure in Figure 12.13 to be formulated. The existence of con-

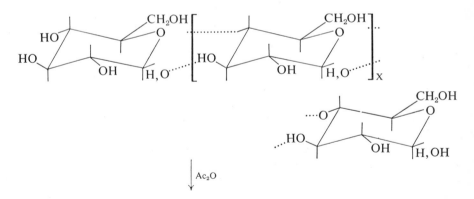

FIGURE 12.13 Representation of cellulose as a linear homopolysaccharide with 1,4 linkages; based on methylation analysis.

tiguous glucopyranose units in the polysaccharide was proved by partial acetolysis and separation and identification of a homologous series of oligosaccharide acetates (Figure 12.14). The configuration of the glycosidic linkage was established as β based on optical rotation and enzymic susceptibility of the disaccharide unit.

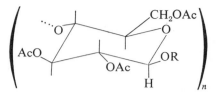

FIGURE 12.14 Structure of homologous oligosaccharides isolated after acetolysis of cellulose. R = acetate or an acetylated β-D-glucopyranose unit; *n* ranges from 2–6.

Careful fractionation of the hydrolysis products of fully methylated cellulose resulted in the isolation of 2,3,4,6-tetra-*O*-methyl-D-glucopyranose. The ratio of this derivative to the tri-*O*-methyl derivative was 1:1000, a figure in agreement with the release of formic acid on periodate oxidation (Figure 12.15). The formula may now be written as shown in Figure 12.16.

Chain residue:

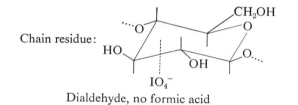

Dialdehyde, no formic acid

Nonreducing end:

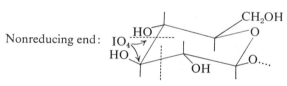

Dialdehyde + 1HCO$_2$H

FIGURE 12.15 Action of periodate on cellulose.

There is a considerable amount of x-ray data available on the arrangement of glucose residues in cellulose, especially crystalline versus noncrystalline regions. The sugar residues are in the normal ring conformation and both

β-D-glucopyranosyl

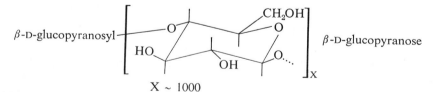

β-D-glucopyranose

X ~ 1000

FIGURE 12.16 Structure of cellulose based on methylation, periodate, and molecular weight studies.

hydrogen bonds and van der Waals forces contribute to the stabilization of the three-dimensional structure.

Amylopectin

Amylopectin is the predominant polysaccharide component of the starch granule and is composed exclusively of glucose. End-group analysis based on either formic acid release after periodate oxidation, or the yield of tetra-*O*-methyl glucose from hydrolysis of fully methylated amylopectin indicated a chain length of about 25 residues. However, molecular weight determinations were grossly different from this figure (about 500,000) and there was no detectable reducing group.

Analysis of the products of hydrolysis of fully methylated amylopectin showed the presence of 2,3,6-tri-*O*-methylglucose (about 90 percent) and about 4 percent of 2,3-di-*O*-methyl glucose. This evidence suggested that the reducing end of one chain of glucose residues (about 25 units) was joined to another chain by a glycosidic linkage to the C-6 hydroxyl (Figure 12.17).

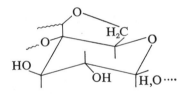

FIGURE 12.17 Schematic structure for amylopectin based on results of methylation analysis.

Partial acid hydrolysis of the parent polysaccharide led to the isolation of crystalline isomaltose which could also be recovered after acetolysis under mild conditions.

Because not all branch points may be 1,6, additional data were obtained by periodate oxidation. The main chain contains 1,4 linkages (Figure 12.18), and

Main chain:

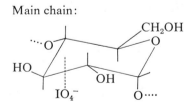

FIGURE 12.18 Possible branch point in an amylopectin chain. If either the C2 or C3 hydroxyl is substituted, such glucose residues will be resistant to the action of periodate.

every such residue will consume 1 mole of periodate. If branching occurs at C-2 or C-3, these residues will be resistant to oxidation whereas those substituted at C-6 will still be oxidized between C-2 and C-3. In the case where branch point linkages are via the hydroxyl group at C-6, after periodate oxidation all glucose residues should be destroyed. This prediction was experimentally confirmed.

The structures in Figure 12.19 can be proposed on the basis of the above data.

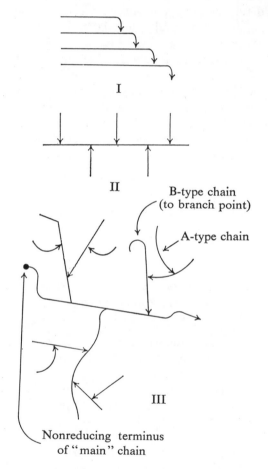

FIGURE 12.19   Possible structures for amylopectin. Type I has all chains of substantially the same size with branching occurring at a fixed distance from a terminus; Type II has a main chain "core" with side branches; and Type III is a rebranched, tree-like structure.

Distinguishing between these alternate structures is not possible on chemical grounds alone but can be achieved by enzymatic degradation. The following enzymes will degrade amylopectin:

1. β-amylase cleaves residues from nonreducing termini but is unable to cleave beyond a branch point.

2. Amylo 1,6-glucosidase (debranching enzyme) catalyzes hydrolysis of 1,6 linkages.

3. Phosphorylase catalyzes phosphorolysis[7] of 1,4 linked residues from nonreducing ends, but cannot act at branch points. In addition, its action on an A-type chain stops 3 units from a branch, but on a B-type chain it stops when it is 5 or 6 residues from the branch point.

The first model will yield a constant percentage of branch points on sequential degradation with amylase and debranching enzyme. The second model would be completely degraded after the sequential action of amylase, debranching enzyme and amylase (or phosphorylase), and the third model would require several successive enzymatic treatments before complete degradation was achieved. This latter model also would give a progressively smaller number of degradation products after each treatment (Figure 12.20).

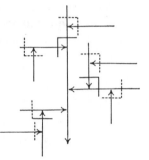

FIGURE 12.20 Residues remaining after enzymatic digestion of a "rebranched" molecule. ––– Limit of first enzymatic digestion of regularly rebranched molecule. —— Limit of second enzymatic digestion.

The second formulation is in agreement with most experimental results; and the model structure in Figure 12.21 may be written for amylopectin.

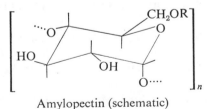

Amylopectin (schematic)

FIGURE 12.21 Formula for amylopectin based on methylation, enzymatic, and molecular weight studies. About one R in 25 is a chain of glucopyranosyl units linked α 1–4. The size of *n* is not known.

---

[7] Hydrolysis with addition of the elements of phosphoric acid rather than water.

Glycogen, on the other hand, appears to have a rebranched structure similar to the third formulation.

Xylans

Analysis of xylans obtained from plant structures reveals the presence of more than 90 percent xylose with small amounts of other sugars, particularly L-arabinose and D-glucuronic acid. The structural questions are formulated as follows:

1. The linkage of the xylose units.
2. Are the xylose residues in furanoside or pyranoside ring form or both?
3. Are the minor components present as contaminants?
4. If not, what is their mode of linkage to the xylose units?

Hydrolysis of fully methylated xylan yields 2,3-di-*O*-methyl xylose. The strong negative optical rotation of xylan combined with its relative stability to acid hydrolysis suggested a structure of predominantly β-1,4 linked xylopyranose units (Figure 12.22).

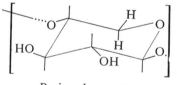

Basic xylan structure

FIGURE 12.22 Structure of main chain of xylan based on methylation analysis.

Evidence that at least 2 adjoining xylose units were of this form was provided by acetolysis of the polymer, and these results were extended by isolation and characterization of a homologous series of xylose oligosaccharides up to a degree of polymerization of 6.

A small percentage of 2-*O*-methyl-xylopyranose was found after hydrolysis of methylated xylan, suggesting some branching to C-3. This was confirmed by periodate studies wherein a comparable amount of xylose was not destroyed by the oxidation.

The xylans that contain arabinose are water soluble but the arabinose may be removed by mild acid to yield an insoluble xylan containing only β-1,4 linked xylose. Thus, the arabinose units are apparently attached to the xylose backbone and are probably furanosides, this latter conclusion resulting from their ease of hydrolysis (Figure 12.23). This was confirmed by enzymatic hydrolysis which yielded oligosaccharides containing arabinofuranose directly linked to xylose.

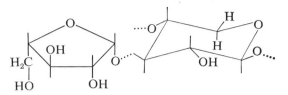

FIGURE 12.23 Attachment of L-arabinose units as furanosides is indicated by ease of hydrolytic cleavage.

Some natural xylans may contain as much as 40 percent arabinose, all residues attached in this fashion.

Similar results are found for the glucuronic acid containing polymers; the glucuronopyranosyl residues appear to be linked either to C-2 or C-3 of the xylose. The general structures in Figure 12.24 agree with current data.

$$(X1 \xrightarrow{\beta} 4X)_n$$

$$X1 \xrightarrow{\beta} 4X1 \xrightarrow{\beta} 4X1 \xrightarrow{\beta} 4X$$

$$\underset{\begin{array}{c}3\\\uparrow\beta\\1\\A\end{array}}{}$$

$$X1 \xrightarrow{\beta} 4X1 \xrightarrow{\beta} 4X1 \xrightarrow{\beta} 4X$$

$$\underset{\begin{array}{c}2\\\uparrow\\1\\GA\end{array}}{}$$

A = L-arabinofuranose

GA = D-glucuronic acid

Schematic xylan structures; X = xylopyranose

FIGURE 12.24 Schematic xylan structures.

Chondroitin 4-sulfate [8, 9]

The presence of complex anionic polysaccharides in connective tissues has been known for nearly 100 years. One of the first to be described was obtained after alkali extraction of cartilage and its empirical formula and products identified after acid hydrolysis, agreed with the following composition:

Uronic acid

Acetic acid

Sulfate

Amino sugar

The amino sugar was obtained in crystalline form but due to the lack of unequivocal synthetic methods for the preparation of amino sugars, its structure was not definitely established until 1945 (Figure 12.25).

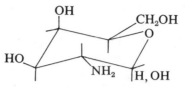

Amino sugar in chondroitin sulfate
(2-amino 2-deoxy D-galactopyranose)

FIGURE 12.25   Amino sugar isolated after hydrolysis of chondroitin sulfate. 2-amino sugars in general, are stable to strong acid conditions.

The uronic acid was identified as D-glucuronic acid both by direct hydrolysis and by oxidative conversion to D-glucosaccharic acid (Figure 12.26). Because the

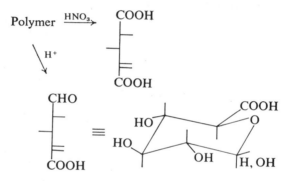

FIGURE 12.26   Confirmation of the presence of D-glucuronic acid in the chondroitin sulfate by isolation of glucosaccharic acid as well as small amounts of glucuronic acid by direct hydrolysis.

polysaccharide did not react with nitrous acid, and the release of acetic acid on acid hydrolysis paralleled formation of free amino groups, the acetate was presumed to be substituted at the amino group (Figure 12.27). The markedly

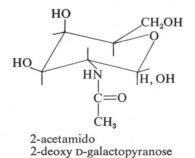

2-acetamido
2-deoxy D-galactopyranose

FIGURE 12.27   Position of the acetyl group determined by the release of acetic acid as compared with the release of free amino groups.

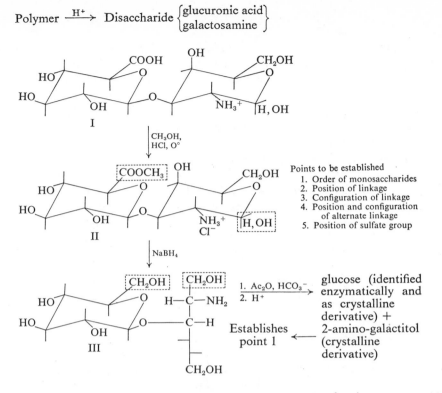

Polymer $\xrightarrow{\text{H}^+}$ Disaccharide $\begin{cases} \text{glucuronic acid} \\ \text{galactosamine} \end{cases}$

Points to be established
1. Order of monosaccharides
2. Position of linkage
3. Configuration of linkage
4. Position and configuration of alternate linkage
5. Position of sulfate group

glucose (identified enzymatically and as crystalline derivative) + 2-amino-galactitol (crystalline derivative)

Establishes point 1

N-acetylation necessary in reaction 1 because hydrolysis of amino compound is very slow due to protonation of nitrogen

Product of N-acetylation susceptible to hydrolysis by β-glucosidase (point 3)

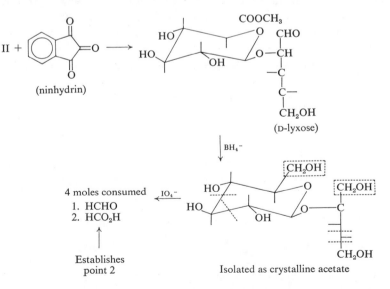

(ninhydrin)

(D-lyxose)

4 moles consumed
1. HCHO
2. HCO₂H

Establishes point 2

Isolated as crystalline acetate

FIGURE 12.28 Structural analysis of disaccharide isolated after acid hydrolysis of chondroitin sulfate.

anionic character of the polysaccharide made methylation studies impractical. Accordingly, further structural work was carried out by partial acid hydrolysis.

Acid hydrolysis of the polymer followed by resolution of the products by ion-exchange chromatography resulted in the isolation of a deacetylated, desulfated disaccharide in 65 percent yield. Its structure was established by the sequence of reactions shown in Figure 12.28. The structure of the glucosido-lyxitol was established by periodate oxidation and that of the parent disaccharide ultimately confirmed by synthesis [10].

Enzymatic digestion of the original polysaccharide yielded oligosaccharides that could be further degraded by acid hydrolysis to the above disaccharide. Because there was no material that was resistant to enzymatic hydrolysis, the polymer was presumed to have a straight chain structure (Figure 12.29).

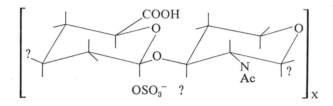

FIGURE 12.29 Structure for chondroitin sulfate based on disaccharide and hydrolytic data.

Esterification of the polymer followed by reduction with sodium boro-hydride gave a product which could be satisfactorily methylated. Hydrolysis of the methylated polymer yielded a monomethyl amino sugar identified as 2-deoxy 2-amino 6-*O*-methyl D-galactose. Thus, the sulfate ester group was apparently on C-4 of the amino sugar (Figure 12.30). This was confirmed by desulfation of the polymer with methanol-HCl under mild conditions, followed

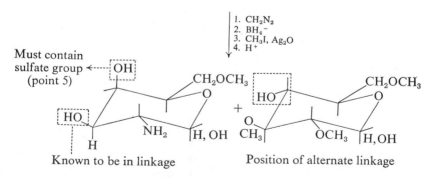

FIGURE 12.30 Sequence establishing position of sulfate group and hexo-saminidic linkage.

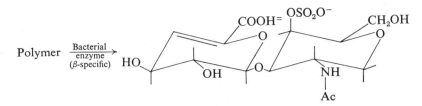

FIGURE 12.31 Action of bacterial enzyme on chondroitin sulfate.

by a methylation sequence similar to the one above. 2-deoxy 2-amino 4,6-di-*O*-methyl-D-galactose was isolated and identified as was 2,3,6-tri-*O*-methyl-D-glucose [11].

Finally, the desulfated polymer was shown to be susceptible to a bacterial enzyme which cleaves 4-substituted glucuronides by an elimination reaction producing an unsaturated product (Figure 12.31) [12]. The polysaccharide was therefore assigned the structure illustrated in Figure 12.32.

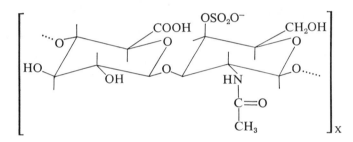

FIGURE 12.32 Structure for chondroitin sulfate based on chemical and enzymatic studies.

More recent evidence indicates that this polymer occurs in tissue covalently linked to a polypeptide chain via the hydroxyl group of serine, and thus has no reducing end. The types of covalent linkages that have been observed for polysaccharide protein complexes are illustrated in Figure 12.33.

The ready β-elimination reaction of the serine glycosides explains the early observations on extraction of the polysaccharide with alkali.

Molecular weight studies on isolated chondroitin sulfate chains free of protein gave a figure of 13,000, with almost no polydispersity [13]. A consideration of such data suggests that, here, polymerization takes place at a number of equally reactive sites (polypeptide serines, for example), that all are available simultaneously, and that ultimate chain size is controlled by some kind of termination step. The expected molecular weight distribution for this type of multichain polymerization agrees with the experimental values. Possible chain termination steps that are also applicable to any polysaccharide biosynthesis include the following:

1. Limitation of precursor supply.

2. Removal from synthetic locus: (a) gelation due to critical chain size; (b) extrusion into extracellular space.

3. "Capping" of chains by a nonreactive anomalous residue.

4. Alteration of peptide structure so as to inhibit further polymerization.

5. Inhibition of polymerization (or a critical enzyme) as a function of chain length.

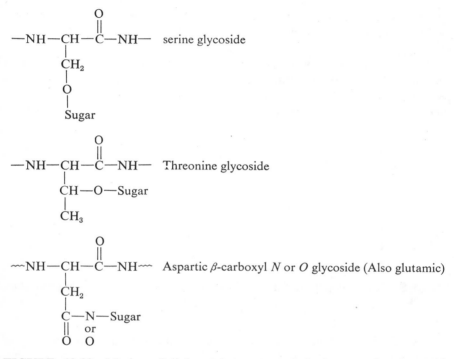

FIGURE 12.33 Modes of linkage between carbohydrate and polypeptide chains.

The over-all structure of the complex can thus be represented as shown in Figure 12.34.

One difference between this class of polysaccharides and glycogen or amylopectin is that the "main chain" is peptide rather than polysaccharide.

These structural examples illustrate several of the methods employed to study increasingly complex polysaccharides. An extension of those techniques already described plus correlation of chemical and physical (size, shape) data will solve most polysaccharide structures. It is apparent that accurate data on size and shape of the polymers are a necessary adjunct to chemical information.

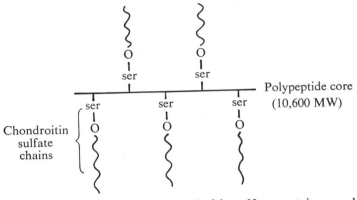

FIGURE 12.34   Structure of chondroitin sulfate-protein complex.

12.6 Methods of Measuring Size and Shape of Polysaccharide Molecules

The physical properties of such polymers will be very dependent upon their molecular weight distribution; it is impossible to draw any conclusion regarding molecular weight from a consideration of a single molecular parameter. Studies that have been carried out on polysaccharides indicate that the majority of such molecules are polydisperse. There are a variety of fractionation techniques that have been employed for polysaccharides.

Fractional Precipitation from Aqueous Solution by the Addition of a Nonpolar Solvent

The most common situation is fractionation of aqueous solutions by the addition of ethanol or acetone. It is also possible to carry out such fractionations by removal of solvent or by control of temperature. The various sub-fractions obtained in this manner are then examined for homogeneity by chromatography, electrophoresis, or centrifugation.

Fractional Extraction

Successive or repeated extractions of insoluble or undissolved polymer yields fractions which may then be examined for homogeneity. It is also possible to carry out liquid–liquid extraction or fractional elution of polysaccharide material when the polymer has been precipitated onto an inert support, such as cellulose, or onto a support, such as ion-exchange resin, when charged functional groups are present in the molecule.

This procedure usually is carried out by use of temperature gradients or by changing the nature of the solvent. The more regular and more crystalline the polymer structure, the more difficult it is to achieve fractionation by this technique.

Chromatographic Methods, Particularly Gel Filtration Techniques

Ion-exchange methods separate molecules largely on the basis of charge similarity. Gel filtration behavior on dextran or polyacrylamide is a function of the effective volume of the polymer. Such gels are cross-linked to varying degrees and have pore sizes that will permit infiltration of molecules only to a certain size limit (Figure 12.35). Larger molecules are excluded from the gel

FIGURE 12.35 Schematic diagram of gel filtration. Small molecules such as salt, oligosaccharides, and so on, (·) penetrate gel and are retarded whereas higher molecular weight materials (•) are excluded. Exclusion limit is a function of degree of crosslinking.

and appear in the eluate at the "excluded" column volume; small molecules are appropriately retarded. This technique is commonly used for desalting macromolecules but has potential use for polymer fractionation as well. When suitable methods have been worked out for the determination of polymer size and shape, some indication as to homogeneity can be obtained by gel fractionation. These methods are limiting in the sense that it is not possible to subfractionate very low molecular weights or very high molecular weights, and it is rather difficult to tell where effects of diffusion begin and end. Thus, precise information is not available.

In addition to fractionation methods based on solvent solubility and molecular dimension (separations carried out by gel filtration techniques), methods such as ultracentrifugation and electrophoresis can in some circumstances be used as purification tools, in addition to their more obvious utility as characterization methods.

When substantial differences in sedimentation behavior exist, then the forces achieved in the ultracentrifuge, which run upwards of 200,000 gravities, may be employed to achieve separation of macromolecular components, particularly when utilized with density gradients. In this latter technique, material of known buoyant density can be predictably sedimented through a solution of variable density until it reaches an area where its density is equal to that of the solvent. The material will then band or form a zone, and subsequent fractionation at the end of the run permits the isolation of this zone with relatively little admixture with adjoining materials. Polymers in a mixture that have different density characteristics can be separated by means of this technique.

The use of electrophoresis has found relatively little application in the purification of polysaccharides. Although several polysaccharides have charged functional groups, particularly pectins, bacterial capsular and cell wall polysaccharides, and those found in connective tissue, the necessity for employing a supporting medium has rendered preparative use of electrophoresis rather limited. The difficulties in using free electrophoresis include limited sample size, diffusion problems, and inability to resolve complex mixtures. A continuous flow electrophoresis apparatus has been developed that can be operated without the use of a supporting medium. This has found some application in the polysaccharide field and will probably come into wider use as the technology develops.

In several cases, ultrafiltration through membrane filters with graded pore size has been used for separating high molecular weight polymers [14]. Several types of dextrans, and hyaluronic acid from synovial fluid have been separated from smaller molecules (for example, protein) by taking advantage of their very high molecular weight and the ability of membrane filters to retard molecules of this size. This is a relatively limited technique and only of advantage where there are gross differences in properties between the molecules under consideration.

Fractionation techniques must ultimately depend on assessment of the homogeneity of the products. Consideration of the mode of biological formation of most macromolecules of this type and those few situations where experimental data are available regarding the distributions of material isolated from natural sources, leads to the conclusion that the synthesis of these molecules occurs so as to give products of random degree of polymerization. Control is exerted by the number of growing chains, kinetic factors such as egress from a cellular environment or the combined action of degradative enzymes. When the synthesizing enzyme is extracellular, as in the case of dextran sucrase, and where degradative enzymes are not present or the cell system is unable to utilize the synthesized material as a substrate, then the molecular weights of the product polymers may become very high. Dextrans frequently have molecular weights upwards of 50 million. The more complex biological polymers that are synthesized by enzymes residing within a cell have molecular weight ranges that are appreciably less.

Polysaccharides such as glycogen, which are synthesized in the cell and which reside in the cell for their biological life, serve as energy sources. This is true for most animal cells and plants; lower animals such as insects rely largely on trehalose as an energy source. The polymer synthesis is usually under control at several "biological levels" and macromolecular structure may grow to very great proportions. Glycogen, for example, is frequently found in a particulate form and it is doubtful if accurate molecular weights have ever been measured for this type of molecule. The vast majority of structural polysaccharides encountered in animal systems are extracellular in nature and apparently remain covalently linked to a polypeptide matrix throughout their biological life. This complicates measurement of the molecular weights to a very considerable degree. The over-all macro complex may have molecular weights of half a million or more but the individual polysaccharide chains have much lower molecular weights.

12.7 Molecular Weight

Introduction

There are a wide variety of methods available for determining molecular weight. Each of these has application to the polysaccharide field and, as expected, each has limitations and advantages. The specialized problems of molecular weight distributions[8] and polymer shape require extensions or combinations of techniques and will be discussed separately.

Chemical Methods (Number Average)

The estimation of polysaccharide chain length by direct chemical assay can be done in one of two ways. When the polymer contains a reducing terminus, reaction of this with reagents specific for the carbonyl group provides a direct measure of the number of such ends per chain.

Stoichiometric iodine consumption can be employed but the limitations of quantitative assay make this method applicable to oligosaccharides having a degree of polymerization of 25 or less. In addition, as chain length increases, the probability of incomplete reaction becomes greater and small errors will introduce large variation in calculated values.

The use of nonstoichiometric reducing sugar methods is complicated by the inability to provide appropriate standards. In these procedures, several moles of oxidant are consumed by a free monosaccharide and substitution at chain hydroxyls alters this value to a very considerable degree. Thus, 1,3,1,4 and 1,6 substituted residues will all consume different amounts of oxidant. Where the linkage is known and an appropriate oligosaccharide is available for use as a standard, satisfactory values may be obtained. These reactions are usually carried out under more drastic conditions than those for iodine consumption, and incomplete oxidation is unlikely.

Two more sensitive methods employing radioactive techniques have been

---

[8] Not encountered with proteins or "small" molecules but very possibly a biological parameter for a given polysaccharide. However, this is a problem of considerable importance to synthetic polymer chemistry.

developed. The reaction of a polysaccharide reducing end group with radio-active cyanide will result in the incorporation of 1 molecule of cyanide per chain (Figure 12.36).

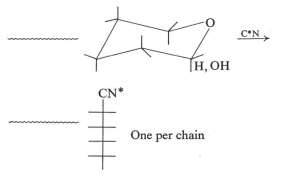

CN*

One per chain

FIGURE 12.36 Reaction of radioactive cyanide with polysaccharide chain. This procedure is only valid when the polymer is known to have a reducing end; see text.

The unreacted cyanide is easily separated from polymeric material and the latter assayed for radioactivity. If the specific activity[9] of the starting cyanide is known, the total number of moles of cyanide incorporated into the polymer can be calculated. Comparing this figure with the total amount of carbohydrate present gives a direct measure of average chain length.

A similar procedure depends on reduction of the terminal carbonyl with tritium labeled sodium borohydride (Figure 12.37).

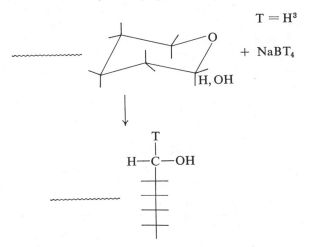

$T = H^3$

$+ NaBT_4$

FIGURE 12.37 Reaction of reducing end of polysaccharide chain with tritium-labeled sodium borohydride. Tritium incorporated into hydroxyl groups is lost by exchange with solvent.

[9] Disintegrations per unit time per mole.

Both methods depend on quantitative reaction; the latter procedure may be more reliable in this regard.

It has already been mentioned that several of the natural occurring polysaccharides may not have a reducing terminus (for example, dextran, chondroitin sulfate). It is possible, however, to estimate nonreducing ends. If this is done in conjunction with structural studies (branching), then an assessment of chain length can be made. The most convenient procedure involves complete methylation, hydrolysis, and estimation of the methylated products.

Separations are readily carried out by gas–liquid chromatography and sensitivity is high. As above, complete reaction is necessary.

Osmotic Pressure (Number Average)

This method is based on the same principles as the procedures of freezing point depression or boiling point elevation. However, pressure differences are more easily measured and small molecule impurities can usually be readily removed and thus do not introduce serious errors.

The osmotic pressure of an ideal solution may be expressed as

$$\frac{\pi}{C} = \frac{RT}{M} \tag{12.4}$$

π = osmotic pressure of solution with concentration C.

However, most polysaccharides, even at low concentrations, show significant deviations from this relationship probably due to a marked entropy change on dilution. The usual procedure is to measure the osmotic pressure as a function of concentration and to extrapolate to zero concentration [15].

Because this procedure counts the *number* of molecules, high molecular weight materials exhibit very low pressures, errors are large, and extrapolation correspondingly more difficult. Even when extrapolation is carried out, however, the experimental results rarely follow the ideal relationship. Equations of the form

$$\frac{\pi}{C} = \frac{RT}{\overline{M}_n} + v_2 C + \cdots \tag{12.5}$$

($\overline{M}_n$ = number average molecular weight)

have been proposed where v_2 is the second virial coefficient. Several attempts have been made to evaluate this parameter, and the proper choice of solvent and temperature appears critical. The procedure has been applied to amylose in aqueous salt and amylose acetates in organic solvents.

Sedimentation

The most pertinent advance in the determination of the molecular weight distribution of polysaccharides has come from the use of the ultracentrifuge. The application of interference optics has made it possible to examine soluble polysaccharide molecules at concentrations such that particle–particle interaction is reduced to a noninterfering minimum. Ancillary information required are the partial specific volume of the molecule and the refractive index increment. These are readily obtained experimentally, and analysis of equilibrium sedimentation data then permits determination of the molecular weight distribution.

The molecular weight distribution of dermatan sulfate isolated from skin was studied by this technique [16] (Figure 12.38). The types of molecular weight measured are the number average $\overline{M}_n$

$$\overline{M}_n = \frac{\sum\limits_{i=1}^{\infty} (n_i M_i)}{\sum\limits_{i=1}^{\infty} n_i} = \frac{\sum\limits_{i=1}^{\infty} C_i}{\sum\limits_{i=1}^{\infty} \left(\dfrac{C_i}{M_i}\right)} \tag{12.6}$$

the weight average $\overline{M}_w$

$$\overline{M}_w = \frac{\sum\limits_{i=1}^{\infty} (n_i M_i^2)}{\sum\limits_{i=1}^{\infty} n_i M_i} = \frac{\sum\limits_{i=1}^{\infty} (C_i M_i)}{\sum\limits_{i=1}^{\infty} C_i} \tag{12.7}$$

(n_i = the number of molecules of molecular weight, M_i and C_i is their concentration.)

and the Z average $\overline{M}_z$

$$\overline{M}_z = \frac{\sum\limits_{i=1}^{\infty} (n_i M_i^3)}{\sum\limits_{i=1}^{\infty} n_i M_i^2} = \frac{\sum\limits_{i=1}^{\infty} (C_i M_i^2)}{\sum\limits_{i=1}^{\infty} C_i M_i} \tag{12.8}$$

(for a pure protein, for example, these are all equal.)

The pertinent conclusions were as follows[10]:

The polymer was found to be polydisperse with respect to molecular size. The number, weight, and Z average molecular weights were 23, 27, and 41 thousand, respectively. The types of polymerization processes that would lead to such molecular weight distributions are random polymerization from which low molecular weight species (approximately 5000 or less) have been removed by some artificial means, or multichain condensation where chain length is controlled by any of several methods mentioned previously. Because the

[10] The general theory of sedimentation equilibrium including a thermodynamic treatment may be found in several standard texts. The specialized treatment utilized for this study is briefly summarized in Appendix 2.

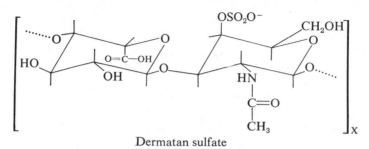

Dermatan sulfate

X ranges from 40 to 80

FIGURE 12.38   Structural formula of dermatan sulfate. Polymer is probably linked to protein in its "natural state". X ranges from 40 to 80.

sample had been subjected to periods of dialysis during its preparation, the former process is in keeping with the experimental results, but the possible presence of low molecular weight fragments in the "native" material was not determined.

The application of the ultracentrifuge to problems of this type offers a very considerable advantage. Several of the technological problems present in viscosity or light scattering measurements and the relatively limited information that can be obtained from osmotic pressure determinations at low concentrations (the situation where the osmotic pressure relationship holds, but which becomes very difficult to measure experimentally for high molecular weight materials) are overcome.

Viscosity

The viscosity average molecular weight or the viscometric measure of molecular size gives information different from osmotic pressure or sedimentation. The specific viscosity of a solution is defined as

$$\eta_{sp} = \eta - \eta_0 \tag{12.9}$$

where η is the viscosity of the solution and η_0 that of the solvent. Extrapolation of this function to zero concentration yields the intrinsic viscosity

$$\frac{\eta_{sp}}{c \to 0} = [\eta] = \text{intrinsic viscosity} \tag{12.10}$$

This value has been related to the molecular weight by an equation of the form:

$$[\eta] = KM^\alpha \tag{12.11}$$

where K and α are constant for a given system [17].

A study of amylose in dimethyl sulfoxide gave experimental data which agreed with values of 1.25×10^{-3} for K and 0.87 for α [18]. In neutral salt, however, values of 0.112 and 0.50, respectively, were derived from experimental data.

The non-Newtonian behavior of polymer solutions, wherein the solution exhibits a viscosity that depends on the applied shear rate, will be dependent upon molecular weight, concentration, and the solvent. Even upon extrapolation to infinite dilution, it is also necessary to extrapolate to 0 rate of shear. When the molecule is a rigid asymmetric particle, the theoretical treatments can explain both shear dependence and the observed molecular weight distributions. However, with macromolecules that behave as flexible random coils, the theory has not been adequately developed to permit any conclusions from viscosity studies with regard to size and shape.

Light Scattering

Measurements of molecular dimensions *per se* can be obtained by light scattering. Because the light scattered by small particles is symmetrical about a position normal to the incident beam (Rayleigh scattering), the amount scattered will be a function of the dimension of the soluble particle relative to the wavelength of the incident light. The amount of light scattered will decrease as the dimension of the solute exceeds approximately 5 percent that of the wavelength of the incident light, and is usually somewhat less than Rayleigh scattering at all angles. This departure from the theoretical scattering or Rayleigh scattering increases with size and is somewhat dependent on shape because tightly coiled molecules will have quite different behavior than fully extended ones.

The most commonly used method for evaluating light scattering data is the extrapolation procedure of Zimm [19]. The value of the particle scattering factor, which is the ratio of the intensity of angle theta to that at 0 angle, is taken as 1 and the equation for molecular weight is as follows (see Figure 12.39):

$$\frac{KC}{R_0} = \left(\frac{1}{\overline{M}_w}\right) + 2\frac{V_2 C}{RT} + \text{higher terms} \qquad (12.12)$$

Hence, if R_0 can be found, the weight average molecular weight can be calculated, independently of any knowledge of the molecular shape. R_0 is not measurable directly but can be extrapolated from the values obtained at sufficiently low angles. The method of Zimm employs extrapolation to zero both for concentration and angle. The limiting gradient of the 0 concentration line is a measure of the molecular dimensions of the molecule and yields the mean-square end-to-end distance for a molecule of Z-average molecular weight.

It is also true that for anisotropic scattering particles, depolarization of the scattered light occurs. Because this influences the angular distribution, it is sometimes necessary to introduce a correction factor.

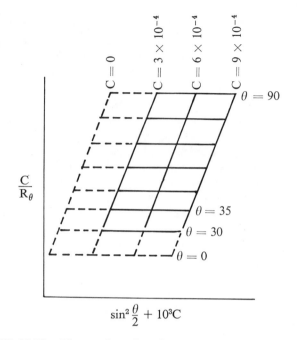

$$\sin^2\frac{\theta}{2} + 10^3C$$

FIGURE 12.39 Zimm plot of typical light scattering data.

The main difficulty in light scattering measurements is methodological. An inspection of the equations reveals that heavy particles are weighted much more strongly than light ones, and thus total clarification of solutions is a necessity. Particles of dust, small amounts of aggregates, and so on, will introduce profound errors.

Summary

It is expected that as centrifugation techniques improve, sedimentation equilibrium will become the molecular weight method of choice for most molecules up to a size of 1 million. The use of interference optics and appropriate methodology for calculating distributions of molecular weights, together with short column equilibrium techniques have made these measurements feasible in the range from 5000 up. Solutions that absorb ultraviolet light can be examined using absorption optics, which renders even greater dilution possible so that higher molecular weights can be examined. Because the sedimentation equilibrium method is based upon equilibrium thermodynamics, it is undoubtedly the most reliable of the centrifuge techniques. The work of Archibald has provided data for the measurement of molecular weights during the approach to sedimentation equilibrium, but the most rigorous results are reached after equilibrium has been obtained and suitable corrections for depletion of solute at the meniscus and crowding at the bottom of the centrifuge cell can be made.

Relatively few polysaccharides have been studied by these techniques; most studies have been carried out on proteins and nucleic acids.

12.8 Conformation of Polysaccharides

Although all of the above molecular weight procedures when applied to a single macromolecular species will give information about the size distribution of the polymer molecule, none of them with the exception of light scattering say very much about the shape. Even the light scattering results give information only about the general shape or the flexibility of the macromolecule and offer very little about the relationship of the individual monomer units to one another, or how the ring forms may be distorted by the presence of bulky substituents. In solution, the total number of conformations that a molecule can adopt, even with imposed restrictions on ring forms, can be exceedingly large, and thus only average dimensions can be measured. Hydrodynamic behavior, solvent and ion binding will all reflect shape in solution.

One parameter that is used to define a model system is the so-called mean-square radius of gyration described in Equation (12.13), where n is the total number of segments and $\bar{\rho}^2$ is the average square distance of one segment from the center of gravity of the molecule:

$$\bar{\rho}^2 = n^{-1} \sum_{i=1}^{n} \bar{\rho}^2 \tag{12.13}$$

From this figure can be derived the mean-square end-to-end distance of the molecule

$$6\bar{\rho}^2 = r \tag{12.14}$$

(r = mean-square end-to-end distance.)

This is distinct from the fully extended length which is a fixed value independent of solvent or temperature (Figure 12.40).

Geometric consideration permits calculation of an excluded volume for the polymer. It is obvious that if the polymer is fully extended in solution, it will occupy an excluded volume equal to that of a sphere whose radius is half the length of the polymer molecule. Because it is unlikely that this fully extended form is present for most natural polymers, whether in their native state or examined under laboratory conditions, some information regarding the occupied space is certainly pertinent before methods of molecular weight determination become meaningful in terms of shape.

The most difficult problems encountered in determining the shape of macromolecules are those concerned with the behavior of flexible polyelectrolytes. These substances have the properties of both electrolytes and polymers, and will have both large conductances and high intrinsic viscosity numbers. The

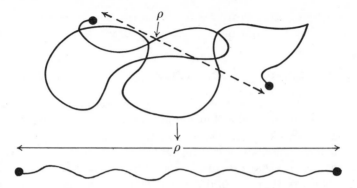

FIGURE 12.40 Representation of polysaccharide chain as random coil or extended rod. Mean-square end to end distance obviously varies with shape.

conformation adopted will depend on many factors including the ionic strength of the solution in which they are examined. Relationships between the extension of the polymer chain and degree of ionization of the polyelectrolyte have been derived. The *p*H in most biological systems will be such that all carboxyl, phosphate, and sulfate groups will be ionized. Simplifying assumptions that include the concept that there is both a conformational and electrostatic contribution to total free energy have proven to be unsatisfactory. The limiting viscosity of a polyelectrolyte is a function of the ionic strength. This is shown in Figure 12.41. Curve 1 represents polyelectrolyte in water, where ionization will increase on increasing dilution and the mutual repulsion of the charged groups causes the macromolecule to expand [20]. This is probably somewhat of an oversimplification because molecular models of such polymers indicate that the

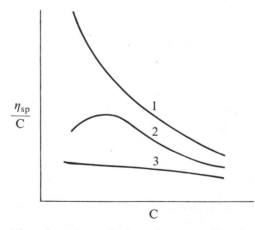

FIGURE 12.41 Viscosity of a polyelectrolyte as a function of its concentration (C) and salt concentration. See text.

dimensions between charged functional groups are of such magnitude that interactions of this type are small. Nevertheless, an effect on η is expected. The concentration range normally employed for measurement shows considerable molecular interaction. As indicated in curve 2, electrolytes such as sodium chloride can be added and the viscosity is appreciably reduced. When the electrolyte concentration becomes high as in curve 3, the ionization effects of the polyelectrolyte become depressed and the hydrodynamic behavior of the polyelectrolyte is similar to that of an uncharged polymer. This would then seem to be the ideal system for examining polymers for properties such as polydispersity. When polyfunctional groups are present, the nature of the electrolyte will affect the apparent molecular weight. Thus, divalent ions may serve as bridges between adjacent molecules. Sulfated polysaccharides, for example, will be both fully ionized and interacting with protein, mono, and divalent cations and small uncharged molecules as well.

Nevertheless, it is conceivable if not likely, that the fine points of conformation are relatively unimportant and that the gross average structures which can be derived suffice to define the physiological role of these molecules.

CHAPTER 13

De Novo
Synthesis of Carbohydrates

13.1 Introduction

One of the problems of considerable contemporary interest is the tracing of evolutionary pathways by means of chemical similarities throughout the phylogenetic scheme. Proteins such as cytochrome c or specific enzymes and several complex connective tissue polysaccharides have been studied with a view toward elucidating possible relationships between chemical structure and evolution. However, to take an even more distant view, antedating the appearance of metabolizing and biosynthetic systems on the planet, we may well ask the question, "How did molecules such as carbohydrates originate?" The *de novo* synthesis of carbohydrate, largely carried out by plants (CO_2 fixation), can be discussed separately. However, we must formulate a mechanism that will begin with compounds which might reasonably have been expected to be present in primitive atmospheres and, by some sequence of understandable chemical transformations, convert these to the level of carbohydrates. It is simply a further logical extension of this construction to synthesize polysaccharides by random condensation reactions carried out under extreme conditions of temperature or pressure. Similarly, amino acids, peptides, purines, pyrimidines, and so on, can be so formed. Although the majority of experimental work in this area has centered on the synthesis of simple amino acids, it is reasonable to assume that the initial formation of carbohydrates follows a scheme not terribly dissimilar from several that have been experimentally devised in the laboratory [1]. The chemical chronology of these laboratory sequences probably is inversely related to their historical origin.

13.2 Aldehyde Condensations

Formaldehyde, when treated with base, will undergo self-condensation reactions and form a complex mixture of carbohydrates. This reaction was initially described over 100 years ago, although the carbohydrate moieties were

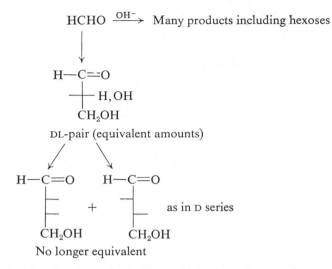

FIGURE 13.1 Condensation of formaldehyde to form carbohydrates up to the level of hexoses. After the trioses, asymmetric induction results in unequal yields of higher products.

not identified at that time. The initial products of such a condensation probably reach the level of trioses, as illustrated in Figure 13.1. Because there can be no selective asymmetry at this level, a compound like glyceraldehyde would be formed as a DL mixture. However, subsequent additions to either the D or the L glyceraldehyde will not occur with unprejudiced stereochemistry. When the hexose level is reached, the expectation is that all 16 aldoses will not be present in equivalent amounts.

Fischer studied this general reaction in detail. Reaction of formaldehyde and glyceraldehyde in the presence of alkali yielded D and L mannose, D and L fructose, and D glucose. It is not entirely clear from the experimental data that all of these were present in the initial mixture because some of the subsequent manipulations may have resulted in isomerization. The initial reaction products were isolated as osazones which were then converted to osones and reduced to

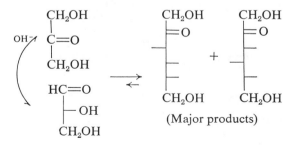

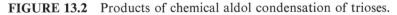

FIGURE 13.2 Products of chemical aldol condensation of trioses.

the individual sugars. Nevertheless, this sequence established the formation of 6-carbon sugars from simple precursors [2].

Aldol condensations in general can produce hexose sugars. Glyceraldehyde and its isomerization product, dihydroxyacetone, undergo ready aldol condensation in the presence of a mild alkali to yield a keto hexose (Figure 13.2). This reaction is similar to the enzyme catalyzed formation of fructose 1-6-diphosphate illustrated in Figure 13.3 [3]. The equilibrium constant of both the

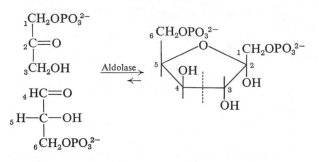

FIGURE 13.3   Enzymatic aldol condensation.

enzymatic and nonenzymatic reactions is strongly in favor of the hexose product. The *trans* configuration at carbons 3 and 4 is specifically formed in the enzymatic synthesis and favored in the nonenzymatic condensation. A list of aldose and keto sugars that have been synthesized by application of aldol condensations is given in Table 13.1.

TABLE 13.1

Carbohydrates synthesized by aldol condensations.

PRODUCTS	PRECURSORS
D-fructose + D-sorbose	D-glyceraldehyde + dihydroxyacetone
D-arabinose + D-xylose	D-glyceraldehyde + glycolaldehyde
2-deoxy D-ribose	IPD-glyceraldehyde + acetaldehyde
L-galactoheptulose	Dihydroxyacetone + tetrose
D-ascorbic acid	Glyoxylic ethyl ester + D-threose (CN$^-$ catalyzed, similar to benzoin condensation).
Fructose-6-phosphate	D-glyceraldehyde + dihydroxy acetone phosphate (enzymatic-only 1 product)

13.3 *Hydroxylation of Unsaturated Precursors*

Just before the turn of the century, Griner was able to show that compounds such as acrolein when treated under hydrogenating conditions gave rise to products that had the properties of divinyl glycols (Figure 13.4) [4].

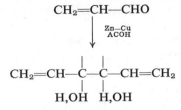

$$CH_2{=}CH{-}CHO$$

$$\downarrow \begin{array}{c} \text{Zn—Cu} \\ \text{ACOH} \end{array}$$

$$CH_2{=}CH{-}\underset{\underset{H,OH}{|}}{C}{-}\underset{\underset{H,OH}{|}}{C}{-}CH{=}CH_2$$

FIGURE 13.4 Synthesis of 6-carbon compounds by condensation of acrolein.

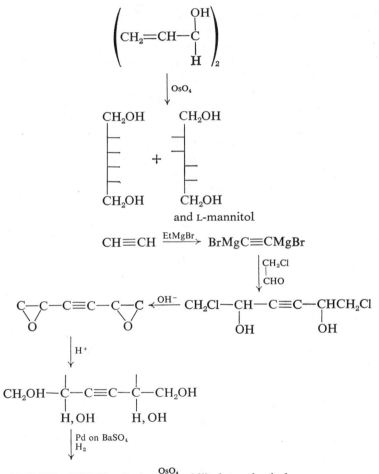

and L-mannitol

$$CH{\equiv}CH \xrightarrow{EtMgBr} BrMgC{\equiv}CMgBr$$

FIGURE 13.5 Synthesis of hexitols by hydroxylation of unsaturated derivatives.

The resulting divinyl glycols could then be hydroxylated to form hexitols (Figure 13.5).

It is not necessary to start these condensations from acrolein because even acetylenic compounds can be made to undergo similar transformations. It is interesting to note that again, in this case, preferential products are formed at the hexose level; the primary ones are allitol, mannitol, and glucitol.

It seems reasonable to consider that intermediates such as acetylene or acrolein would have existed under primitive earth conditions and that the initial condensation to form carbohydrates took place by mechanisms not terribly dissimilar from this one.

The condensation of aldehyde sugar acetates with carbethoxymethylene triphenylphosphorine proceeds under mild conditions to yield the corresponding *trans* 2,3-dehydro, 2,3-dideoxy aldonic acids. Treatment of this product under hydroxylating conditions with osmium tetraoxide results in the formation of partially acetylated aldonic acids. This is a rather novel method for the extension of the carbohydrate chain and should make available quite a large number of isomers although it will probably be restricted to aldoses. The results of hydroxylation studies indicated the *trans* configuration for the double bond in the aldonic acids.

It is also possible to condense the phosphorine with unprotected monosaccharides to give *trans* 2,3-dehydro, 2,3-dideoxy aldonic acids directly. Arabinose on reaction with the phosphorine in dimethylformamide gave an excellent yield of the D-arabinoheptonate derivative (Figure 13.6) [5, 6].

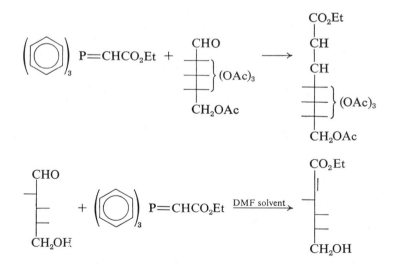

FIGURE 13.6 Synthesis of dideoxy sugars by condensation with a phosphine derivative. A variant of the Wittig reaction applied to carbohydrates. The unsaturated product can be further reacted.

13.4 Biosynthesis

Introduction

The current broad distribution of carbohydrates in nature reflects an unusual ability and diversity on the part of biological systems to form what are presumably functionally different carbohydrates. Most of these are 5 or 6 carbon sugars, but when we consider the possibilities for functional group substitution, oxidation, and reduction, and we add this to the number of possible polymeric products which may be formed, the sum is a truly enormous figure. Despite this amazing diversity, there is only one really fundamental reaction that permits net carbohydrate synthesis to take place. This is the fixation of carbon dioxide by green plants to ultimately yield 6-carbon sugars which are then transformed by a variety of enzymatic steps into all of the commonly occurring carbohydrates.

Photosynthesis

The fixation of CO_2 by green plants under the influence of light is a two-stage reaction, with the formation of the new carbon–carbon bond not requiring

$$6CO_2 + 6H_2O \xrightarrow{h\nu} 6O_2 + C_6 \text{ sugar}$$

FIGURE 13.7   Over-all equation for photosynthesis.

light [7]. The over-all expression may be written as shown in Figure 13.7. During the light phase of the photosynthetic step, high-energy phosphate and

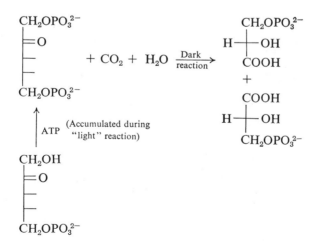

FIGURE 13.8   Primary carbon dioxide fixation step in photosynthesis.

reducing power are accumulated in the plant cell by transduction of electro-magnetic energy from the incident light. The fixation of CO_2 requires this high-energy phosphate because the immediate acceptor of the carbon dioxide is a phosphorylated 5-carbon keto sugar, D-ribulose 1-5-diphosphate (Figure 13.8).

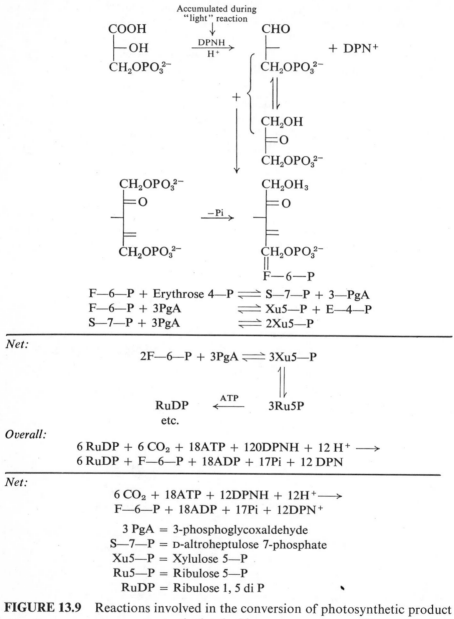

F—6—P + Erythrose 4—P $\rightleftharpoons$ S—7—P + 3—PgA
F—6—P + 3PgA $\rightleftharpoons$ Xu5—P + E—4—P
S—7—P + 3PgA $\rightleftharpoons$ 2Xu5—P

Net:

$$2F{-}6{-}P + 3PgA \rightleftharpoons 3Xu5{-}P$$

$$RuDP \xleftarrow{ATP} 3Ru5P$$
etc.

Overall:

6 RuDP + 6 CO_2 + 18ATP + 120DPNH + 12 H^+ $\longrightarrow$
6 RuDP + F—6—P + 18ADP + 17Pi + 12 DPN

Net:

6 CO_2 + 18ATP + 12DPNH + 12H^+ $\longrightarrow$
F—6—P + 18ADP + 17Pi + 12DPN$^+$

3 PgA = 3-phosphoglycoxaldehyde
S—7—P = D-altroheptulose 7-phosphate
Xu5—P = Xylulose 5—P
Ru5—P = Ribulose 5—P
RuDP = Ribulose 1, 5 di P

FIGURE 13.9   Reactions involved in the conversion of photosynthetic product to the level of hexoses.

Although we would predict that this fixation would result in the formation of a branched 6-carbon sugar, the initial product observed in such systems is 3-phosphoglyceric acid (Figure 13.8). Through a series of condensations and transfer reactions illustrated in Figure 13.9, the 3-phosphoglyceric acid is reconverted to ribulose 1,5 diphosphate and, at the same time, $\frac{1}{6}$ of a molecule of hexose is synthesized. Repetition of this cycle through 6 turns allows the synthesis of 1 hexose molecule from 6 carbon dioxides, 6 waters, and electromagnetic radiation. The remainder of the products involved in this synthetic transformation are catalytic in nature and do not appreciably change in concentration.

Interconversion of Sugars

It is almost universally true in living systems that D-glucose serves as the primary carbohydrate source in all transformations. Isotopic tracer studies that have been carried out substantiate this conclusion and show that D-glucose serves as a precursor for molecules as far removed as L-fucose or D-galactosamine. There are two possible pathways for such conversions. One involves dissimilation of ingested glucose to the level of trioses or lower, with subsequent stereospecific recondensation to build up the desired product. The second pathway would require specific epimerizations, oxidations, substitutions, and so on, to be carried out at the hexose level. In general, the carbohydrate interconversions occur without randomization of the carbon chain or without carbon–carbon cleavage in the hexose skeleton. These transformations involve several general reactions, many of which have their counterparts in the chemical laboratory, although in the latter case, the specificity or yield does not approach the biosynthetic mechanism.

Isomerases. These were discussed in some detail when considering the mechanism of the Lobry de Bruyn transformation. The most common is the conversion of glucose-6-phosphate to fructose-6-phosphate. Similar transformations also take place for pentoses and trioses.

Oxidation. The formation of uronic acids in biological systems occurs at the level of the sugar nucleotide. A typical example is the oxidation of uridine diphospho-D-glucose to uridine diphospho-D-glucuronic acid [3] (Figure 13.10). Mannuronic acid is formed by a similar oxidation but several of the other uronic acids are derived in turn from uridine diphospho-D-glucuronic acid by yet another transformation.

Epimerization. The ability of enzyme systems to catalyze epimerization of sugars such as glucose and galactose is another tribute to their remarkable stereospecificity. This conversion takes place in the animal organism by the sequence of reactions illustrated in Figure 13.11. The actual epimerization step is of considerable mechanistic interest and has been extensively studied. As

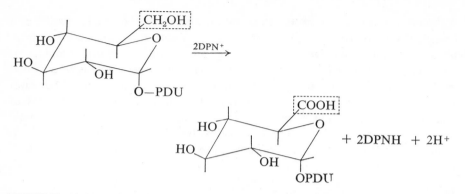

FIGURE 13.10 Biological oxidation of hexoses to hexuronic acids. This enzyme (uridine diphosphoglucose dehydrogenase) is widely distributed in plant and animal sources.

noted in the equation in Figure 13.11, the enzyme catalyzing this transformation has an absolute requirement for a hydrogen acceptor; in this case, diphosphopyridine nucleotide. Thus, we might envision transient oxidation of the glucose moiety of the nucleotide to a keto intermediate with subsequent reduction forming an epimeric mixture of products. Careful studies on this transformation have demonstrated the following:

1. If the reaction is carried out in the presence of tritiated water, tritium is not incorporated into the product sugar. Because the reduction step requires a proton, we might expect that such tritium exchange would occur. However, the proton might go only to hydroxyl and thus be lost again to the solvent.

2. Hydrogen from externally added reduced pyridine nucleotide is not

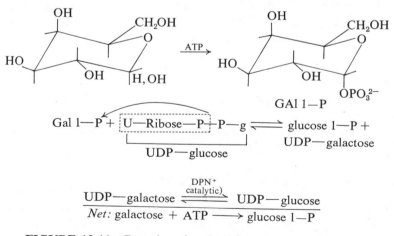

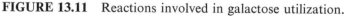

FIGURE 13.11 Reactions involved in galactose utilization.

incorporated into the product sugar and the reduced pyridine nucleotide actually is an inhibitor of the reaction even in the case where the parent enzyme has been completely freed of its pyridine nucleotide coenzyme.

3. Studies carried out with uridine diphosphoglucose, specifically labeled with tritium in the C_4 position of the glucose moiety, have demonstrated that there is no loss of tritium to the solvent during conversion of the sugar to uridine diphosphogalactose (Figure 13.12).

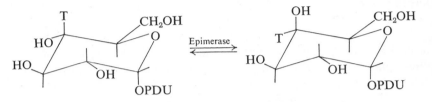

FIGURE 13.12 Reaction catalyzed by UDP-glucose 4-epimerase.

4. Studies carried out with material labeled with both tritium and carbon-14 show that during the course of the reaction, the ratio of tritium to carbon-14 is altered, but that at the end of the reaction, it has been restored to its initial condition. This indicates that in some fashion the tritium is lost from the C-4 position but that it is stereospecifically restored *without exchange*.

5. Fluorescent studies of the enzyme during the course of the reaction indicate that reduced pyridine nucleotide is formed as a transitory, enzyme

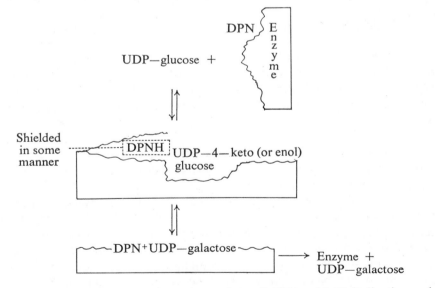

FIGURE 13.13 Illustration of reaction of Figure 13.12 indicating role of enzyme and pyridine nucleotide.

bound intermediate. The over-all course of the reaction can be schematically formulated as indicated in Figure 13.13 [9].

Other carbohydrate epimerases include those for the C-5 position of uronic acids [10], the C-4 position of hexosamines [11], the C-2 position of *N*-acetyl hexosamine [12], and the C-3 position of keto pentoses [13]. The latter two reactions utilize sugar phosphates as substrates and not the nucleotide linked sugar.

Reduction. The introduction of a deoxy function (terminal) is accomplished by a series of transformations, illustrated in the conversion of guanosine diphospho-D-mannose to guanosine diphospho-L-fucose (Figure 13.14) [14].

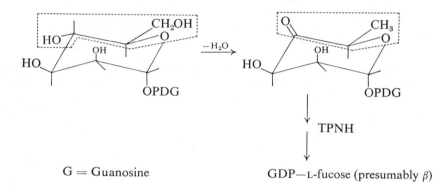

G = Guanosine   GDP—L-fucose (presumably β)

FIGURE 13.14 Reactions involved in the biosynthesis of 6-deoxy sugars.

The initial step is an internal reduction-oxidation occurring on carbon 4 and carbon 6. The 4-keto 6-deoxy nucleotidyl linked sugar is then epimerized at carbon 5 and subsequently reduced to form the desired deoxy sugar product. Similar mechanisms appear to be general for the formation of other 6-deoxy sugars.

Amination. The reactions by which nitrogen is fixed into organic compounds are those catalyzed by glutamic dehydrogenase, glutamine, and carbamyl phosphate synthetases. The formation of hexosamine also represents a nitrogen fixation, but into a carbohydrate chain. Because the ultimate degradation product of amino sugars is ammonia, this fixation is transitory and does not appear in protein. However, it still represents a net nitrogen gain for most organisms. The mechanism of hexosamine synthesis was described previously and involves the condensation of D-fructose-6-phosphate with glutamine to form D-glucosamine-6-phosphate. Amino sugars such as galactosamine and mannosamine are formed by epimerizations from glucosamine derivatives. The biogenesis of deoxy amino sugars, 3 and 4 amino sugars, and the unusual sugars occurring in antibiotics is virtually unknown but undoubtedly follows pathways similar to those described above.

Esters.   Most amino sugars occur as *N*-acetyl derivatives and, in addition, several *O*-acetyl sugars have been described. The synthesis of the latter class of compounds has not been investigated but the synthesis of acetyl function of amino sugars occurs by transfer of a C-2 unit from acetyl coenzyme *A* to glucosamine-6-phosphate (Figure 13.15) [15].

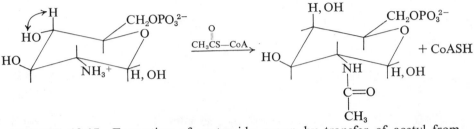

FIGURE 13.15   Formation of acetamido group by transfer of acetyl from acetyl coenzyme A.

In those compounds where phosphate and sulfate esters occur in polymeric or macromolecular products, the bulk of evidence indicates that the polymeric products are synthesized prior to the addition of these substituent groups. The possibility remains that some intermediate small molecular weight precursor might be the initial anion acceptor. Typical reactions are illustrated in Figure 13.16.

Branched Chain Sugars.   There are several naturally occurring branched chain sugars, particularly in the cardiac glycosides. The biosynthesis of these

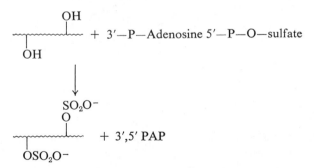

FIGURE 13.16   Illustration of level at which sulfate ester groups are introduced into polysaccharide chains. The hydroxyl acceptors are on specific monosaccharides in the polysaccharide chain. Phosphate esters may be introduced by a similar mechanism utilizing adenosine triphosphate as the phosphate donor.

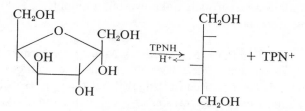

FIGURE 13.17   Reaction catalyzed by D-mannitol dehydrogenase. As in most reductive reactions, the equilibrium is markedly in favor of the reduced product.

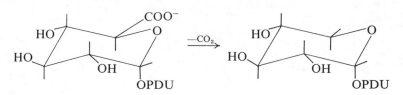

FIGURE 13.18   Synthesis of xylose by enzymatic decarboxylation of uridine diphosphoglucuronic acid.

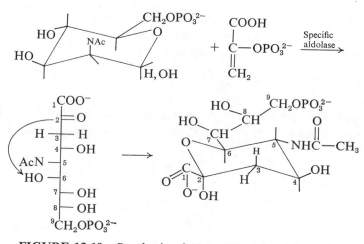

FIGURE 13.19   Synthesis of *N*-acetyl neuraminic acid.

has not been extensively investigated but it seems likely that the introduction of a methyl or hydroxymethyl group takes place via 1-carbon transfer.

Reduction.   Conversion of aldoses or ketoses to the level of sugar alcohols is generally accomplished by pyridine nucleotide specific enzymes in which the equilibrium constant is strongly in favor of the reduced product. The stoichiometry of a typical reaction shows that this is pH dependent. These reactions are frequently used as specific assays (Figure 13.17) [16].

Decarboxylation. The formation of L-arabinose from D-xylose takes place through an epimerization sequence but most xylose arises from the enzymatic decarboxylation of uridine diphospho-D-glucuronic acid (Figure 13.18) [17].

Condensations. Aldol-type condensations have been mentioned. The synthesis of fructose-1,6-diphosphate and deoxy ribose-5-phosphate are typical examples. One unusual condensation is that between *N*-acetyl mannosamine 6-phosphate and phosphoenolpyruvate to form a 9-carbon keto acid, *N*-acetylneuraminic acid (Figure 13.19) [18].

This unusual sugar acid is widely distributed in nature, especially in complex lipids and proteins where it is found as a peripheral, nonreducing terminus.

A summary of these transformations is given in Table 13.2.

TABLE 13.2

Summary of enzymatic sugar interconversions.

REACTION TYPE	SUGARS INVOLVED
Isomerase	Mannose 6-P; Glucose 6-P; Glyceraldehyde 3-P; L-fucose; L-rhamnose; Ribose 5-P
Oxidation (C-1)	Glucose 6-P; 6-P gluconic acid
Oxidation (C-6)	UDP-glucose; GDP-mannose
Decarboxylation	UDP-glucuronic (to -xylose)
Epimerization	N-Ac-glucosamine 6-P (C-2); Ribulose 5-P (C-3); UDP-glucose ⎫ UDP-*N*-Ac-glucosamine ⎭ C-4 UDP-glucuronic acid; C-4 and C-5
Amination	Fructose 6-P
Esterification	Glucosamine 6-P (*N*-Ac) Galactosamine 6-P (*N*-Ac)
Reduction	Numerous simple sugars in bacterial systems; GDP-mannose (to L-fucose)
Aldol condensation	Triose phosphates; Phosphoenol pyruvate and *N*-Ac-mannosamine 6-P

CHAPTER $\boxed{14}$

Analytical Methodology

14.1 Introduction

It is extremely infrequent that a practicing chemist encounters problems at the level described in a text. Much of the preliminary work and ancillary information required to approach a given reaction or transformation is usually assumed by the author or left to the reader's discretion and understanding. However, in actual laboratory practice, problems such as identification of unknown materials, quantitation of specific components, and separation of closely related isomers form a routine part of the analytical procedures necessary during any structural investigation. The theoretical basis of many of the analytical methods has been largely unstudied in favor of developing suitable empirical conditions. However, classification can be made on such grounds although, as with any empirical procedure, success can only be measured by experiment.

14.2 Reducing Sugar Procedures

The ability of carbohydrates to act as reducing agents has been known for some time and this property is widely utilized in devising quantitative methods for their estimation.

Nonstoichiometric

In general, nonstoichiometric methods are empirical; therefore, precise attention to reaction time, pH control, temperature, concentrations, and use of appropriate standards is required before such methodology can be employed as a quantitative tool. When assaying compounds for which suitable standards are available, precision of the order of 3 percent is not uncommon.

The reaction of cupric copper with aldose or ketose sugars in the presence of alkali (most frequently carbonate) takes place according to the following:

$$\text{Sugar} \xrightarrow[\text{CO}_3^=]{\text{Cu}^{++}} \text{Mixed products, 4–5 Cu}^+ \qquad (14.1)$$
$$\text{(potential free carbonyl)}$$

The intermediate transformations that the sugar undergoes have not been completely defined but compounds such as metasaccharinic acids and osones have been identified (Figure 14.1). The number of moles of oxidant ultimately

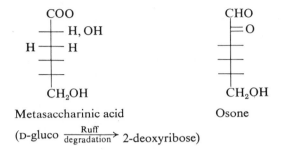

Metasaccharinic acid · · · · · · · · · · · Osone

(D-gluco $\xrightarrow[\text{degradation}]{\text{Ruff}}$ 2-deoxyribose)

FIGURE 14.1 Products formed on treatment of carbohydrates with alkali. D-glucometasaccharinic acid can be degraded to 2-deoxy D-ribose by treatment with hydrogen peroxide in the presence of ferrous ion (Ruff degradation).

consumed depends upon the conditions of the reaction, structure of the sugar, and the exact reagents employed. Because degradation of the carbon chain does take place, sugars that are substituted with groups which may resist further degradation give much lower molar reducing equivalents compared to a standard such as glucose. Other structural relationships to reducing power have not been formulated, but it is known that glucose, galactose, and mannose give different reducing values per mole. Fructose and keto sugars generally undergo these reactions much more readily than do the aldose analogs.

The cuprous oxide formed during the reaction may be measured in several ways. The initial techniques were iodimetric but the demand of current work places a strong emphasis on micro or semimicro methodology, which resulted in the development of indirect colorimetric procedures. The reagent most commonly employed is arsenomolybdic acid; reaction with cuprous oxide proceeds as follows [1]:

$$Cu^{++} \xrightarrow{\text{Sugar}} Cu^{+}$$

$$Cu^{+} + HAsMoO_4(\text{ox}) \longrightarrow Cu^{++} + HAsMoO_4(\text{red}) \qquad (14.2)$$

$$\underset{\uparrow}{\text{yellow}} \qquad\qquad\qquad\qquad \underset{\uparrow}{\text{blue}}$$

The amount of reduced arsenomolybdic acid formed is proportional to the amount of cuprous oxide formed and in that sense proportional to the amount of sugar oxidized.

A second, more sensitive method for reducing sugars uses ferricyanide as the oxidizing agent and measures ferrocyanide by reaction to form prussian blue [2]:

$$Fe(CN)_6^{\equiv} \xrightarrow{\text{Sugar}} Fe(CN)_6^{\equiv}$$

$$Fe(CN)_6^{\equiv} + Fe^{++} \longrightarrow Fe_2[Fe(CN)_6] \qquad (14.3)$$
$$\text{prussian blue}$$

This method measures less than 1 μg of sugar with reasonably high precision. The conditions of the over-all oxidation reaction are similar to those of the copper oxidation procedure. There are several other oxidation procedures which involve organic dyes or silver ion but these have their primary application in chromatographic analysis and will be discussed subsequently.

Stoichiometric Methods

The reaction of aldoses with iodine has been previously discussed as a preparative technique and is often employed as a quantitative end-group method. The stoichiometry is illustrated below and the reaction can be scaled to measure several micromoles of sugar. The major advantage in this procedure is that ketoses are unreactive (Figure 14.2).

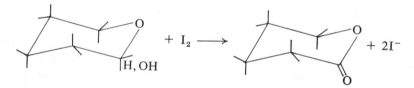

FIGURE 14.2 Stoichiometry of reaction of aldoses with iodine.

Radioactive cyanide or borohydride can be used for determining extremely small quantities of reducing compounds, but the handling is difficult. The major problem with cyanide is the completeness of the reaction, whereas the problem with borohydride is the quantitative removal of interfering substances before radioactive assay can be carried out. Neither of these methods has been extensively employed.

Procedures such as periodate consumption can be used under conditions where the structure of the compound is known and quantitation is desired by means of oxidation of specific functional groups.

Strong Acid Methods (Table 14.1) [3]

Introduction. The ring form of the carbohydrates is relatively stable to acid hydrolysis but under extreme conditions the molecule can be dehydrated to form furfural derivatives, which may further degrade to aliphatic compounds

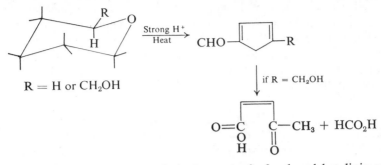

FIGURE 14.3 Conversion of carbohydrates to furfural and levulinic acid by treatment with strong acid. Both aldoses and ketoses react.

such as levulinic acid (Figure 14.3). These aromatic or unsaturated aldehydes undergo condensations with a wide variety of organic substances to yield chromogens whose structure has rarely been determined but whose absorption properties have been commonly used for a quantitative assay of carbohydrates. A brief description of the more commonly employed techniques follows:

Pentoses. Pentoses on treatment with hot concentrated hydrochloric acid are converted to furfural in a reasonably high yield. The condensation of furfural with orcinol in the presence of ferric iron yields a green complex with an absorption maximum at about 600 mμ. The sensitivity of this method is of the order of 0.01 micromoles. As with all methods in this category, it is subject to considerable interference from comparable structures. See Table 14.1 for details.

Hexoses. The treatment of hexoses with concentrated sulfuric acid yields hydroxymethyl furfural and levulinic acid (Figure 14.3). These are then

TABLE 14.1

Colorimetric methods of carbohydrate analysis.

REAGENT	SPECIFICITY
Resorcinol	Ketohexoses
Cysteine-carbazole	Ketoses (3 to 7 carbons)
Carbazole	Uronic acids
Cysteine	Methyl pentoses, hexoses
Anthrone	Aldo and keto hexoses, uronic acids
Orcinol	Pentoses, uronic acids
Naphthoresorcinol	Uronic acids
Diphenylamine	2-deoxypentose
Indole	2-deoxypentose
Acetylacetone *p*-dimethylamino- benzaldehyde	Amino sugars

condensed with a variety of aromatic alcohols or ketones (such as phenol or anthrone) to yield chromogens. Aldoses, ketoses, methyl pentoses, and uronic acids all undergo this reaction. However, the nature of the chromogen formed is somewhat different in each case and some distinction is possible. The measurement of small amounts of aldoses in the presence of large amounts of other materials is difficult.

Hexuronic acids. Heating uronic acids in the presence of concentrated hydrochloric acid initially produces decarboxylation so that the end product is the same as that derived from pentoses, furfural. The orcinol procedure mentioned above may also be applied to the determination of uronic acids.

The treatment of uronic acids with concentrated sulfuric acid under conditions where dehydration is more rapid than decarboxylation leads to the formation of 2-formyl furoic acid (Figure 14.4). This is subsequently condensed

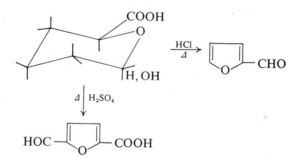

FIGURE 14.4 Reactions of uronic acids with strong mineral acid.

with carbazole to yield a pink product, λ max at 530 mμ. This intermediate also condenses with anthrone but the carbazole method appears to be the most sensitive and specific for the uronic acid grouping [4].

Methyl Pentoses. The reactions described for methyl pentoses depend on the condensation of methyl furfural with cysteine to yield a yellow complex. The specificity of this reaction is reasonably high and can be used for estimation of methyl pentose in the presence of large amounts of hexose or hexosamine. The chromogen formed has λ_{max} just at the limit of the visible spectrum (400 mμ), whereas most other sugars yield yellow chromogens with higher absorption maxima [5].

Ketoses. Ketoses, due partially to their less stable ketal structure and to the fact that many of them occur in the form of furanoside rings undergo reactions under less vigorous conditions than those required for aldoses. The reaction of ketoses in acid solution at mildly elevated temperatures with resorcinol is reasonably specific and not subject to interference by significant

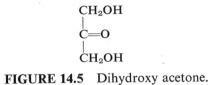

FIGURE 14.5 Dihydroxy acetone.

amounts of aldose. The cysteine-carbazole procedure can be used for ketoses as simple as dihydroxy acetone (Figure 14.5) [6].

Deoxy Ribose and Similar Sugars.

1. SCHIFF BASE FORMATION. Specific reactions for deoxy ribose initially developed through histochemical procedures for the detection of deoxyribonucleic acids. The most commonly employed is the aldehyde fuchsin reagent, which takes advantage of the substantial portion of the deoxy ribose that exists as the free aldehyde form. The formation of the Schiff base chromogen can be specifically observed (Figure 14.6).

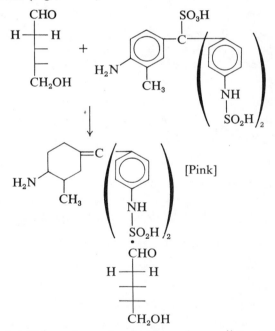

FIGURE 14.6 Schiff base formation between deoxy ribose and leucofuchsin.

2. THIOBARBITURIC ACID. Prior oxidation of deoxy ribose by periodate yields a malondialdehyde intermediate which may then be condensed with thiobarbituric acid (Figure 14.7) [7]. This reaction is highly sensitive and has also been employed for the determination and estimation of *N*-acetyl neuraminic

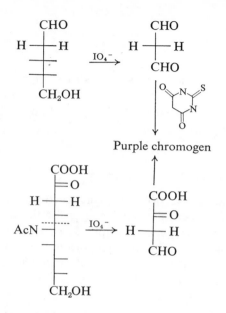

FIGURE 14.7   Reaction of deoxy ribose with periodate followed by condensation with thiobarbituric acid.

FIGURE 14.8   Periodate oxidation of *N*-acetyl neuraminic acid to yield oxalacetic acid semialdehyde.

acid (Figure 14.8). Compounds that do not give rise to this intermediate cannot be measured in this manner.

Due to the relative stability of sugar alcohols and aldonic acids very few suitable methods are available for their direct colorimetric estimation by strong acid procedures. There is, however, one general procedure that can be employed for all sugar alcohols and aldonic acids although it is subject to obvious

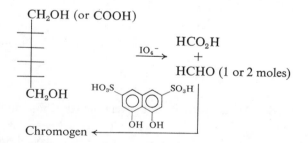

FIGURE 14.9   Reaction of aldonic acids or sugar alcohols with periodate followed by condensation of the formaldehyde produced with chromotropic acid.

interference from neutral sugars as well. However, when preliminary separations have been carried out, quantitation by this technique can be employed. The periodate oxidation of the sugar yields formic acid and formaldehyde. The formaldehyde is in turn measured colorimetrically by means of the chromotropic acid reaction (Figure 14.9). Any sugar that forms formaldehyde can be assayed and this technique is frequently used to measure glycerol.

Summary

All of the methods listed above are applicable not only to low molecular weight materials, but to polymeric materials as well. The strenuous acid conditions are sufficient to hydrolyze most polymers to their constituent monosaccharides which then undergo the degradative reactions. However, for given reaction conditions, a free sugar may yield a certain amount of chromogen but an equivalent amount of the same sugar in a polymer may give quite a different yield. This depends on the relative rates of hydrolysis of the polymer, the relative stability of the intermediates formed under the reaction conditions, and so on. In many circumstances, it is advisable to examine several reaction conditions to obtain optimal yields or else to relate every reaction to some known experimental standard as nearly like the substance being studied as possible. If this is not done, accurate quantitative estimation is not possible.

Hexosamine Determinations

The marked stability of 2-deoxy 2-amino sugars to acid hydrolysis conditions makes it impossible to estimate their content directly in polymeric structures. They must first be released by acid hydrolysis and subsequently determined by a specialized procedure. Problems of hydrolysis conditions and resolution from interfering substances have been dealt with elsewhere and this discussion will be restricted to considering only analytical methods.

Acetylacetone Procedure [8]. The most commonly employed method for hexosamine analysis involves the condensation of the amino sugar with 2,4-pentanedione in basic solution. The formation of the intermediate complex requires that the amino group be α to the aldehyde carbonyl. The intermediate is then reacted with p-dimethylaminobenzaldehyde in acid to form a product with λ_{max} at 530 mμ. This reaction is highly specific and none of the commonly occurring neutral or acidic carbohydrates interfere. The λ_{max} for 6-deoxy amino sugars and 3-substituted amino sugars are slightly different so that they can be differentiated. Glucosamine and galactosamine, the most commonly occurring 2-amino sugars, yield identical amounts of chromogen on a molar basis.

Acetyl Hexosamine Procedure [9]. *N*-acetyl hexosamines react with alkali (most frequently borate buffer at pH 9) to produce an intermediate pyrrole which reacts with paradimethylaminobenzaldehyde in glacial acetic acid.

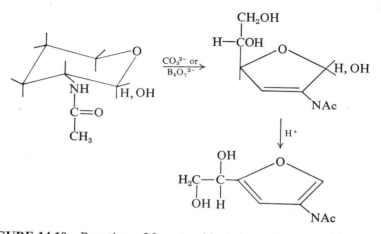

FIGURE 14.10   Reaction of 2-acetamido 2-deoxy hexoses with alkali.

λ_{max} of the product is at 580 mμ. The nature of the intermediate is illustrated in Figure 14.10. This reaction is particularly useful in conjunction with the former one, because the color yields for acetylglucosamine and acetylgalactosamine are markedly different. Analysis of a mixture of these 2-amino sugars by both procedures gives two simultaneous equations which may be solved as illustrated below:

$$a = \frac{gm}{A_1 gm} \qquad b = \frac{galm}{A_1 galm} \qquad\qquad (14.4)$$

$$c = \frac{gm}{A_2 gm} \qquad d = \frac{galm}{A_2 galm} \qquad\qquad (14.5)$$

gm, galm = Hexosamine concentration (standard)
A_1gm = Absorbancy of glucosamine in acetylacetone procedure
A_2gm = Absorbancy of glucosamine in acetylhexosamine procedure

$$gm \text{ factor} = \alpha_{gm} = \frac{ac}{(ad - bc)}$$

$$galm \text{ factor} = \alpha_{galm} = \frac{bd}{(ad - bc)}$$

Unknown mixture yields absorbancies A_1 and A_2

$$gm = \alpha_{gm}(dA_1 - bA_2)$$
$$galm = \alpha_{galm}(aA_1 - cA_2)$$

Deamination Reactions.   Treatment of amino sugars with nitrous acid yields a diazo intermediate which decomposes by internal attack to form an

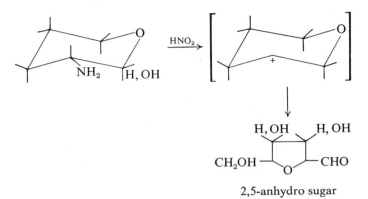

2,5-anhydro sugar

FIGURE 14.11 Nitrous acid deamination reaction of amino sugars.

anhydro sugar which may then be determined by a strong acid reaction. This method has the advantage that only amino sugars will give rise to such products on nitrous acid treatment (Figure 14.11) [10].

Enzymatic Procedures

In theory these methods offer ideal conditions for quantitative specific analysis of carbohydrates. The reagents exhibit a high degree of stereoselectivity and many methods are known that are virtually unique for a single sugar. Most of these procedures can be scaled to semimicro levels so that extremely small amounts of carbohydrate can be measured. There are several methods for the common sugars such as glucose and galactose, fewer methods for less common sugars, and none at all for rare sugars. This reflects both the natural development of enzymatic pathways and the extent of work that has been devoted to developing methodology.

Most methods for convenient biochemical analysis allow direct spectrophotometric measurement of the reaction under study. Reactions involving oxidations or reductions are usually coupled to pyridine nucleotide coenzymes with their associated change in absorbancy at 340 mμ. Because the reactions are uniformly stoichiometric and the molar extinction coefficient of the pyridine nucleotide at this wavelength is known, the change in absorption is a direct measure of the amount of sugar which has undergone reaction. A typical reaction sequence is shown in Figure 14.12.

In addition to these methods, both glucose and galactose oxidases (previously mentioned) are commonly employed. The former is probably the most widely employed specific enzymatic reagent with application in clinical chemistry, monitoring of blood and urine sugar, and routine glucose analyses. Isomerases, kinases, phosphatases, epimerases, and condensing enzymes have all been used for carbohydrate analyses and many determinations involve coupling of several enzymatic reactions. The obvious convenience of such techniques for routine

$$\text{Glucose} \xrightarrow[\text{hexokinase}]{\text{ATP}} \text{Glucose } 6-\text{P} + \text{ADP}$$

$$\Bigg\downarrow \begin{array}{l} \text{TPN}^+ \\ \text{G6-P-dehydrogenase} \end{array}$$

$$6-\text{P}-\text{gluconolactone} + \text{TPNH} + \text{H}^+$$

Assay by measuring ΔA_{340} due to TPNH formation

FIGURE 14.12   Reaction sequence for the enzymatic determination of glucose with hexokinase and glucose 6-phosphate dehydrogenase.

measurements is apparent, but it is the rare laboratory that has all the requisite tools.

A summary of the more common enzymatic determinations and their mechanism or pathway is given in Table 14.2 [11].

TABLE 14.2

Enzymatic methods of carbohydrate analysis.

SUGAR	ASSAY
Glucose	Glucose oxidase
	Hexokinase-G6P-dehydrogenase
Glucosamine	Hexokinase-deaminase-isomerase-G6P-dehydrogenase
Fructose	Hexokinase-isomerase-G6P-dehydrogenase
Fucose	Isomerase (+colorimetric ketose analysis)
D-xylulose	Dehydrogenase (*to* xylitol)
Galactose	Galactose oxidase
Mannose	Isomerase or dehydrogenase (*to* mannitol)
Sorbitol	Dehydrogenase

Chromatographic Procedures

Introduction.   The development of chromatographic procedures for the separation of closely related substances has undoubtedly been one of the major causes for the tremendous impetus in carbohydrate chemistry and every area of natural products study. The use of thin-layer chromatography, for example, permits rapid separation of microgram amounts of material and obviates the necessity for processing large quantities by fractional crystallization, solvent extraction, or some similar means. It is important to point out that absolute identification by this technique is dangerous. An unknown compound may have similar chromatographic properties to a standard in several systems but this does not suffice for complete characterization. The exclusion of a structure is much more easily made because compounds of the same structure will obviously always have the same mobility. When chromatographic behavior is different in any system, even though it may be similar in several others, it can be concluded that the compounds in question are not identical. The most common chromatographic techniques employed are thin-layer or paper partition, thin-layer or column adsorption, ion-exchange and gas–liquid chromatography.

Paper and Thin-layer Chromatography. The relationship between conformational stability and chromatographic mobility was briefly described in Chapter 5. In principle, partition chromatography systems depend on the distribution of a given compound between a mobile organic phase and a stationary aqueous phase. The more hydrophilic the compound in question is, the less solubility it has in the organic phase and consequently the slower its mobility. When resolving compounds such as methylated sugars, high mobility may be expected and much less polar solvents will be employed; sugar phosphates have low mobilities and require the use of highly polar solvents to achieve resolutions. The great advantages of thin-layer chromatography are the extremely rapid development of the chromatograms (5 min to 2 hours). This permits screening of intermediates in a single reaction, examination of reaction course as a function of time, and determination of optimal systems for preparative separations. Unsubstituted sugars usually show properties on thin-layer plates similar to those observed for paper systems. Typical separations are given in Table 14.3 [12].

TABLE 14.3

Paper chromatographic mobility of sugars.

SUGAR	$R_g{}^a$	$R_f{}^b$	$R_f{}^c$
Maltose	0.02	0.11	$\cdots$
Galactose	0.07	0.16	0.18
Glucose	0.09	0.18	0.20
Sorbose	0.10	0.20	0.24
Mannose	0.11	0.20	0.24
Fructose	0.12	0.23	0.24
Gulose, arabinose	0.12	0.21	0.23
Xylose	0.15	0.28	0.28
Altrose	0.17	$\cdots$	0.22
Idose	0.18	$\cdots$	0.31
Talose, lyxose	0.19	$\cdots$	0.29
Ribose, fucose	0.21	0.31	0.33
Rhamnose	0.30	0.37	0.38
4,6-Dimethylglucose	0.44	$\cdots$	$\cdots$
2,4,6-Trimethylglucose	0.76	$\cdots$	$\cdots$
2,3,4,6-Tetramethylglucose	1.00	$\cdots$	$\cdots$

[a] Mobility relative to tetramethyl glucose. Solvent is butanol-ethanol-water (5:1:4; top layer).
[b] Mobility relative to solvent front. Solvent in butanol-acetic acid-water (4:1:5).
[c] Mobility relative to solvent front. Solvent is ethyl acetate-pyridine-water (2:1:2).

The techniques used to locate carbohydrates on either paper or thin-layer chromatograms depend on reactions not dissimilar from the nonstoichiometric reactions described above. The most common procedures involve reduction of silver ion or heating with acid in the presence of an organic molecule to form an easily located chromogen. A summary of detection techniques is given in Table 14.4 [13].

TABLE 14.4

Reagents used to detect carbohydrates on chromatograms.

SPRAY	SPECIFICITY
$AgNO_3^-$ base	Reducing compounds: 1 μg or less
Aniline-phthalate heat	Reducing compounds; 0.1 μg, fluorescent under ultraviolet light
Urea-phosphoric acid	Ketoses
Anthrone	Reducing compounds
Triphenyl tetrazolium	Reducing compounds
Naphthoresorcinol-trichloracetic acid	Ketoses
NH_2OH-Fe^{+++}	Esters (acetates, methyl esters)
Ninhydrin	Amino sugars
Acetylacetone-p-Me_2N-benzaldehyde	Amino sugars and acetylamino sugars

Adsorption Chromatography. This technique is widely used in the lipid and steroid field where inert adsorbents such as alumina, clays, or silica gels are used and compounds sequentially eluted by solvents of increasing polarity. Fully acetylated sugars can be separated by column chromatography on silica gel or alumina. Advantage has also been taken of the relatively higher affinity of equatorial hydroxyls for adsorbents, such as alumina, in separation of partially blocked carbohydrate derivatives. In most cases, solvents such as ethyl acetate or benzene with increasing amounts of alcohol are employed for elution systems.

Ion-exchange Chromatography. Carbohydrates with charged functional groups can usually be readily resolved by ion-exchange procedures. In most cases, the substituent groups are anionic, such as phosphate, sulfate, or carboxyl, and anion exchange resins have been most extensively investigated. Resolution of most sugar phosphates and sulfates can be carried out by use of gradient elution systems which vary both in ionic strength and pH. Methods of detection again depend on reactions similar to those described above. In some cases, the functional groups may permit direct measurement by ultraviolet absorption spectroscopy. It is possible to separate axial and equatorial phosphates, primary and secondary sulfates, and so on. Some typical separations are illustrated in Table 14.5 [14, 15].

TABLE 14.5

Ion-exchange separations of carbohydrates.

SUGARS	SYSTEM
Uronic acid epimers	Dowex 1 acetate
Monosaccharide sulfates	Dowex 1 chloride
Amino sugars	Dowex 50 hydrogen
Homologous series of uronides	Dowex 3 formate
	Amberlite IR-4B
	Dowex 1 formate
Monosaccharide phosphates	Dowex 1 chloride

Gas–liquid Chromatography.

INTRODUCTION. The development of gas–liquid chromatography was initially in the lipid field, but has become of increasing importance to the carbohydrate chemist.

Columns are most frequently prepared with a highly viscous immobile, nonvolatile organic liquid, such as neopentylglycol or silicone oil, on an inert adsorbent such as firebrick. There is rapid flow of gas through the column and the derivative is partitioned between the flowing gas phase and the stationary liquid phase adsorbed on its inert support. The emergence of material from the column may be followed by several means, the most common being flame ionization measurements. The sensitivity of these procedures is remarkably high and amounts of 0.01 μg or less can be readily detected. The theoretical plates in such columns may run upward of 250,000, making possible separations that would be totally impractical under normal operating laboratory conditions. Runs are usually complete in 10 min to 2 hours.

It should be noted that the relation between carbon chain length and retention time is frequently of an exponential type, so that higher homologs of a given sugar series may take extremely long times to emerge from the column. This may also introduce complications due to possible breakdown during the extended periods required for chromatography.

Materials that are slower moving on the column tend to diffuse; thus, peaks broaden so that direct measurement of peak height is not sufficient to serve as a quantitative assay. Peak area can be measured graphically or more easily by transducing the output signal to a suitable integrating device. The retention time for a given compound will be a function of the nature of the liquid phase so that comparisons are meaningful only of the same liquid phase.

The most reliable method for identification is measurement of retention time relative to a constant internal standard. By this means, small variations in column packing, flow rates, column temperatures, and rate of heating will be essentially eliminated.

The detection devices have a variable response depending upon the ionization potential of the compound being eluted; when quantitative determinations are desired, it is important to run standards of comparable structure.

The major obstacle is the preparation of suitably volatile carbohydrate derivatives which will have sufficient thermal stability to survive the chromatographic conditions.

METHYLATED SUGARS.   The free sugars themselves are not of sufficient volatility or stability to permit direct analysis but methylated derivatives and methyl glycosides can readily be separated. This facilitates analysis of methylation products of polymeric materials where several different derivatives are formed and only small amounts are available. The resolving power of GLC is usually sufficiently good so that quantitative estimation of each of these may be made. Retention times of methylated methylglucopyranosides are given in Table 14.6 [19].

TABLE 14.6

Retention times of methylated sugars in gas–liquid chromatography.

SUGAR	150°		220°	
	I[a]	II	I	II
Di-*O*-methyl-α			4.02	3.90
Di-*O*-methyl-α				7.90
Di-*O*-methyl-α				11.00
4,6-di-*O*-methyl-α			4.58	4.92
4,6-di-*O*-methyl-β				6.10
3,4,5-tri-*O*-methyl-α	2.61	2.89	2.23	2.18
2,4,6-tri-*O*-methyl-α	3.52	3.68	2.64	2.59
2,4,6-tri-*O*-methyl-β	2.38	2.12	2.02	
2,3,6-tri-*O*-methyl-α	3.52	3.68	2.64	2.59
2,3,6-tri-*O*-methyl-β	2.50	2.19	2.02	2.18
2,3,4-tri-*O*-methyl-α	2.11	2.18	1.91	1.84
2,3,4-tri-*O*-methyl-β	1.80	1.68	1.75	
2,3,4,6-tetra-*O*-methyl-α	1.00	1.00	1.00	1.00
2,3,4,6-tetra-*O*-methyl-β	0.70	0.75	0.79	0.72

[a] See legend for Table 14.7.

ACETATES AND CYCLIC DERIVATIVES.   In addition to methylated methyl glycosides, fully acetylated aldoses and alditols may be separated via GLC and excellent resolution of acetates ranging from glycerol to octitol have been reported. Cyclic sugar acetals and ketals have also been resolved by GLC and this technique has been of particular value in studying the course of cyclic derivative formation, particularly for sugar alcohols. Typical separations are listed in Tables 14.7 and 14.8 [16, 17].

TABLE 14.7

Separations of fully acetylated sugar alcohols or pyranosides relative to penta-*O*-acetyl arabinitol. I is butane diol-succinate on chromosorb W and II is a mixture of I and Apiezon M grease on glass beads. Column temperature was 213 degrees.

SUGAR	I	II
Glycerol	0.120	0.122
Erythritol	0.378	0.393
Ribitol	0.918	0.944
Arabinitol	1.00	1.00
Xylitol	1.18	1.20
Mannitol	2.13	2.16
Glucitol	2.39	2.73
Galactitol	2.42	2.75
Iditol	2.74	2.85
Xylose-α	0.72	0.61
Xylose-β	0.91	0.78
Galactose-α	2.04	1.92
Galactose-β	2.70	2.55
Glucose-α	2.14	2.21
Glucose-β	2.57	2.41
Mannose-α	2.72	2.26
Mannose-β	2.74	2.64
Ribose-α	1.00	0.99
Altrose-α	2.52	2.50
Lyxose-α	0.84	0.80

FREE SUGARS. The most pertinent recent development has been the use of trimethylsilyl (TMS) ethers of simple sugars [18]. The advantage of this derivative is that it is readily prepared in nearly quantitative yield from free sugars under rather mild conditions, thus permitting rapid analysis. This avoids preparation of acetates which proceeds in relatively lower yield and usually requires longer reaction times. The reaction involved is indicated in Figure 14.13. This technique has been extended to oligosaccharides and sugar phosphates. The presence of groups such as carboxyl, phosphate, or sulfate in a carbohydrate reduces the volatility to such a degree that substitution is usually necessary before GLC is possible.

Under the conditions for TMS ether formation, the free sugars always give rise to mixtures of α and β anomers. Sugars such as galactose, that have a significant amount of furanoside, form this derivative as well. These are all readily recognized and separated but there are obvious problems when dealing with mixtures because, in this case, overlap is inevitable. This can be controlled in

TABLE 14.8

Retention volumes relative to 1,2,5,6 di-isopropylidene
D-glucofuranose. IDP-isopropylidene; ETD-ethrylidene;
Me-methylene. Packing as for column II in Table 14.7;
$T = 206$ degrees.

SUGAR	R_{IPDG}
1,2-IPD-glucofuranose-5,6-carbonate	0.58
Me-2,3,4,6-di-IPD-α-D-mannopyranoside	0.66
2,3-IPD-rhamnose	0.79
1,2,4,5-di-IPD-fructose	0.82
1,2,5,6-di-IPD-glucose	1.00
2,3,5,6-di-IPD-mannose	1.20
4,6-ETD-1,2-IDP-galactose	1.67
4,6-ETD-2,3-IDP-mannose	1.86
1,2-IDP-fructose	2.70
1,3,2,4-di-Me-glucitol	8.88
1,2,5,6-di-IPD-3-tosylglucose	25.6

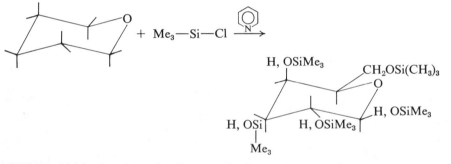

FIGURE 14.13   Reaction leading to the formation of trimethylsilyl ethers.
Both anomers are usually obtained.

several ways including prior formation of methyl glycosides, reduction to sugar
alcohols, and formation of oximes by reaction with hydroxylamine before
derivatization with trimethylsilylchloride. Typical retention times are illustrated
in Table 14.9 [20].

STRUCTURAL CORRELATIONS.   Although this technique has been widely
used in the carbohydrate field for only the past 4 or 5 years, several generalizations can be made relating structure and retention time:

1. Anomeric methyl-*O*-methylglycopyranosides. The anomer that has
the methoxyl at C-2 *cis* to the glycosidic oxygen has the higher retention volume.
If the C-2 hydroxyl group is unsubstituted, the order of elution is reversed.

TABLE 14.9

Retention time of trimethylsilyl derivatives of
selected sugars.[a]

SUGAR	RETENTION TIME (minutes)	
	I	II
D-ribose-α	2.40	
D-ribose-β	2.60	
Arabinose-α	2.45	
Arabinose-β	2.04	
Xylose-α	3.16	
Xylose-β	5	
Lyxose-α	1.97	
Lyxose-β	2.64	
Glucose-α		1.2
Glucose-β		1.46
Sucrose		12.6
Maltose-α		14.0
Maltose-β		15.8

[a] I is Apiezon L on firebrick, 180 degrees. II is SE-52
silicone oil on Chromosorb W, 210 degrees.

2. Fully methylated glycosides of the arabinose, galactose, and fructose families have the furanosides emerging before the pyranosides, whereas the reverse is true for xylose and glucose.

3. For fully acetylated alditols, isomers with the larger number of ester groups on the same side of the planar carbon chain have the highest retention volumes. When two isomers have the same number of ester groups on the same side of the molecule, the one with the groups closer together will have the larger retention volume. There are similar relationships with the acetylated aldoses and the trimethylsilyl derivatives but these are not as generally followed.

4. The replacement of an equatorial by an axial substituent at any position but carbon 1 tends to increase the relative retention time in acetylated aldoses.

5. For the trimethylsilyl ethers, the introduction of an axial group either at carbon 1 or in the chain causes decreased retention volume.

6. Compounds are almost always eluted in order of their molecular weight—that is, pentoses before hexoses, and so on.

7. Nonpolar substituents such as deoxy functions result in increased mobility.

Summary. The application of gas–liquid chromatography to the carbohydrate field is still increasing rapidly. The great resolving power and sensitivity combined with rapid separation (usually complete in an hour) make this method ideally suited to checking purity of products, kinetic studies, examining reactions for intermediates, and so on. In addition, because it is possible to measure physical properties such as ionization potential, it is not necessary to have a specific functional grouping such as the terminal aldehyde present before analysis can be carried out. The major drawbacks of the methodology are the requirement of both volatility and relative stability for the compounds being separated, the possible reactions that may occur during the elevated temperatures required for GLC, possible rearrangements, and the frequent necessity for extensive empirical investigations before applications can be made to a given system. Nevertheless, there is no question that gas chromatography has a very major role in analytical carbohydrate chemistry.

14.3 Mass Spectrometry

Introduction

The general utility of mass spectra analysis as an aid in structural determination has been abundantly demonstrated, particularly in the steroid and alkaloid fields. Although simple sugars are relatively nonvolatile, several standard derivatives have properties that permit cracking patterns to be obtained. At the present time, insufficient experimentation has been carried out to make any broad conformational correlations, but as techniques and data accumulate, this may be feasible. In any case, certain structural features are readily recognized and ancillary information such as molecular weight can also be obtained.

Principle

Cracking patterns are obtained by exposing molecules to electron bombardment which gives rise to a series of ions. These ions are refocused by a magnetic field and a spectrum is obtained by scanning the field or by placing a photographic plate at an appropriate location and recording the lines corresponding to each mass. The sensitivity is extremely high, of the order of ± 2 millimass units, permitting distinction between species as closely related as carbon monoxide, nitrogen, and ethylene. The intensity of each mass line can be quantitated and the parent compound frequently reconstructed from a knowledge of the functional groups present, or directly from the peaks present in the cracking pattern [21].

Bombarding a molecule with electrons[1] produces reactions of the following type:

$$e + RCH_2R' \longrightarrow \overset{+}{RCHR'} + 2e$$

[1] Usually of 50–100 electron-volt energy.

$$\overset{+}{}$$

The molecular ions $(R\overset{+}{C}HR')$ then break down by fragmentation including re-arrangements, eliminations, and hydrogen transfer reactions. These reactions, because they involve an ionic species, may not parallel the normal chemical behavior of the compound. Only those fragments that are charged are recorded on the photographic plate.

The following general nomenclature is employed: carbon atoms attached to a functional group, R, are designated α, β, and so on, in the usual way (Figure 14.14).

$$\overset{\gamma}{\underset{\gamma}{-C}}-\overset{\beta}{\underset{\beta}{C}}-\overset{\alpha}{\underset{\alpha}{C}}-X$$

FIGURE 14.14 General nomenclature of carbon chain employed when discussing cracking patterns obtained in mass spectra analysis.

Electronegative substituents favor cleavage of the α bond or β bond, accompanied by hydrogen transfer (Figure 14.15).

$$R\overset{+}{C}H_2R' \longrightarrow R^+ + R'CH_2$$
$$\longrightarrow R'\overset{+}{C}H + RH$$
$$C—C—C\overset{|}{\div}X \longrightarrow C—C—C + X$$

when X is electronegative

FIGURE 14.15 Typical cleavage reactions observed in mass spectra.

The use of isotopically substituted materials, particularly deuterium, can frequently localize the origin of ions which may have arisen through extensive rearrangement.

Application to Carbohydrates

The most useful derivatives are acetates, thioacetals, and cyclic acetals and ketals. Structural differences such as pentose versus hexose, furanoside versus pyranoside, or aldose versus ketose are easily recognized. Epimers have very similar spectra but substituents in an unfavorable conformation are occasionally detectable by differences in peak intensities.

A study by Biemann and co-workers on monosaccharide acetates revealed the following [22].

1. The molecular ion, mass 390, is of low intensity due to the high degree of substitution on the parent molecule.

2. The most intense peak is at $m/e = 46$ (CH_3CO^+) and is about 10 times the magnitude of the next most prominent unit.

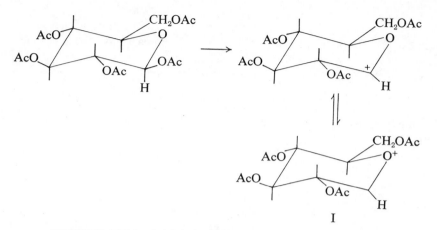

FIGURE 14.16   Initial cleavage of β-D-glucose pentaacetate.

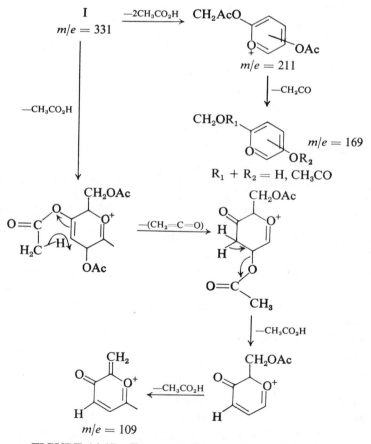

FIGURE 14.17   Fragmentation reactions of above.

3. Peaks are observed at $m/e = 347$ (M—CH$_3$CO), $m/e = 331$ (M—CH$_3$CO$_2$) and $m/e = 317$ (M—CH$_3$COOCH$_2$).

4. Loss of acetic acid is frequently accompanied by loss of ketene especially in polyacetates.

5. The C-1 acetoxy group is preferentially lost, probably due to stabilization of the ionic species formed (Figure 14.16).

6. Further fragmentation proceeds as outlined in Figure 14.17.

Although this technique requires unusual instrumentation and considerable background data before interpretation can be made with assurance, its application to specialized structural problems can be very useful. Amino sugars, branched chain sugars, and deoxy sugars will all exhibit very characteristic patterns, permitting considerable structural assignment on very small amounts of material, 1 mg or less.

14.4 Degradative Techniques

The utility of degradative techniques largely depends on the intended goal. Methodology employed for structural proof and that used in establishing the isotopic distribution of carbohydrates isolated from natural systems are likely to be different from one another and both may differ from that employed for synthetic purposes. In the latter case, for example, neither quantitative yields nor annoying byproducts need to be seriously considered as long as the desired homolog can be isolated in pure form and in satisfactory yield. However, for structural proof, one must have some reasonable assurance that the product of some degradation scheme represents a reasonable contribution in the parent structure. Finally, when dealing with degradation of isotopically labeled material, or for synthetic sequences involving radioactively labeled compounds, high yields, and some knowledge as to the course of the reaction, the nature of by-products and stereochemistry all become significantly important.

The following methods are the ones most commonly employed for the degradation of carbohydrates, whereby the reducing carbon is removed and the sugar converted to the next lower aldose.

1. The Zemplen modification of the procedure of Wohl involves treatment of the carbohydrate with hydroxylamine to yield a sugar oxime. The oxime is generally not isolated but treated directly with acetic anhydride and sodium acetate to form a fully acetylated open chain nitrile (Figure 14.18). Treating the nitrile with sodium methoxide in methanol results in removal of the nitrile function and of the acetoxy groups and formation of the next lower aldose [23]. The over-all yields are from 40 to 50 percent. Because the acetates are usually obtained in crystalline form, this route is still frequently used. A modification of this procedure involves treating the aldose oxime in basic

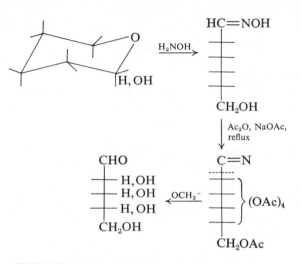

FIGURE 14.18 Wohl-Zemplen degradation.

solution with dinitrofluorobenzene (Figure 14.19) [24]. The mechanism of this reaction has not been worked out but might involve dehydration of the oxime and subsequent elimination. The nitrile may be formed as an intermediate and the over-all sequence has the advantage of not being required to proceed through the acetate. Because the reactions take place in the open chain form, there is relatively little stereochemical hindrance involved.

2. A second method for the degradation of carbohydrates involves initial treatment with ethyl mercaptan in the presence of acid, followed by acetylation to yield the fully acetylated diethylmercaptal (Figure 14.20) [25]. This derivative (usually obtained in excellent yield), is oxidized with a per acid, such as perpropionic acid, to yield the aldose disulphone, which, on exposure to weak alkali, decomposes to the next lower aldose and bis-ethyl sulfonyl ethane.

This degradation seems rather complicated but actually proceeds in excellent yield because formation of the diethylmercaptal is nearly quantitative and

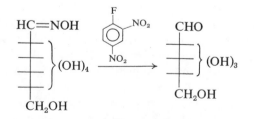

FIGURE 14.19 Modified Zemplen degradation employing dinitrofluorobenzene.

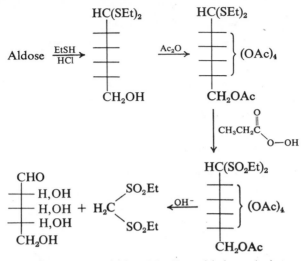

FIGURE 14.20 Fischer-MacDonald degradation.

in the reaction with alkali, all of the apparent intermediate products which may be formed also decompose to yield the next lower aldose.

3. The removal of carbon 1 of aldonic acids can be accomplished in several ways. The reaction of the amide with sodium hypochlorite in alkali gives an isocyanate intermediate (presumed), which in alkaline solution decomposes to form the next lower aldose (Figure 14.21). This reaction will not

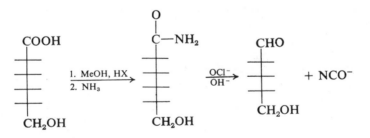

FIGURE 14.21 Isocyanate degradation.

take place without the presence of a free α-hydroxy group and provides a convenient test for the presence of such a functional group. This test is based on the identification of the isocyanate ion because it condenses with semicarbazide to yield an easily identifiable, insoluble hydrazochromogen.

An alternative to the above is to treat the aldonic acid with hydrazoic acid to form the azide. This decomposes in alkali to yield CO_2 from carbon 1 and an amine product (Figure 14.22) [26]. This degradation does not require an

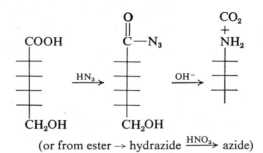

(or from ester → hydrazide $\xrightarrow{HNO_2}$ azide)

FIGURE 14.22   Azide degradation. Because any carboxylic acid reacts in this sequence, this method is frequently employed in analysis of isotopically labeled carbohydrates.

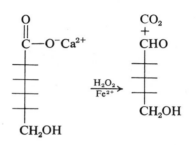

FIGURE 14.23   Ruff degradation.

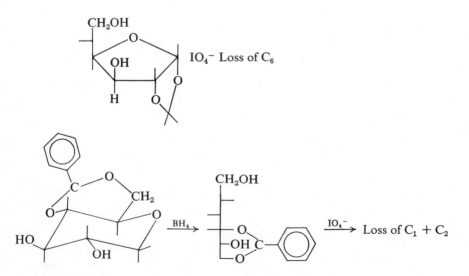

FIGURE 14.24   Use of periodate in degradation of carbohydrates.

α-hydroxy group and is commonly employed in isotope studies because the yield of CO_2 is nearly quantitative.

The procedure developed in 1899 by Ruff involves treatment of the calcium salt of the aldonic acid with hydrogen peroxide in the presence of ferrous ion (Figure 14.23). Although this procedure is still used to a limited extent today, it is of relatively minor interest.

4. In addition to the methods mentioned above, the use of periodate or lead tetraacetate on suitably blocked carbohydrate derivatives can be employed to remove C-1, C-6, or in appropriate cases, two carbons (Figure 14.24).

The above methods generally involve removal of carbon 1 and have been widely employed as synthetic and structural tools. Their use in structural proof is limited because the asymmetry at carbon 2 is destroyed, thus limiting identification to one of two parent products. However, additional adjunct information usually suffices for complete structural proof. In the synthesis of new sugars, the Zemplen and sulfone degradations are the methods of choice, where periodate or lead tetraacetate cannot be employed.

Degradation of Isotopically Labeled Sugars

The degradation of isotopically labeled carbohydrates presents other problems. The information most often desired requires isolation of *individual carbon atoms* without cross contamination. The best method for achieving this result usually combines bacterial and chemical procedures. However, in many experiments involving hexoses, a knowledge of isotope content in carbon 1, carbon 2, and carbon 6 is sufficient to answer the questions asked. This is most readily obtained using benzimidazole derivatives.

The formation of an aldo benzimidazole can be carried out via the intermediate synthesis of the aldonic acid or by direct condensation of the aldose in the presence of an oxidizing agent such as cupric ion. This latter technique is particularly desirable when small amounts of material are being handled which would preclude intermediate synthesis and isolation of the aldonic acid. Treatment of the aldose or aldonic acid with orthophenylenediamine at elevated temperatures in an inert solvent yields a polyhydroxyalkyl benzimidazole. These are isolated as crystalline heavy-metal salts because the benzimidazole group has an ionizable proton. The free benzimidazoles are crystalline as well and can usually be recrystallized quite readily. In addition, the aromatic ring has a characteristic ultraviolet absorption spectrum permitting the tracing of small quantities of material after chromatography on a suitable cation-exchange resin. The resulting derivative has carbon 1 in the imidazole ring and carbons 2 to 6 exocyclic. Note that no loss of asymmetry takes place at C-2 (glucose and mannose yield different products, for example), which represents a considerable advantage over most other derivatives. Further degradation of this intermediate is carried out by oxidation with periodate. Carbon 6 is released as formaldehyde,

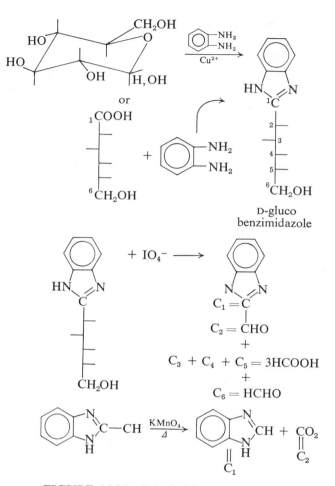

FIGURE 14.25 Benzimidazole degradation.

carbons 3, 4, and 5 as formic acid, and carbons 1 and 2 appear in formyl benzimidazole (Figure 14.25).

Oxidation of the latter compound with permanganate, followed by decarboxylation in refluxing ethylene glycol, yields benzimidazole itself, containing carbon 1 of the parent sugar, and carbon dioxide quantitatively from carbon 2. Thus, carbons 1, 2, and 6 are obtained separately and carbons 3, 4, and 5 are combined and isolated as formic acid. Methyl pentoses will give acetaldehyde from C_5–C_6 in the periodate step, which may be further degraded to separate C_5 and C_6. Pentoses follow the identical sequence giving C_1, C_2, and C_5 separately and C_3 and C_4 as formic acid.

Periodate oxidation of the methyl glycosides of aldopyranosides yields only carbon 3 as formic acid; thus, this carbon may be determined separately

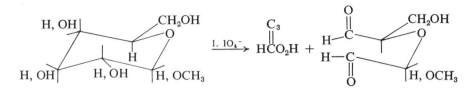

FIGURE 14.26 Direct analysis of carbon 3 by periodate oxidation of methyl pyranoside.

(Figure 14.26). When carbon 4 must be separated from carbon 5, appropriate derivatives must be prepared that permit selective isolation of these carbons. One such route for glucose is illustrated in Figure 14.27.

Complete bacterial fermentation of glucose by Leuconostoc mesenteroides P-60 proceeds according to the scheme shown in Figure 14.28 [27].

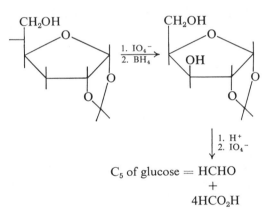

C_5 of glucose = HCHO

+

$4HCO_2H$

FIGURE 14.27 Method of determination of the radioactivity of C4 of glucose. Carbon 5 is obtained as formaldehyde and all other positions by methods outlined above. C4 radioactivity may then be determined by difference.

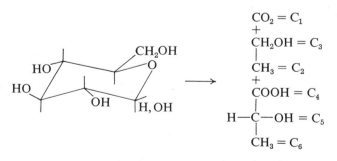

$$CO_2 = C_1$$
$$+$$
$$CH_2OH = C_3$$
$$|$$
$$CH_3 = C_2$$
$$+$$
$$COOH = C_4$$
$$|$$
$$H-C-OH = C_5$$
$$|$$
$$CH_3 = C_6$$

FIGURE 14.28 Bacterial degradation of D-glucose.

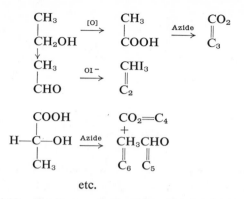

FIGURE 14.29   Further analysis of bacterial degradation products.

Further degradation of the lactic acid and ethanol is carried out as shown in Figure 14.29. By this technique, each carbon of the parent glucose is isolated separately and may be examined for specific radioactivity. A similar degradation is applicable to glucosamine if the bacterial cells are preadapted to the amino sugar. Most other sugars are degraded by chemical techniques.

APPENDIX 1

RULES OF CARBOHYDRATE NOMENCLATURE[1]

Rule 1. The names "aldose" or "ketose" will be used in a generic sense to denote the respective character of the reducing, or potentially reducing group of the monosaccharide or derivative thereof. In an aldose, the carbon atom of the aldehyde function is atom number one; and in a ketose, the carbonyl carbon atom has the lower possible number.

For indicating the number of carbon atoms in the normal chain, the appropriate one of the following names will be used: triose, tetrose, pentose, hexose, heptose, octose, nonose, and so on.

Rule 2. Configurational relationships will be denoted by the capital letter prefixes D and L, which in print will be small capital Roman letters and which are pronounced "dee" and "ell" (not "dextro" and "levo"). Such symbols will be placed immediately before the sugar stem name and be employed only with compounds which have been definitively related to the reference standard glyceraldehyde (see Rule 3). In a definitive name, the configurational symbol shall not be omitted.

If the optical rotational sign under specified conditions is to be indicated, this may be done by adding (*dextro*) or (*levo*), which are italicized in print, or by adding (+) or (−). Racemic modifications may be indicated by the prefixes DL, or (±).

Rule 3. Carbohydrates having the same configuration of the highest numbered asymmetric carbon atom as that of D-(*dextro*)-glyceraldehyde will belong to the D-configurational series; those having the opposite configuration will belong to the L series.

Rule 4. The configuration of a group of consecutive but not necessarily contiguous asymmetric carbon atoms $\left(\text{such as } \rangle\text{CHOH, } \rangle\text{CHOCH}_3, \rangle\text{CHOAc, or } \rangle\text{CHNH}_2\right)$, containing one to four asymmetric carbon atoms, will be designated by the appropriate one of these prefixes:

Asymmetric Carbons	Prefixes
one	*glycero*
two	*erythro, threo*
three	*arabino, lyxo, ribo, xylo*
four	*allo, altro, galacto, gluco, gulo, ido, manno, talo*

---

[1] Reprinted from the *Journal of Organic Chemistry* **28**, 281 (1963).

Rule 5. Ketoses having the carbonyl group at carbon atom number two will be named by means of the suffix "-ulose"; before this will be a prefix denoting the number of carbon atoms in the chain, which, in turn, will be preceded by the prefix denoting the configuration of the group of asymmetric centers present (see Rule 4).

Rule 6. When an alcoholic hydroxyl group of a monosaccharide is replaced by a hydrogen atom, the compound will be named by attaching a hyphen, before the sugar name, the appropriate numeral (indicating position), a hyphen, and the prefix "deoxy." The configuration of the sugar will be designated, when necessary, as given in Rule 4.

COMMENT. Trivial names, established by usage, include: D-fucose (6-deoxy-D-galactose) and L-rhamnose (6-deoxy-L-mannose).

Rule 7. When the hydrogen atom of an alcoholic hydroxyl group of a carbohydrate is replaced, an italic capital letter *O* (for oxygen) will be attached by a hyphen directly before the replacement prefix.

Rule 8. An ester formed from a sugar or sugar derivative by reaction with one or more of its alcoholic hydroxyl groups may be named by placing, after the sugar name and separated therefrom by a space, the appropriate numeral (indicating position) and a hyphen, as prefix to the name of the group derived from an acid.

Rule 9. The anomeric prefix (α- or β-), which can only be used in conjunction with a configurational prefix (D or L), will immediately precede the latter. The configurational prefix will directly precede the stem name (see Rule 4).

Rule 10. The acylic nature of a sugar or derivative containing an uncyclized CHO or CO group as the primary function will be indicated by inserting the italicized prefix *aldehydo* or *keto*, respectively, immediately before the configurational prefix and stem name.

Rule 11. The size of the ring in the heterocyclic forms of monosaccharides (both aldoses and ketoses) may be indicated by replacing, in the sugar name, the letters "se" by "furanose" for the 5-atom ring, "pyranose" for the 6-atom ring, and "septanose" for the 7-atom ring. Likewise, for the glycosides (both aldosides and ketosides), the size of the ring may be revealed by replacing the syllable "-side" by "furnanoside," "pyranoside," or "septanoside."

Rule 12. The root "glyc" (as in glycose or glycoside) will be used in a generic sense to denote any sugar or derivative thereof, rather than some specified sugar.

Rule 13. A glycoside is a mixed acetal resulting from the exchange of an alkyl or aryl radical for the hydrogen atom of the hemiacetal hydroxyl group of a cyclic form of an aldose or ketose. It is named by substituting "ide" as a suffix in place of the terminal "e" of the corresponding sugar name and placing before this word, separated by a space, the name of the organic substituent.

Rule 14. If the hemiacetal hydroxyl group is detached from a cyclic modification of an aldose or ketose, the residue is a glycosyl (glycofuranosyl, glycopyranosyl, glycoseptanosyl) radical. It is named by substituting "yl" as a suffix in place of the terminal "e" of the corresponding sugar name.

EXAMPLE:

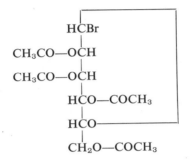

Tetra-*O*-acetyl-α-D-mannopyranosyl bromide

Rule 15. Names for the polyhydric alcohols (alditols) are derived from the names of the corresponding aldose sugars by changing the suffix "ose" to "itol." For nonmeso compounds, the same family-determining asymmetric carbon atom as that characterizing the name of the sugar is used.

Rule 16. Aldonic acids, formed from aldoses by oxidation of only the hemiacetal or aldehydic carbon atom to —CO—OH, may be named by substituting "onic acid" as a suffix in place of "ose" of the corresponding aldose name. Acid chlorides, amides, esters, lactones, nitriles, salts, and the like, are named in the conventional manner.

Rule 17. Uronic acids, formed from aldoses having a terminal —CH₂OH group by oxidation only of this group to —CO—OH, will be named by substituting "uronic acid" as a suffix in place of "ose" of the corresponding aldose name. The hemiacetal or aldehydic carbon atom is carbon number one, and the syllable "ur" has the significance of "ω."

Rule 18. If the glycoside radical (see Rule 13) of an aldose glycoside possesses a terminal —CH₂OH group, and, if this group of the glycoside is oxidized to a carboxyl group, the product will be named by substituting "uronic acid" as a suffix in place of the terminal "e" of the parent glycoside name. The glycosidic hemiacetal carbon atom is carbon number one, and the syllable "ur" has the significance of "ω."

Rule 19. Dicarboxylic sugar acids (aldaric acids), formed by the oxidation of aldoses at both terminal carbon atoms, will be named by substituting "aric acid" as a suffix in place of "ose" of the corresponding aldose name.

Rule 20. The "glycosides of ortho ester structure" may be named as the ortho esters, with the carbohydrate group given as the first term in the name.

Rule 21. Cyclic acetals formed by the reaction of carbohydrates with aldehydes or ketones may be named in accordance with Rule 7 with bivalent radicals as prefixes.

Rule 22. An intramolecular anhydride, formed by the elimination of the elements of water from two hydroxyl groups of a monosaccharide molecule (aldose or ketose), is named by attaching by a hyphen before the sugar name the prefix "anhydro"; this, in turn, is preceded by a pair of numerals identifying the two hydroxyl groups involved. Anhydrides of sugar acids, alcohols, lactones, and the like, are named similarly.

Rule 23. An oligosaccharide is a compound which, on complete hydrolysis, gives monosaccharide units only, in relatively small number per molecule (in contrast to the high-polymeric polysaccharides).

DISACCHARIDES. A nonreducing disaccharide may be named as a glycosyl glycoside, and a reducing disaccharide as a glycosyl–glycose, from its component parts.

EXAMPLES:

(*a*) *Nonreducing*

Sucrose: β-D-fructofuranosyl α-D-glucopyranoside or α-D-glucopyranosyl β-D-fructofuranoside

(*b*) *Reducing*

α-Lactose: 4-*O*-β-D-galactopyranosyl-α-D-glucopyranose or *O*-β-D-galactopyranosyl-(1 → 4)-α-D-glucopyranose

(*c*) *Derivatives of reducing disaccharides*

I. Methyl α-lactoside: methyl 4-*O*-β-D-galactopyranosyl-α-D-glucopyranoside or methyl *O*-β-D-galactopyranosyl-(1 → 4)-α-D-glucopyranoside

TRI- AND HIGHER OLIGO-SACCHARIDES

(*a*) *Nonreducing*

Raffinose: *O*-α-D-galactopyranosyl-(1 → 6)-α-D-glucopyranosyl β-D-fructofuranoside

Gentianose: *O*-β-D-glucopyranosyl-(1 → 6)-α-D-glucopyranosyl β-D-fructofuranoside

(*b*) *Reducing*

Beginning with the first nonreducing component, and following Rule 14, the first glycosyl portion with its configurational prefixes is delineated. This is followed by two numbers which indicate the respective positions involved in this glycosidic union; these numbers are separated by an arrow (pointing from the glycosyl carbon atom number to the number for the hydroxylic carbon atom involved) and are enclosed in parentheses inserted into the name by hyphens. The next disaccharide linkage is treated similarly (and so on), and the last portion of the name delineates the reducing sugar unit.

EXAMPLE:

α-Cellotriose:

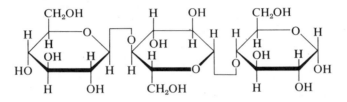

O-β-D-glucopyranosyl-($1 \rightarrow 4$)-O-β-D-glucopyranosyl-($1 \rightarrow 4$)-α-D-glucopyranose

APPENDIX 2

CALCULATION OF MOLECULAR WEIGHT DISTRIBUTIONS

The data obtained from interference patterns after attainment of sedimentation equilibrium can be treated in the following way. The vertical position f of a fringe at a distance r from the center of rotation is proportional to the concentration of solute at that point

$$f = \delta h \left(\frac{dn}{dC} \right) \frac{C}{\lambda} \equiv KC \tag{A1}$$

Delta is the distance between adjacent fringes in microns, h the thickness of the solution column in the ultracentrifuge cell, dn/dC the refractive increment of the solute, λ the wavelength of light used, and C the concentration. It may happen that a fringe position corresponding to 0 concentration cannot be established and therefore observed values of f will be only relative and contain an unknown constant. However, the difference between f values at any two positions is given directly and the calculations may be based on values of $f - f_a$, the fringe height at the upper meniscus

$$f - f_a = K(C - C_a) \tag{A2}$$

The observed values of $f - f_a$ are integrated according to the following expression:

$$\int_a^b (f - f_a)r dr = K \int_a^b Cr dr - K \int_a^b C_a r dr$$
$$= \tfrac{1}{2}(r_b^2 - r_a^2)(f_0 - f_a) \tag{A3}$$

r_b represents the position of the lower meniscus, C_0 is the initial uniform concentration of solute in the solution, and f_0 is equal to kC_0. $f_0 - f_a$ as determined from experimental data from Equation (A3) must approach f_0 at high speeds and large values of $r_b - r_a$. For a homogeneous solute, the equation for f_a would be:

$$\frac{f_a}{f_0} = \frac{C_a}{C_0} = \frac{H\rho^{-H}}{\sinh H} \tag{A4}$$

420

where H is related to the molecular weight M by

$$H = \frac{M}{4} \frac{(1 - \bar{v}\rho)\omega^2(r_b{}^2 - r_a{}^2)}{RT} \tag{A5}$$

In this equation, $\bar{v}$ is the partial specific volume of the solute, ρ the solution density, and ω the rotor speed in radians per second. f_a should approach 0 as $\omega^2(r_b{}^2 - r_a{}^2)$ becomes large independently of solute molecular weight.

Plots of $\ln f$ versus r^2 can be made and the relative curvature of such plots indicate the heterogeneity of the molecular size. The molecular weight averages indicative of such heterogeneity are obtained as follows:

$$\overline{M}_w{}^0 = \frac{2RT}{(1 - \bar{v})\omega^2(r_b{}^2 - r_a{}^2)} \frac{f_b - f_a}{f_0}$$

The weight average of that part of the solute which lies at any position r in the centrifuge cell designated $\overline{M}_{wr}$ is obtained from the slope of the plot of $\ln f$ versus r^2.

$$\overline{M}_{wr} = \frac{2RT}{(1 - \bar{v}\rho)\omega^2} \frac{d \ln f}{dr^2} \tag{A6}$$

From the limiting value of this parameter at $r = r_b$, we can determine the z average molecular weight of the sample according to the following expression:

$$\overline{M}_z{}^0 = \overline{M}_{wb} \frac{1 - (f_a/f_b)(\overline{M}_{wa}/\overline{M}_{wb})}{1 - f_a/f_b} \tag{A7}$$

In order to calculate a number average molecular weight, it is necessary that the integral $\int_a^r fr\,dr$ be computed at each point of the cell. The local number average molecular weight is related to this integral as follows:

$$\frac{f}{\overline{M}_{nr}} = \frac{f_a}{\overline{M}_{na}} + \frac{(1 - \bar{v}\rho)\omega^2}{RT} \int_a^r fr\,dr \tag{A8}$$

where $\overline{M}_{na}$ is the value of $\overline{M}_{nr}$ at the upper meniscus. $\overline{M}_{nr}$ can be unequivocally determined if f_a is equal to 0. However, when f_a is not 0, $\overline{M}_{nr}$ is indeterminate. This error can only be minimized by calculating number average molecular weights from runs where f_a is quite small. The number average of the original sample $\overline{M}_{n_0}$ can be calculated from the following relationship:

$$\overline{M}_n{}^0 = \frac{\frac{1}{2}f_0(r_b{}^2 - r_a{}^2)}{\int_a^b \frac{fr}{\overline{M}_{nr}}\,dr} \tag{A9}$$

However, the data obtained from the upper part of the cell makes an appreciable contribution to the integral denominator of this expression. The percentage error of determining f is very large and a modification of a procedure described by Yphantis can be employed. An arbitrary value of r is selected above which the percentage error in f is no longer appreciable. The value of f over $\overline{M}_{nr}$ can be considered an unknown parameter, and evaluated according to the following expression:

$$\frac{f}{\overline{M}_{nr}} + \left(\frac{f}{\overline{M}_{nr}}\right)_{r'} + \frac{(1 - \bar{v}\rho)\omega^2}{RT} \int_{r'}^{n} frdr \tag{A10}$$

An arbitrary number M^* is now chosen for the value of $\overline{M}_{nr}$ at $r = r'$. A plot of $\overline{M}_{nr}$ against a suitable parameter representing position in the cell can be made. The parameter ϕ represented by

$$\phi = \int_{a}^{r} \frac{frdr}{\tfrac{1}{2}f_0(r^2 - a^2)} \tag{A11}$$

is that fraction of all of the solute which lies between the upper meniscus and the point r. $\overline{M}_{nr}$ is either independent of r, or increases as r increases and thus should be a monotonically increasing function of r. A single value of M^* can be chosen within limits so that the plot of $\overline{M}_{nr}$ versus the weight fraction of total solute between r_a and the point of measurement satisfies this condition. Once M^* is known, the value of f is established and the number average molecular weight can be correctly obtained. The over-all error of this computation is in the order of 10 percent but for most samples is an entirely satisfactory procedure of approximation.

GENERAL REFERENCES

Chapter 1

E. L. Eliel, *Stereochemistry of Carbon Compounds*, McGraw-Hill Book Company Inc., New York, 1962.

E. L. Eliel, N. L. Allinger, S. J. Angyal, and G. A. Morrison, *Conformational Analysis*, Interscience Publishers, Inc., New York, 1965.

M. Hanack, *Conformation Theory*, Academic Press Inc., New York, 1965.

W. Kauzmann, J. E. Walter, and H. Eyring, Chem. Revs. **26**, 339 (1940).

Chapter 2

W. N. Haworth, *The Constitution of Sugars*, Edward Arnold & Company, London, 1929.

C. S. Hudson, J. Chem. Educ. **18**, 353 (1941).

E. G. V. Percival and E. Percival, *Structural Carbohydrate Chemistry*, J. Garnet Miller Ltd., London, 1962.

W. Pigman, *The Carbohydrates*, Academic Press, Inc., New York, 1957.

Polarimetry, Saccharimetry, and the Sugars, Circular C440, National Bureau of Standards, 1942.

J. Stanek, M. Cerny, J. Kocourek, and J. Pacak, *The Monosaccharides*, Academic Press, Inc., New York, 1962, Vol. 1.

Advances in Carbohydrate Chemistry, Yearly Series, Academic Press, Inc., New York, 1946, Vol. 1.

Chapter 3

E. L. Eliel, *Stereochemistry of Carbon Compounds*, McGraw-Hill Book Company, Inc., New York, 1962.

E. L. Eliel, N. L. Allinger, S. J. Angyal, and G. A. Morrison, *Conformational Analysis*, Interscience Publishers, Inc., New York, 1965.

M. Hanack, *Conformation Theory*, Academic Press Inc., New York, 1965.

D. H. R. Barton, Experientia **6**, 316 (1950).

D. H. R. Barton, O. Hassel, K. Pitzer, and V. Prelog, Science **119**, 49 (1953).

O. Hassel and B. Ottar, Acta Chem. Scand. **1**, 929 (1947).

Chapter 4, Nuclear Magnetic Resonance:

N. Bhacca and D. H. Williams, *Applications of NMR Spectroscopy in Organic Chemistry*, Holden-Day, San Francisco, 1964.

R. H. Bible, *Interpretation of NMR Spectra*, Plenum Press, New York, 1965.

L. D. Hall, *NMR Spectra of Carbohydrates in Advances in Carbohydrate Chemistry*, Academic Press, Inc., New York, 1964, Vol. 19.

J. A. Pople, W. G. Schneider, and H. J. Bernstein, *High Resolution Nuclear Magnetic Resonance*, McGraw-Hill Book Company, Inc., New York, 1959.

J. D. Roberts, *An Introduction to the Analysis of Spin–Spin Splitting in High Resolution NMR Spectra*, W. Benjamin, New York, 1961.

K. B. Wiberg and B. J. Nist, *The Interpretation of NMR Spectra*, W. A. Benjamin, Inc., New York, 1962.

Infrared Spectroscopy:

L. J. Bellamy, *The Infra-red Spectra of Complex Molecules*, Methuen, London, 1958, 2nd edition.

K. Nakanishi, *Infra-red Absorption Spectroscopy*, Holden-Day, San Francisco, 1964.

W. B. Neely, *The Infra-red Spectra of Carbohydrates in Advances in Carbohydrate Chemistry*, Academic Press, Inc., New York, 1957, Vol. 12.

H. Spedding, *Infra-red Spectra and Carbohydrate Chemistry in Advances in Carbohydrate Chemistry*, Academic Press, Inc., New York, 1964, Vol. 19.

Optical Rotation:

P. Crabbe, *Optical Rotatory Dispersion and Circular Dichroism in Organic Chemistry*, Holden-Day, San Francisco, 1965.

C. Djerassi, *Optical Rotatory Dispersion*, McGraw-Hill Book Company, Inc., New York, 1960.

Chapter 5, Conformation:

E. L. Eliel, N. L. Allinger, S. J. Angyal, and G. A. Morrison, *Conformational Analysis*, Interscience Publishers, Inc., New York, 1965, Chap. 6.

H. S. Isbell, J. Res. Natl. Bur. Stand. **18**, 505 (1937); **20**, 97 (1938).

R. E. Reeves, *Advances in Carbohydrate Chemistry*, Academic Press, Inc., New York, 1951, Vol. 6.

Physical Properties:

B. Capon and W. G. Overend, *Advances in Carbohydrate Chemistry*, Academic Press, Inc., New York, 1960, Vol. 15.

A. B. Foster, *Advances in Carbohydrate Chemistry*, Academic Press, Inc., New York, 1963, Vol. 18.

Chapter 6

W. A. Bonner, *Advances in Carbohydrate Chemistry*, Academic Press, Inc., New York, 1951, Vol. 6.

L. J. Haynes, *Advances in Carbohydrate Chemistry*, Academic Press, Inc., New York, 1963, Vol. 18.

K. Heyns and H. Paulsen, *Advances in Carbohydrate Chemistry*, Academic Press, Inc., New York, 1962, Vol. 17.

H. El Khadem, *Advances in Carbohydrate Chemistry*, Academic Press, Inc., New York, 1963, Vol. 18; 1965, Vol. 20.

N. K. Richtmeyer, *Advances in Carbohydrate Chemistry*, Academic Press, Inc., New York, 1951, Vol. 6.

J. C. Speck, Jr., *Advances in Carbohydrate Chemistry*, Academic Press, Inc., New York, 1958, Vol. 13.

R. L. Whistler and M. L. Wolfrom, eds., *Methods in Carbohydrate Chemistry*, Academic Press, Inc., New York, 1962, Vols. 1 and 2.

Chapter 7

R. U. Lemieux, *Advances in Carbohydrate Chemistry*, Academic Press, Inc., New York, 1954, Vol. 9.

J. W. F. McOmie, *Advances in Organic Chemistry*, Interscience Publishers, Inc., New York, 1963, Vol. 3.

J. A. Mills, *Advances in Carbohydrate Chemistry*, Academic Press, Inc., New York, 1955, Vol. 10.

F. Shafizadeh, *Advances in Carbohydrate Chemistry*, Academic Press, Inc., New York, 1958, Vol. 13.

J. F. Sugihara, *Advances in Carbohydrate Chemistry*, Academic Press, Inc., New York, 1953, Vol. 8.

Chapter 8

J. M. Bobbitt, *Advances in Carbohydrate Chemistry*, Academic Press, Inc., New York, 1956, Vol. 11.

E. L. Jackson, *Organic Reactions*, John Wiley & Sons, Inc., New York, 1944, Vol. 2.

A. S. Perlin, *Advances in Carbohydrate Chemistry*, Academic Press, Inc., New York, 1959, Vol. 14.

Chapter 10

J. D. Dutcher, in *Advances in Carbohydrate Chemistry*, Academic Press, Inc., New York, 1963, Vol. 18.

A. B. Foster and D. Horton, in *Advances in Carbohydrate Chemistry*, Academic Press, Inc., New York, 1959, Vol. 14.

A. B. Foster and M. Stacey, in *Advances in Carbohydrate Chemistry*, Academic Press, Inc., New York, 1952, Vol. 7.

R. Jeanloz and E. Balazs, eds., *The Amino Sugars*, Academic Press, Inc., New York, 1965, Vol. 1.

Chapter 11

D. M. Brown, in *Advances in Organic Chemistry*, Interscience Publishers, Inc., New York, 1963, Vol. 3.

H. G. Khorana, *Some Recent Developments in the Chemistry of Phosphate Esters of Biological Interest*, John Wiley & Sons, Inc., New York, 1961.

Chapter 12

W. Banks and C. T. Greenwood, in *Advances in Carbohydrate Chemistry*, Academic Press, Inc., New York, 1963, Vol. 18.

J. S. Brimacombe and J. M. Webber, *Mucopolysaccharides*, Elsevier, Amsterdam, 1964.

H. Gibian, *Mucopolysaccharide and Mucopolysaccharidases*, Deuticke, Vienna, 1959.

C. T. Greenwood, in *Advances in Carbohydrate Chemistry*, Academic Press, Inc., New York, 1956, Vol. 11.

R. L. Whistler, ed. *Methods in Carbohydrate Chemistry*, Academic Press, Inc., New York, 1965, Vol. 3 (Cellulose); Vol. 4 (Starch); Vol. 5 (General Polysaccharides).

R. L. Whistler and C. L. Smart, *Polysaccharide Chemistry*, Academic Press, Inc., New York, 1953.

Chapter 13

L. F. Leloir, C. E. Cardini, and E. Cabib, Comp. Biochem. **2**, 97 (1960).

R. Lespieau, in *Advances in Carbohydrate Chemistry*, Academic Press, Inc., New York, 1947, Vol. 2.

E. F. Neufeld and W. Z. Hassid, in *Advances in Carbohydrate Chemistry*, Academic Press, Inc., New York, 1963, Vol. 18.

Chapter 14

G. Ashwell, in *Methods in Enzymology*, S. P. Colowick and N. O. Kaplan, eds., Academic Press, Inc., New York, 1957, Vol. 3.

C. D. Bishop, in *Advances in Carbohydrate Chemistry*, Academic Press, Inc., New York, 1964, Vol. 19.

H. Budzkewicz, C. Djerassi, and O. H. Williams, *Structure Elucidation of Natural Products by Mass Spectrometry*, Holden Day, San Francisco, 1965.

R. L. Whistler and M. L. Wolfrom, eds., *Methods in Carbohydrate Chemistry*, Academic Press, Inc., New York, 1962, Vol. 1.

REFERENCES

CHAPTER 1

[1] M. S. Newman, J. Chem. Educ. **32**, 344 (1955).
[2] J. S. Pitzer, Disc. Faraday Soc. **10**, 66 (1951).
[3] F. A. Loewus, B. Vennesland, and F. Westheimer, J. Am. Chem. Soc. **75**, 5018 (1953).
[4] P. Fresnel, Bull. Soc. Philomat 147 (1824).
[5] J. B. Biot, Ann. Chim. Physique **4**, 90 (1817).
[6] P. Drude, *Theory of Optics* (English translation), S. Hirzel, Leipzig, p. 415 (1907).
[7] W. Kauzmann, *Quantum Chemistry*, Academic Press, New York, 1957.

CHAPTER 2

[1] C. S. Hudson, J. Chem. Educ. **18**, 353 (1941).
[2] M. A. Rosanoff, J. Am. Chem. Soc. **28**, 114 (1906).
[3] *The Collected Works of C. S. Hudson*, Two vols., Academic Press, New York, 1946–48.

CHAPTER 3

[1] W. N. Haworth, *The Constitution of Sugars*, Edward Arnold and Son, London, 1929.
[2] A. Baeyer, Ber. **18**, 2269 (1885).
[3] H. Sachse, Ber. **23**, 1363 (1890); Z. Physik Chem. **10**, 203 (1892).
[4] F. R. Jensen, D. S. Noyce, C. H. Sederholm, and A. J. Berlin, J. Am. Chem. Soc. **84**, 386 (1962).
[5] E. L. Eliel, N. L. Allinger, S. J. Angyal, and D. A. Morrison, *Conformational Analysis*, Interscience, New York, 1965, p. 36.
[6] D. H. R. Barton and A. J. Head, J. Chem. Soc. 932 (1956).

CHAPTER 4

[1] M. Karplus, J. Chem. Phys. **30**, 11 (1959).
[2] H. Conroy, in *Advances in Organic Chemistry, Methods and Results*, Interscience, New York, 1960, Vol. **2**, p. 311.
[3] G. E. McCasland, S. Furuta, L. F. Johnson, and J. N. Shoolery, J. Org. Chem. **28**, 894 (1963).

[4] F. R. Jensen, D. S. Noyce, C. H. Sederholm, and A. J. Berlin, J. Am. Chem. Soc. **84**, 386 (1962).

[5] R. U. Lemieux, R. K. Kullnig, H. J. Bernstein, and W. J. Schneider, J. Am. Chem. Soc. **80**, 6098 (1958).

[6] R. U. Lemieux, R. K. Kullnig, H. J. Bernstein, and W. J. Schneider, Can. J. Chem. **39**, 116 (1961).

[7] A. C. Richardson and K. A. McLauchlan, J. Chem. Soc. 2499 (1962); S. A. Barker, J. Homer, N. C. Keith, and L. F. Thomas, J. Chem. Soc. 1538 (1963); P. Perchemlides and E. A. Davidson, unpublished results.

[8] R. D. Guthrie and L. F. Johnson, J. Chem. Soc. 4166 (1962); F. A. L. Anet, R. B. Bernard, and L. D. Hall, Can. J. Chem. **41**, 2331 (1963).

[9] W. Hofheinz, H. Grisebach, and H. Friebolin, Tetrahedron **18**, 1265 (1962).

[10] Reference 9.

[11] A. S. Perlin, Can. J. Chem. **41**, 399 (1963).

[12] R. U. Lemieux, J. D. Stevens, and R. R. Fraser, Can. J. Chem. **40**, 1955 (1962).

[13] R. D. Abraham, L. B. Hall, L. Hough, and K. A. McLauchlan, J. Chem. Soc. 3699 (1962); 748 (1963).

[14] L. Mester and E. Moczar, J. Org. Chem. **29**, 247 (1964).

[15] R. H. Marchessault, Can J. Chem. **41**, 1612 (1963).

[16] V. S. R. Rao and J. F. Foster, J. Phys. Chem. **67**, 951 (1963).

[17] E. F. L. J. Anet, Chem. Ind. 1035 (1963).

[18] M. Sundaralingham, J. Am. Chem. Soc. **87**, 599 (1965).

[19] O. Jardetsky, J. Am. Chem. Soc. **85**, 1823 (1963).

[20] C. A. Beevers, T. R. R. McDonald, J. H. Robertson, and F. Stern, Act. Cryst. **5**, 689 (1952); G. M. Brown and H. Ahern, Science **141**, 921 (1963).

[21] S. A. Barker, E. J. Bourne, M. Stacey, and D. H. Whiffen, J. Chem. Soc. 171 (1954); S. A. Barker, E. J. Bourne, R. Stephens, and D. H. Whiffen, J. Chem. Soc. 3468, 4211 (1954).

[22] H. S. Isbell, F. A. Smith, E. C. Creitz, H. L. Frush, J. D. Moyer, and J. E. Stewart, J. Res. Natl. Bur. Std. **59**, 41 (1957).

[23] H. B. Henbest, G. D. Meakins, B. N. Choles and A. A. Wagland, J. Chem. Soc. 1462 (1957).

[24] H. Spedding, J. Chem. Soc. 1317 (1961).

[25] W. B. Neeley, Adv. Carb. Chem. **12**, 13 (1957).

[26] M. Stacey, R. H. Moore, S. A. Barker, H. Weigel, E. J. Bourne, and D. H. Whiffen, Proc. U.N. Intern. Conf. Peaceful Uses of Atomic Energy, Geneva, 1958, Vol. **20**, p. 251.

[27] S. F. D. Orr, Biochim. Biophys. Acta **14**, 173 (1954).

[28] N. Baggett, M. A. Burkhart, A. B. Foster, J. Lehman, and J. M. Webber, J. Chem. Soc. 4157 (1963).

[29] S. A. Barker, A. B. Foster, A. H. Haines, J. Lehman, and J. Zweifel, J. Chem. Soc. 4161 (1963).

[30] J. S. Brimacombe, A. B. Foster, and A. H. Haines, J. Chem. Soc. 2582 (1960).

[31] C. N. Pace, C. Tanford, and E. A. Davidson, J. Am. Chem. Soc. **86**, 3160 (1964).

[32] V. S. R. Rao and J. F. Foster, Nature **200**, 570 (1963).

[33] I. Listowsky, G. Avigad, and S. England, J. Am. Chem. Soc. **87**, 1765 (1965).

CHAPTER 5

[1] R. Reeves, J. Am. Chem. Soc. **71**, 215 (1949).

[2] R. Reeves, J. Am. Chem. Soc. **72**, 1499 (1950).

[3] J. Boseken, Adv. Carb. Chem. **4**, 189 (1949).

[4] S. J. Angyal and D. J. McHugh, J. Chem. Soc. 423 (1957).

[5] A. B. Foster, J. Chem. Soc. 4214 (1957).

[6] H. S. Isbell, J. Res. Natl. Bur. Std. **66A**, 233 (1962).

[7] K. Heyns and H. Paulsen, Adv. Carb. Chem. **17**, 169 (1962).

[8] J. A. Snyder and K. P. Link, J. Am. Chem. Soc. **74**, 1883 (1952); **75**, 1758 (1953).

[9] I. Johansson, B. Lindberg, and O. Theander, Acta Chem. Scand. **17**, 13 (1963).

[10] C. A. Bunton, T. A. Lewis, D. R. Llewellyn, and C. A. Vernon, J. Chem. Soc. 4419 (1955).

[11] J. F. Smith and T. M. Lowry, J. Chem. Soc. 666 (1928).

[12] B. Anderson and H. Degu, Acta Chem. Scand. **16**, 215 (1962).

[13] B. Capon and W. G. Overend, Adv. Carb. Chem. **15**, 16 (1960).

[14] C. S. Hudson and E. Yanovsky, J. Am. Chem. Soc. **39**, 1013 (1917).

[15] F. A. Isherwood and M. A. Jermyn, Biochem. J. **48**, 515 (1951).

[16] D. H. Whiffen, Chem. Ind. 964 (1956).

[17] J. H. Brewster, J. Am. Chem. Soc. **81**, 5475, 5483 (1959).

[18] O. Hassel and B. Ottar, Acta Chem. Scand. **19**, 29 (1947).

CHAPTER 6

[1] R. Wilstätter and G. Schudel, Ber. **51**, 780 (1918).

[2] S. Moore and K. P. Link, J. Biol. Chem. **133**, 293 (1940).

[3] B. P. Ridge and A. H. Little, J. Textile Inst. **33**, 133 (1942).

[4] H. S. Isbell, J. Res. Natl. Bur. Std. **29**, 227 (1942).

[5] O. Ruff, Ber. **31**, 1573 (1898); **34**, 1362 (1901).

[6] H. S. Isbell, J. V. Karabinos, H. L. Frush, N. B. Holt, A. Schwebel, and T. Galkowski, J. Res. Natl. Bur. Std. **48**, 163 (1952); H. L. Frush and H. L. Isbell, J. Res. Natl. Bur. Std. **54**, 267 (1955).

[7] R. Prince and T. Reichstein, Helv. Chim. Acta **20**, 101 (1937).

[8] E. Fischer, Ber. **22**, 2204 (1889); R. Kuhn and P. Klesse, Ber. **91**, 1989 (1958).

[9] H. S. Isbell, J. V. Karabinos, H. L. Frush, N. B. Holt, A. Schwebel, and T. Galkowski, Chem. Abstr. **47**, 3873 (1953).

[10] H. S. Isbell, H. L. Frush, and N. B. Holt, J. Res. Natl. Bur. Std. **64a**, 363 (1959).

[11] L. Henry, Compt. Rend. **120**, 1265 (1895).

[12] J. C. Sowden and H. O. L. Fischer, J. Am. Chem. Soc. **69**, 1963 (1947).

[13] J. C. Sowden, J. Am. Chem. Soc. **72**, 3325 (1950).

[14] H. ElKhadem, Adv. Carb. Chem. **20**, 139 (1965).

[15] L. F. Fieser and M. Fieser, *Organic Chemistry*, D. C. Heath and Company, Boston, 1944, p. 351.

[16] R. M. Hann and C. S. Hudson, J. Am. Chem. Soc. **66**, 735 (1944).

[17] H. ElKhadem, M. H. Meshreki, and G. H. Labib, J. Chem. Soc. 2306 (1964).

[18] L. Mester, J. Am. Chem. Soc. **77**, 4301 (1955).

[19] J. Zemplen, L. Mester, A. Messner, and E. Eckhart, Acta Chim. Acad. Sci. Hung. **2**, 25, (1952).

[20] W. T. Hoskins and C. S. Hudson, J. Am. Chem. Soc. **61**, 1266 (1939).

[21] M. L. Wolfrom and A. Thompson, J. Am. Chem. Soc. **53**, 622 (1931).

[22] R. U. Lemieux and M. J. Chu, Abst. 133 Amer. Chem. Soc. Meeting, 31N (1958).

[23] D. L. MacDonald, J. Org. Chem. **27**, 1107 (1962).

[24] P. Perchemlides, E. A. Davidson, and N. Aronson, Abstracts, 147 Amer. Chem. Soc. Meeting 1C (1964).

[25] L. J. Haynes and F. H. Newth, Adv. Carb. Chem. **10**, 207 (1955).

[26] L. J. Haynes and A. R. Todd, J. Chem. Soc. 303 (1950).

[27] W. J. Hickenbottom, J. Chem. Soc. 1676 (1929).

[28] R. U. Lemieux, Can. J. Chem. **29**, 1079 (1951).

[29] F. Micheel, A. Klemer, M. Nolte, H. Nordiek, L. Tork, and H. Westermann, Ber. **19**, 1612 (1957).

[30] F. Micheel, A. Klemer, and R. Flitsch, Ber. **91**, 653 (1958).

[31] F. Micheel and D. Borrmann, Ber. **93**, 1143 (1960).

[32] A. Bertho and H. Nussel, Ber. **63**, 836 (1930).

[33] D. Horton and D. H. Hutson, Adv. Carb. Chem. **18**, 123 (1963).

[34] J. Stanek, K. Malkovsky, M. Novak, and D. Petricek, Coll. Czech. Chem. Comm. **23**, 336 (1958).

[35] W. A. Bonner, J. Am. Chem. Soc. **70**, 3491 (1948); W. Schneider and A. Bangar, Ber. **64** 1321 (1931).

[36] E. F. Izard and P. W. Morgan, Ind. Eng. Chem. **41**, 617 (1949).

[37] E. Fischer, Ber. **28**, 1145 (1895); J. A. Cadotte, F. Smith, and D. Spriestersbach, J. Am. Chem. Soc. **74**, 1501 (1952).

[38] W. Koenigs and E. Knorr, Ber. **34**, 957 (1901).

[39] L. W. Mazzeno, J. Am. Chem. Soc. **72**, 1039 (1950).

[40] B. Helferich, Ber. **77**, 194 (1944); H. Feier and O. Westphal, Ber. **89**, 589 (1956).

[41] B. Helferich, Am. Chem. Soc. **7**, 210 (1952).

[42] W. A. Bonner, J. Am. Chem. Soc. **81**, 5171 (1959).

[43] R. Lemieux and G. Huber, Can. J. Chem. **53**, 128 (1955).

[44] R. Lemieux, "Rearrangements and Isomerizations in Carbohydrate Chemistry," in *Molecular Rearrangements*, edited by P. DeMayo, John Wiley & Sons, New York, 1963.

[45] E. P. Painter, J. Am. Chem. Soc. **75**, 1137 (1953).

[46] W. A. Bonner, J. Am. Chem. Soc. **83**, 2661 (1961).

[47] C. T. Bishop and F. P. Cooper, Can. J. Chem. **40**, 224 (1962); **41**, 2743 (1963).

[48] D. D. Reynolds and W. L. Evans, Org. Syn. Coll. **3**, 432 (1955).

[49] C. Armour, C. A. Bunton, S. Patasi, L. H. Selman, and C. A. Vernon, J. Chem. Soc. 412 (1961).

[50] M. S. Feather and J. F. Harris, J. Org. Chem. **30**, 153 (1965).

[51] C. D. Hurd and W. A. Bonner, J. Am. Chem. Soc. **67**, 1977 (1945).

[52] W. A. Bonner, Adv. Carb. Chem. **6**, 251 (1951).

[53] L. J. Haynes, Adv. Carb. Chem. **18**, 227 (1963).

[54] C. D. Hurd and R. P. Holysz, J. Am. Chem. Soc. **72**, 2005 (1950).

[55] C. A. Lobry de Bruyn and W. A. van Ekenstein, Rec. Trav. Chim. Pays Bas **14**, 203 (1895); J. C. Speck, Jr. Adv. Carb. Chem. **13**, 63 (1958).

[56] M. L. Wolfrom and W. L. Lewis, J. Am. Chem. Soc. **50**, 837 (1928).

[57] J. Kenner and G. N. Richards, J. Chem. Soc. 2921 (1956).

[58] Y. Topper, J. Biol. Chem. **225**, 419 (1957).

[59] Y. Topper and D. Stetten, J. Biol. Chem. **189**, 191 (1951).

[60] I. A. Rose and E. L. O. Connell, Biochim. Biophys. Acta **42**, 159 (1960).

[61] I. A. Rose, Brookhaven Symposia on Biology **15**, 293 (1962).

[62] S. Kirkwood, Proc. Gord. Res. Conf. on Carbohydrates (1964).

[63] S. Ghosh, H. J. Blumenthal, E. A. Davidson, and S. Roseman, J. Biol. Chem. **235**, 1265 (1960).

[64] J. F. Carson, J. Am. Chem. Soc. **77**, 1881 (1955).

CHAPTER 7

[1] G. C. Swain, J. Am. Chem. Soc. **70**, 1119 (1948).

[2] C. G. Swain, R. B. Mosley, and D. E. Brown, J. Am. Chem. Soc. **77**, 3731 (1955).

[3] E. J. Reist, R. R. Spencer, and B. R. Baker, J. Org. Chem. **24**, 1618 (1959).

[4] E. J. Reist and L. Goodman, Chem. Ind. 1794 (1962).

[5] M. L. Wolfrom, J. Bernsman, and D. Horton, J. Org. Chem. **27**, 4505 (1962).

[6] J. M. Sugihara, Adv. Carb. Chem. **8**, 1 (1953).

[7] A. Fürst and P. A. Plattner, Int. Conf. Pure and Applied Chem. **12**, 405 (1951).

[8] H. Ohle and L. von Vargha, Ber. **62**, 2435 (1929).

[9]   E. M. Montgomery, N. K. Richtmeyer, and C. S. Hudson, J. Am. Chem. Soc. **65**, 1848 (1943).

[10] F. Micheel and A. Klemer, Adv. Carb. Chem. **16**, 85 (1961).

[11] A. S. Meyer and T. Reichstein, Helv. Chem. Acta **29**, 152 (1946).

[12] L. von Vargha, Ber. **87**, 1351 (1954).

[13] P. Perchemlides, Ph.D. Dissertation, Duke University, 1965.

[14] E. Hardegger, R. M. Montavon, and O. Jucker, Helv. Chem. Acta **31**, 1863 (1948).

[15] L. H. Haynes and A. R. Todd, J. Chem. Soc. 303 (1950).

[16] S. Winstein, C. Hanson, and E. Grunwald, J. Am. Chem. Soc. **70**, 812 (1948); S. Winstein and R. Heck, J. Am. Chem. Soc. **74**, 5584 (1952).

[17] R. U. Lemieux, Can. J. Chem. **29**, 1079 (1951).

[18] P. Perchemlides and E. A. Davidson, unpublished observations.

[19] J. E. Hodge and C. E. Rist, J. Am. Chem. Soc. **74**, 1498 (1952).

[20] B. R. Baker, R. Harrison, and A. H. Haines, J. Org. Chem. **29**, 1068 (1964).

[21] C. J. P. Glaudemans and H. G. Fletcher, J. Org. Chem. **29**, 3286 (1964).

[22] A. N. DeBelder, Adv. Carb. Chem. **20**, 219 (1965).

[23] J. A. Mills, Adv. Carb. Chem. **11**, 1 (1955).

[24] R. C. Cookson, Chem. Ind. n23 (1954).

[25] J. A. Mills, Chem. Ind. 633 (1954).

[26] N. K. Richtmeyer and C. S. Hudson, J. Am. Chem. Soc. **63**, 1727 (1941); W. H. Myers and G. J. Robertson, J. Am. Chem. Soc. **65**, 8 (1943).

[27] W. N. Haworth, C. R. Porter, and A. C. Waine, Rec. trav. chim. **57**, 541 (1938).

[28] L. Hough, J. E. Priddle, and R. S. Theobald, Adv. Carb. Chem. **15**, 91 (1960).

[29] W. G. Overend, M. Stacey, and L. F. Wiggins, J. Chem. Soc. 1358 (1949).

[30] W. N. Haworth and C. R. Porter, J. Chem. Soc. 151 (1930).

[31] D. D. Reynolds and W. O. Kenyon, J. Am. Chem. Soc. **64**, 1110 (1942).

[32] J. H. Chapman and L. N. Owen, J. Chem. Soc. 579 (1950).

[33] R. A. Jeanloz, D. A. Prins, and P. Reichstein, Helv. Chem. Acta **29**, 371 (1946).

[34] B. R. Baker and T. L. Huller, J. Org. Chem. **30**, 4038, 4045 (1965).

[35] A. B. Foster, D. Horton, N. Salin, M. Stacey, and J. M. Webber, J. Chem. Soc. 2587 (1960).

[36] B. Helferich and M. Gindy, Ber. **87**, 1488 (1954).

[37] E. L. Jackson, in *Organic Reactions*, edited by R. Adams, J. Wiley & Sons, New York, 1944, Vol. 2.

[38] J. B. Bobbitt, Adv. Carb. Chem. **11**, 1 (1956).

[39] R. Criegee, L. Craft, and B. Rank, Ann. **507**, 159 (1933).

[40] C. A. Bunton and V. J. Shiner, Jr., J. Chem. Soc. 1593 (1960).

[41] V. J. Shiner, Jr., and C. R. Wasmuth, J. Am. Chem. Soc. **81**, 37 (1959).

[42] T. W. Clutterbuck and F. Renter, J. Chem. Soc. 1467 (1935).

[43] D. A. MacFayden, J. Biol. Chem. **158**, 107 (1945).

[44]   G. Dangschat and H. O. L. Fischer, Naturwiss, **27**, 756 (1939).
[45]   K. Heyns, Ann. **558**, 147 (1941).
[46]   O. Theander, Acta Chem. Scand. **11**, 1557 (1957).
[47]   K. Heyns and H. Paulsen, Adv. Carb. Chem. **17**, 169 (1962).
[48]   K. Heyns, Chem. Abstr. **35**, 4396 (1941).
[49]   K. Heyns and W. Koch, Ber. **86**, 110 (1953).
[50]   K. Heyns and H. Paulsen, Ber. **86**, 853 (1953).
[51]   J. G. Post and L. Anderson, J. Am. Chem. Soc. **84**, 471 (1962).
[52]   K. Heyns, H. Gottschalk, and H. Paulsen, Ber. **95**, 2660 (1962).
[53]   H. G. Hers, Biochim. Biophys. Acta **22**, 202 (1956).
[54]   D. Keilin and E. F. Hartree, Biochem. J. **50**, 331 (1952).
[55]   A. St. J. Hugget and D. A. Nixon, Biochem. J. **66**, 12P (1957).
[56]   G. Avigad, D. Amaral, C. Asensio, and B. L. Horecker, J. Biol. Chem. **237**, 2736 (1962).
[57]   J. O. Phillips, Adv. Carb. Chem. **18**, 9 (1963).

CHAPTER 8

[1]   I. J. Goldstein, J. K. Hamilton, and F. Smith, J. Am. Chem. Soc. **81**, 6252 (1959).
[2]   I. J. Goldstein and W. J. Whelan, J. Chem. Soc. 170 (1962).
[3]   V. Barry, J. Chem. Soc. 578 (1942).
[4]   J. C. Sowden, J. Am. Chem. Soc. **74**, 4377 (1952).
[5]   A. S. Perlin, Adv. Carb. Chem. **14**, 9 (1959).
[6]   A. S. Perlin, Can. J. Chem. **40**, 1226 (1962).
[7]   A. S. Perlin, Can. J. Chem. **38**, 2280 (1960).
[8]   A. S. Perlin, Can. J. Chem. **33**, 1216 (1955).
[9]   A. S. Perlin, Can. J. Chem. **34**, 1811 (1956).

CHAPTER 9

[1]   W. N. Haworth, E. L. Hirst, and H. A. Thomas, J. Chem. Soc. 821 (1931).
[2]   R. Kuhn, H. Trischmann, and I. Löw, **67**, 32 (1955).
[3]   I. E. Muskat, J. Am. Chem. Soc. **56**, 2449 (1934).

CHAPTER 10

[1]   G. Ledderhose, Z. Physiol. Chem. **2**, 213 (1878); P. A. Levene and F. B. LaForge, J. Biol. Chem. **18**, 123 (1914).
[2]   R. Kuhn and W. Kirschenlor, Ang. Chem. **67**, 786 (1955).
[3]   J. F. Carson, J. Am. Chem. Soc. **78**, 3728 (1956).
[4]   S. P. James, F. Smith, M. Stacey, and L. F. Wiggins, J. Chem. Soc. 625 (1946).
[5]   W. N. Haworth, W. H. G. Lake, and S. Peat, J. Chem. Soc. 271 (1939).

[6] A. B. Foster, M. Stacey, and S. V. Vardheim, Acta Chem. Scand. **12**, 1605 (1958).

[7] M. L. Wolfrom, F. Shafizadeh, and R. K. Armstrong, J. Am. Chem. Soc. **80**, 4885 (1958).

[8] B. R. Baker and R. E. Schaub, J. Org. Chem. **19**, 646 (1954).

[9] M. L. Wolfrom, J. R. Vercellotti, and D. Horton, J. Org. Chem. **29**, 540 (1964).

[10] R. Kuhn and W. Kirschenlor, Ber. **87**, 1547 (1954).

[11] M. L. Wolfrom, A. Thompson, and I. R. Hooper, J. Am. Chem. Soc. **68**, 2343 (1946); J. Sowden, A. Kirkland, and K. O. Lloys, J. Org. Chem. **28**, 3516 (1963).

[12 B. R. Baker, R. E. Schaub, J. P. Joseph, and J. H. Williams, J. Am. Chem. Soc. **76**, 4044 (1954).

[13] B. R. Baker, R. E. Schaub, and J. H. Williams, J. Am. Chem. Soc. **82**, 77 (1955).

[14] H. H. Baer and H. O. L. Fischer, J. Am. Chem. Soc. **82**, 3709 (1960).

[15] R. Cram and F. AbdELhafez, J. Am. Chem. Soc. **74**, 5828 (1952).

[16] S. Peat and L. F. Wiggins, J. Chem. Soc. 1810 (1938).

[17] M. L. Wolfrom and K. Anno, J. Am. Chem. Soc. **75**, 1038 (1953).

[18] S. Ghosh and S. Roseman, J. Biol. Chem. **240**, 1525 (1965).

[19] J. J. Distler, J. M. Merrick, and S. Roseman, J. Biol. Chem. **230**, 497 (1958)

[20] C. E. Cardini and L. F. Leloir, Arch. Biochim. Biophys. **45**, 55 (1952).

CHAPTER 11

[1] J. R. Barnard, M. D. Montague, R. J. Moss, and M. A. Parsons, J. Chem. Soc. 3786 (1957).

[2] J. Baddiley and A. R. Todd, J. Chem. Soc. 648 (1947); J. Kumamoto and F. H. Westheimer, J. Am. Chem. Soc. **77**, 2515 (1955).

[3] H. G. Khorana and A. R. Todd, J. Chem. Soc. 2257 (1953).

[4] G. M. Kosolapoff, *Organophosphorous Compounds*, John Wiley & Sons, New York, 1950.

[5] P. Brigl and H. Müller, Ber. **72**, 2121 (1939).

[6] F. R. Atherton, H. T. Openshaw, and A. R. Todd, J. Chem. Soc. 382 (1945).

[7] E. Cherbuliez and J. Rabinowitz, Helv. Chim. Acta **39**, 1461 (1956).

[8] J. E. Seegmiller and B. L. Horecker, J. Biol. Chem. **192**, 175 (1951).

[9] H. J. Pontis and C. L. Fischer, Biochim. J. **89**, 452 (1963).

[10] A. B. Foster and W. S. Overend, Quart. Rev. **11**, 61 (1957).

[11] D. L. MacDonald, J. Org. Chem. **27**, 1107 (1962).

[12] T. Y. Kim and E. A. Davidson, J. Org. Chem. **28**, 2475 (1963).

[13] A. H. Olavesen and E. A. Davidson, J. Biol. Chem. **240**, 992 (1965).

[14] P. J. O'Brien, Biochim. Biophys. Acta **86**, 628 (1964).

[15] T. Osawa, P. Perchemlides, R. Jeanloz, and E. A. Davidson, Carb. Res. (to be published).

CHAPTER 12

[1] B. Weissmann and K. Meyer, J. Am. Chem. Soc. **76**, 1753 (1954); R. W. Jeanloz and H. M. Flowers, Biochem. **3**, 123 (1964).

[2] E. A. Davidson and K. Meyer, J. Am. Chem. Soc. **76**, 5686 (1954); **77**, 4796 (1955).

[3] M. B. Mathews and I. Lozaityte, Arch. Biochem. Biophys. **75**, 158 (1958).

[4] E. J. Hehre, Proc. Soc. Exptl. Biol. Med. **54**, 18 (1943).

[5] *Methods in Carbohydrate Chemistry*, edited by R. L. Whistler, Academic Press, New York, 1964, Vol. III.

[6] D. J. Manners, Quart. Rev. **9**, 78 (1955).

[7] E. G. Percival and E. Percival, *Structural Carbohydrate Chemistry*, J. Garnett Miller, London, 1962, 2nd edition, p. 229.

[8] J. S. Brimacombe and J. M. Webber, *Mucopolysaccharides*, Elsevier Amsterdam, 1964, Chap. 4.

[9] E. A. Davidson and K. Meyer, J. Biol. Chem. **211**, 605 (1954).

[10] S. Takanashi, Y. Hirasaka, M. Kawada, and M. Ishidate, J. Am. Chem. Soc. **84**, 3029 (1962).

[11] P. J. Stoffyn and R. Jeanloz, Fed. Proc. **21**, 81 (1962).

[12] P. Hoffman, A. Linker, V. Lippman, and K. Meyer, J. Biol. Chem. **235**, 3066 (1960).

[13] E. Marler and E. A. Davidson, Proc. Natl. Acad. Sci. **54**, 648 (1965).

[14] K. C. B. Wilkie, J. K. N. Jones, B. J. Excell, and R. E. Semple, Can. J. Chem. **35**, 795 (1957).

[15] J. M. G. Cowrie and C. T. Greenwood, J. Chem. Soc. 2658, 2862 (1957).

[16] C. Tanford, E. Marler, E. Jury, and E. A. Davidson, J. Biol. Chem. **239**, 4034 (1964).

[17] H. Mark, Z. Elektrochem. **40**, 449 (1934).

[18] J. M. G. Cowie, Makromol. Chemie. **42**, 230 (1961).

[19] B. H. Zimm, J. Chem. Phys. **16**, 1093 (1948).

[20] B. Rosen, P. Kamath, and F. Eirich, Disc. Faraday Soc. **11**, 135 (1951).

CHAPTER 13

[1] "Evolutionary Biochemistry," *Proceedings of the Sixth International Conference on Biochemistry*, Pergamon Press, London, 1963.

[2] E. Fischer, Ber. **23**, 2114 (1890).

[3] C. B. Fowler, Biochim. Biophys. Acta. **7**, 503 (1951).

[4] R. Lespieau, Adv. Carb. Chem. **2**, 107 (1946).

[5] R. Tripett, in *Advanced Organic Chemistry, Methods and Results*, Interscience Publishers, New York, 1960, Vol. 1, p. 83.

[6] N. Kochetkov and A. Dimitrie, Chem. Ind. 1723 (1964).

[7] J. A. Bassham, *Advanced Enzymology*, Interscience Publishers, New York, 1963, Vol. 25, p. 29.

[8]   D. Wilson, Anal. Biochem. **10**, 472 (1965).
[9]   H. M. Kalckar, *Advanced Enzymology*, Interscience Publishers, New York, 1958, Vol. 20, p. 111.
[10] B. Jacobson and E. A. Davidson, J. Biol. Chem. **237**, 638 (1962).
[11] L. Glaser, J. Biol. Chem. **234**, 2801 (1959). B. Jacobson and E. A. Davidson, Biochim. Biophys. Acta **73**, 145 (1963).
[12] S. Ghosh and S. Roseman, J. Biol. Chem. **240**, 1531 (1965).
[13] J. Hurwitz and B. L. Horecker, J. Biol. Chem. **223**, 993 (1956).
[14] V. Ginsbury, J. Biol. Chem. **235**, 2196 (1960).
[15] E. A. Davidson, H. J. Blumenthal, and S. Roseman, J. Biol. Chem. **226**, 125 (1957).
[16] H. J. Williams-Ashman, J. Banks, and S. K. Wolfson, Jr., Arch. Biochem. Biophys. **72**, 45 (1957).
[17] H. Ankel and D. S. Feingold, Biochem. **4**, 2468 (1965).
[18] S. Roseman, G. W. Jourdian, D. Watson, and R. Rood, Proc. Natl. Acad. Sci. **47**, 958 (1961); L. Warren and G. Felsenfeld, Biochem. Biophys. Res. Conn. **4**, 232 (1961).

CHAPTER 14

[1]   N. Nelson, J. Biol. Chem. **153**, 375 (1954).
[2]   J. T. Park and M. J. Johnson, J. Biol. Chem. **181** 149 (1949).
[3]   Z. Dische, in *Methods in Carbohydrate Chemistry*, edited by R. L. Whistler and M. Wolfrom, Academic Press, New York, 1962, Vol. 1, p. 478.
[4]   Z. Dische, J. Biol. Chem. **176**, 189 (1947).
[5]   Z. Dische, J. Biol. Chem. **181**, 379 (1949).
[6]   Z. Dische and E. Borenfreund, J. Biol. Chem. **192**, 583 (1951).
[7]   L. Warren, J. Biol. Chem. **234**, 1971 (1959).
[8]   E. A Davidson, in *Methods of Enzymology*, edited by E. Neufeld and A. Ginsberg, Academic Press, New York, 1966, Vol. VIII, p. 52.
[9]   W. T. J. Morgan and L. A. Elson, Biochem. J. **26**, 988 (1934); J. L. Reissig, J. L. Strominger, and L. F. Leloir, J. Biol. Chem. **217**, 959 (1955).
[10] Z. Dische and E. Borenfreund, J. Biol. Chem. **184**, 517 (1950).
[11] *Methods of Enzymatic Analysis*, edited by H. U. Bergmeyer, Academic Press, New York, 1963.
[12] E. Lederer and M. Lederer, *Chromatography*, Elsevier, New York, 1953; H. Weigel, Adv. Carb. Chem. **18**, 61 (1963).
[13] S. M. Partridge and R. G. Westall, Biochem. J. **42**, 238 (1948).
[14] J. X. Khym and L. P. Zill, J. Am. Chem. Soc. **73**, 2399 (1951).
[15] B. Weissman, K. Meyer, P. Sampson, and A. Linker, J. Biol. Chem. **208**, 417 (1954).
[16] H. J. Jones, J. K. N. Jones, and M. B. Perry, Can. J. Chem. **40**, 1559 (1962).
[17] S. W. Gunner, J. K. N. Jones, and M. B. Perry, Can. J. Chem. **39**, 1892 (1961).

[18] R. Bentley, C. C. Sweeley, M. Makita, and W. W. Wells, J. Am. Chem. Soc. **85**, 2497 (1963).

[19] J. O Aspinall, J. Chem. Soc. 1676 (1963).

[20] C. T. Bishop, Adv. Carb. Chem. **19**, 95 (1964).

[21] R. I. Reed, *Advanced Inorganic Chemistry, Methods and Results*, Interscience Publishers, New York, 1963, Vol. 3, p. 1.

[22] K. Biemann, D. C. DeJongh, and H. K. Schnoes, J. Am. Chem. Soc. **85**, 1763 (1963).

[23] G. Zemplen and D. Kiss, Ber. **60**, 165 (1927).

[24] F. Weygand and R. Lowenfeld, Ber. **83**, 559 (1950).

[25] D. L. MacDonald and H. O. L. Fischer, J. Am. Chem. Soc. **74**, 2087 (1952).

[26] E. F. Phares, Arch. Biochem. Biophys. **33**, 173 (1951).

[27] M. Gibbs, P. K. Kindel, and M. Busse, in *Methods in Carbohydrate Chemistry*, edited by R. L. Whistler and Wolfrom, Academic Press, New York, 1963, Vol. II, p. 496.

Index